DIFFERENCE EQUATIONS FOR SCIENTISTS AND ENGINEERING

Interdisciplinary Difference Equations

DIFFERENCE EQUATIONS FOR SCIENTISTS AND ENGINEERING

Interdisciplinary Difference Equations

Michael A Radin

Rochester Institute of Technology, USA

World Scientific

NEW JERSEY · LONDON · SINGAPORE · BEIJING · SHANGHAI · HONG KONG · TAIPEI · CHENNAI · TOKYO

Published by

World Scientific Publishing Co. Pte. Ltd.

5 Toh Tuck Link, Singapore 596224

USA office: 27 Warren Street, Suite 401-402, Hackensack, NJ 07601

UK office: 57 Shelton Street, Covent Garden, London WC2H 9HE

Library of Congress Cataloging-in-Publication Data
Names: Radin, Michael A. (Michael Alexander), author.
Title: Difference equations for scientists and engineering : interdisciplinary difference equations /
    Michael A. Radin (Rochester Institute of Technology, USA).
Description: New Jersey : World Scientific, 2019. | Includes bibliographical references.
Identifiers: LCCN 2019008183| ISBN 9789811203855 (hard cover : alk. paper) |
    ISBN 9789811202964 (pbk : alk. paper)
Subjects: LCSH: Difference equations. | Differential equations, Linear. | Nonlinear difference equations.
Classification: LCC QA431 .R3255 2019 | DDC 515/.625--dc23
LC record available at https://lccn.loc.gov/2019008183

British Library Cataloguing-in-Publication Data
A catalogue record for this book is available from the British Library.

For any available supplementary material, please visit
https://www.worldscientific.com/worldscibooks/10.1142/11349#t=suppl

Desk Editor: Liu Yumeng

Typeset by Stallion Press
Email: enquiries@stallionpress.com

PREFACE

Learning about structures and their details is essential for development and enhancement of our intuitions, analytical skills and deducting reasoning skills. For instance, it is pertinent to decipher specific patterns when studying weather systems, when learning to play a musical instrument, when studying a foreign language, when learning computer programming, when studying transportation routes and schedules, when analyzing engineering structures, when studying behaviors and other similar applications.

The aim of this interdisciplinary book is to capture and recognize the emergence of patterns when obtaining an explicit solution to determine the monotonic properties and periodic patterns. We will progressively expand our instincts with repetitive style examples that will inductively guide us to developing theorems and deeper mastery of convergence nature of solutions, oscillatory character of solutions and periodic traits of solutions by addressing the following questions:

- Is the solution monotonically increasing or monotonically decreasing?
- Does the solution approach the limit from above or from below?
- Is the solution oscillatory?
- What is the period of the given cycle? An even ordered or an odd ordered period?
- The existence and uniqueness of periodic cycles? Are periodic cycles unique or is every solution periodic?
- Are all the terms of the cycle positive or negative, and do they alternate?
- When do eventually periodic solutions arise and why?

I invite you to the discovery voyage in deciphering monotonic, oscillatory, periodic and chaotic behavior of solutions of first order, second order and higher order difference equations. We will study the monotonic properties and periodic traits of linear difference equations, rational difference equations in exponential form, piecewise difference equations and max-type difference equations, and discuss various applications in population dynamics, biological sciences, signal processing, economics and neural networking. Our plan is to develop inductive intuition that will help us recognize specific structures of patterns of monotonic properties, periodic cycles and eventually periodic cycles and to develop theorems after numerous repetitive types of examples. The intents are to widen our inductive reasoning skills and to develop techniques such as proof by induction, proof by contradiction and how additional fundamentals such as Number Theory, Combinatorics, Abstract Algebra and analyzing computer observations will blend in as pieces of the puzzle to address deeper research questions and welcome the interdisciplinary research atmosphere. The aim is to enhance efficiency in fast speed computing when we write computer programs that decipher the patterns of the periodic cycles and the transient terms inductively that will lead to new unanswered questions to pioneers.

AUTHOR INTRODUCTION

Michael A. Radin earned his Ph.D. at the University of Rhode Island in 2001 and is currently an associate professor of mathematics at the Rochester Institute of Technology. Michael started his journey analyzing difference equations with periodic and eventually periodic solutions as part of his Ph.D. thesis and has several publications on boundedness and periodic nature of solutions of rational difference equations, max-type difference equations and piecewise difference equations. Michael published several papers together with his Master's students and undergraduate students at RIT and has publications with students and colleagues from Riga Technical University, University of Latvia and several other European Universities.

Michael also has publications in applied mathematics related topics such as Neural Networking, Modelling Extinct Civilizations and Modelling Human Emotions. Michael organized numerous sessions on difference equations and applications at the annual **American Mathematical Society** meetings. Recently Michael published four manuscripts on international pedagogy and has been invited as a keynote speaker at several international and interdisciplinary conferences. Michael taught courses and conducted seminars on these related topics during his spring 2009 sabbatical at the Aegean University in Greece and during his spring 2016 sabbatical at Riga Technical University and at the University of Latvia.

During his spare time Michael spends time outdoors and is an avid landscape photographer. In addition, Michael is an active poet and has several published poems in the **Le Mot Juste**. Spending time outdoors and active landscape photography widens and expands Michael's understandings of nature's patterns and cadences.

CONTENTS

Appendices   305

CHAPTER 1

INTRODUCTION

We notice patterns quite frequently during different occasions. For instance, traffic patterns, musical patterns, nature's patterns, weather patterns, patterns in computer programs and mathematical patterns. Sometime patterns repeat at the same scale and at other times patterns repeat at different scales. In addition, we can discover alternating patterns. The first example that I would like to share is the clouds' patterns repeated at the same scale that we can see from the airplane window as we are flying:

The second example is an aerial photograph of a canyon resembling patterns repeated at different scales:

The next example illustrated patterns of equilateral triangles repeated at different scales of the **Sierpinski Triangle** (image by James W. Wilson from University of Georgia):

The objectives of this textbook are to get acquainted with difference equations. To solve first order, second order, higher order difference equations and systems of difference equations explicitly using the induction method, to determine the monotonic character of solutions, the periodic and oscillatory traits of solutions and stability of solutions. Here are some of the questions that we will remit throughout the book: Does a solution converge monotonically or oscillate? Does a solution diverge to infinity monotonically? We will discuss applications of difference equations in population dynamics, biological sciences, signal processing, economics and neural networking. Analyze specific discrete models such as the Linear Economics Model, Logistic Model, Beverton–Holt model, Ricker Model, Pielou's Model, Host Parasitoid Model, The West Nile Epidemics Model, and the LTI difference equation in signal processing. Furthermore, after working out the details of several rigourous examples we will discover and prove theorems. Our aim is to compare the similarities and differences between periodic cycles of even order and odd order; the contrasts when we have unique periodic cycles versus every solution being periodic. Moreover, we will study specific difference equations that exhibit eventually constant solutions and eventually periodic solutions.

Recently, I had the opportunity to implement the hands-on teaching and learning style in the courses that I regularly teach at RIT and during my sabbatical in Latvia during the spring 2016 semester. This method confirmed to work very successfully for me and my students, kept the students stimulated and engaged and improved their course performance [72, 73]. Therefore, while applying the hands-on teaching and learning style, the intent of this book is to provide the repetitive type examples to enhance the understanding of fundamentals of difference equations and their applications. In fact, several repetitive type examples will help us develop our intuition on patterns' recognition and see the bigger spectrum how concepts relate to each other that will lead to development of theorems and their proofs. This will be an especially essential technique to understand the proof by induction method that will be used to generalize several results.

1.1. Recursive Sequences

We will start refreshing our memories about sequences. First of all, how do we write a formula of a sequence? Second of all, when do we have to write a recursive formula? Furthermore, when we write a recursive formula for a sequence, we will treat it as an **Initial Value Problem**, where the initial value is similar to the starting index of the sequence. We will start with exhibiting examples when we move from one neighbor to the next by adding a constant term. In the very first example we will move from one neighbor to the next by adding a 4.

Example 1. Write a recursive formula for:

$$1, \ 5, \ 9, \ 13, \ 17, \ 21, \ 25, \dots.$$

Solution: Observe that we shift from neighbor to neighbor by adding a 4. Therefore, we can write the following formula of the above sequence:

$$\{4n + 1\}_{n=0}^{\infty}.$$

Alternatively, we can express this as a recursive sequence. By iteration and induction we get:

$$x_1 = 1,$$
$$x_1 + 4 = 1 + 4 = 5 = x_2,$$
$$x_2 + 4 = 5 + 4 = 9 = x_3,$$
$$x_3 + 4 = 9 + 4 = 13 = x_4,$$
$$x_4 + 4 = 13 + 4 = 17 = x_5,$$
$$x_5 + 4 = 17 + 4 = 21 = x_6,$$
$$\vdots$$

Thus for all $n \in \mathbb{N}$:

$$\begin{cases} x_{n+1} = x_n + 4, \\ x_1 = 1. \end{cases}$$

In the next example we move from neighbor to neighbor by multiplying by 2. This is called a **Geometric Sequence**.

Example 2. Write a recursive formula for:

$$7, \ 14, \ 28, \ 56, \ 112, \ 224, \ 448, \ldots.$$

Solution: Notice that we shift from neighbor to neighbor by multiplying by 2. Therefore, we can write the following formula of the above sequence:

$$\{7 \cdot 2^n\}_{n=0}^{\infty}.$$

Alternatively, we can describe this as a recursive sequence. Notice:

$$x_1 = 7,$$
$$x_1 \cdot 2 = 7 \cdot 2 = 14 = x_2,$$
$$x_2 \cdot 2 = 14 \cdot 2 = 28 = x_3,$$
$$x_3 \cdot 2 = 28 \cdot 2 = 56 = x_4,$$
$$x_4 \cdot 2 = 56 \cdot 2 = 112 = x_5,$$
$$x_5 \cdot 2 = 112 \cdot 2 = 224 = x_6,$$
$$\vdots$$

Thus for all $n \in \mathbb{N}$:

$$\begin{cases} x_{n+1} = 2x_n, \\ x_1 = 7. \end{cases}$$

In the next example we will be adding consecutive integers starting at 1.

Example 3. Write a recursive formula for:

$$1, \ 3, \ 6, \ 10, \ 15, \ 21, \ 28, \ldots.$$

Solution: Notice:

$$x_1 = 1,$$
$$x_1 + 2 = 1 + 2 = 3 = x_2,$$
$$x_2 + 3 = 3 + 3 = 6 = x_3,$$
$$x_3 + 4 = 6 + 4 = 10 = x_4,$$
$$x_4 + 5 = 10 + 5 = 15 = x_5,$$
$$x_5 + 6 = 15 + 6 = 21 = x_6,$$
$$x_6 + 7 = 21 + 7 = 28 = x_7,$$
$$\vdots$$

It follows by induction that for all $n \in \mathbb{N}$:

$$\begin{cases} x_{n+1} = x_n + (n+1), \\ x_1 = 1. \end{cases}$$

Example 4. Write a recursive formula for:

$$4, \ 13, \ 25, \ 40, \ 58, \ 79, \ 103, \ldots.$$

Solution: Observe:

$$x_1 = 4,$$
$$x_1 + 3 \cdot 3 = 4 + 9 = 4 + 3 \cdot 3 = 13 = x_2,$$
$$x_2 + 3 \cdot 4 = 13 + 12 = 13 + 3 \cdot 4 = 25 = x_3,$$
$$x_3 + 3 \cdot 5 = 25 + 15 = 25 + 3 \cdot 5 = 40 = x_4,$$
$$x_4 + 3 \cdot 6 = 40 + 18 = 40 + 3 \cdot 6 = 58 = x_5,$$
$$x_5 + 3 \cdot 7 = 58 + 21 = 58 + 3 \cdot 7 = 79 = x_6,$$
$$\vdots$$

Thus for all $n \in \mathbb{N}$:

$$\begin{cases} x_{n+1} = x_n + 3(n+2), \\ x_1 = 4. \end{cases}$$

Example 5. Write a recursive formula for:

$$1, \ 2, \ 6, \ 24, \ 120, \ 720, \ 5040, \ldots.$$

Solution: We obtain the following iterative pattern:

$$x_1 = 1,$$
$$x_1 \cdot 2 = 1 \cdot 2 = 2 = x_2,$$
$$x_2 \cdot 3 = 2 \cdot 3 = 6 = x_3,$$
$$x_3 \cdot 4 = 6 \cdot 4 = 24 = x_4,$$
$$x_4 \cdot 5 = 24 \cdot 5 = 120 = x_5,$$
$$x_5 \cdot 6 = 120 \cdot 6 = 720 = x_6,$$
$$\vdots$$

Thus for all $n \in \mathbb{N}$:

$$\begin{cases} x_{n+1} = (n+1) \cdot x_n, \\ x_1 = 1. \end{cases}$$

This example describes the **Factorial Pattern**.

Now we will advance with more comprehensive properties of difference equations.

1.2. Order of a Difference Equation and Explicit Solution

We will emerge with examples of difference equations of various orders:

(i) $x_{n+1} = 4x_n, \quad n = 0, 1, \ldots.$
(ii) $x_{n+2} = 2x_{n+1} - x_n, \quad n = 0, 1, \ldots.$
(iii) $x_{n+3} = x_{n+2} + x_{n+1} + x_n, \quad n = 0, 1, \ldots.$

In (i), we have a difference equation of first order as x_{n+1} depends on x_n. In (ii), we have a difference equation of second order as x_{n+2} depends on x_{n+1} and x_n. In (iii), we have a difference equation of third order as x_{n+3} depends on x_{n+2}, x_{n+1} and x_n. Now we will define a first order difference equation

(Δ.E. as an abbreviation) as an iterative process (recursive relation) in the form:

$$x_{n+1} = f(x_n), \quad n = 0, 1, \ldots. \tag{1.1}$$

Eq. (1.1) is a **first order Δ.E.** with one initial condition x_0. The function $y = f(x)$ describes Eq. (1.1) on an interval (domain) I. If $f : I \to I$ and $x_0 \in I$, then $x_n \in I$ for all $n \geq 0$. The following example portrays difference equations that are of first order as x_{n+1} depends on x_n.

Example 6. The following two difference equations are of first order:

(i) (Special Case of the **Riccati Δ.E.**)

$$x_{n+1} = \frac{x_n}{x_n - 1}, \quad n = 0, 1, \ldots.$$

(ii) (Special Case of the **Logistic Δ.E.**)

$$x_{n+1} = 4x_n (1 - x_n), \quad n = 0, 1, \ldots.$$

(iii) (Tent-Map, Special Case of **Piecewise Δ.E.**)

$$x_{n+1} = \begin{cases} 2x_n & \text{if } x_n < \dfrac{1}{2}, \\ 2(1 - x_n) & \text{if } x_n \geq \dfrac{1}{2}. \end{cases} \quad n = 0, 1, \ldots,$$

In Chapter 3 we will discover **Chaotic Behavior** in the Logistic Δ.E. and in the Tent-Map.

Now we will discuss a solution to Eq. (1.1). By iterating Eq. (1.1) starting at x_0, we procure:

$$x_0, \ x_1 = f(x_0), \ x_2 = f(x_1) = f^2(x_0), \ldots, \ x_n = f^n(x_0), \ldots.$$

The solution to Eq. (1.1) is defined as a **sequence** $\{x_n\}_{n=0}^{\infty}$. Our aims are to explicitly solve difference equations by iterations (recursively) and inductively as we will see throughout this book.

Example 7. Determine the **explicit solution** to the following Δ.E.:

$$x_{n+1} = ax_n, \quad n = 0, 1, \ldots,$$

where $a \neq 0$.

Solution: By iterations we obtain the following pattern:

$$x_0,$$
$$x_1 = ax_0,$$
$$x_2 = ax_1 = a \cdot [ax_0] = a^2 x_0,$$
$$x_3 = ax_2 = a \cdot [a^2 x_0] = a^3 x_0,$$
$$x_4 = ax_3 = a \cdot [a^3 x_0] = a^4 x_0,$$
$$x_5 = ax_4 = a \cdot [a^2 x_0] = a^5 x_0,$$
$$\vdots$$

Hence for all $n \in \mathbb{N}$:

$$x_n = a^n x_0.$$

This is a solution acquired by induction to the first order linear homogeneous Δ.E. that we will diligently analyze in Chapter 2.

Example 8. Determine the **explicit solution** to the following Δ.E.:

$$x_{n+1} = ax_n + b, \quad n = 0, 1, \ldots,$$

where $a \neq 0, 1$ and $b \neq 0$.

Solution: By iterations we procure the following pattern:

$$x_0,$$
$$x_1 = ax_0 + b,$$
$$x_2 = ax_1 + b = a \cdot [ax_0 + b] = a^2 x_0 + ab,$$
$$x_3 = ax_2 + b = a \cdot [a^2 x_0 + b] = a^3 x_0 + a^2 b + ab + b,$$
$$x_4 = ax_3 + b = a \cdot [a^3 x_0 + b] = a^4 x_0 + a^3 b + a^2 b + ab + b,$$
$$x_5 = ax_4 + b = a \cdot [a^2 x_0 + b] = a^5 x_0 + a^4 b + a^3 b + a^2 b + ab + b,$$
$$\vdots$$

Thus for all $n \in \mathbb{N}$:

$$x_n = a^n x_0 + b \left[\sum_{i=0}^{n-1} a^i \right] = a^n x_0 + b \left[\frac{1 - a^n}{1 - a} \right].$$

This is a solution obtained by induction to a first order linear nonhomogeneous Δ.E. that we will investigate rigorously in Chapter 2.

1.2.1. *Non-autonomous difference equations*

Throughout this book we will encounter several non-autonomous difference equations; non-autonomous linear difference equations and non-autonomous rational difference equations including the non-autonomous Riccati Difference Equations. First we will introduce examples of first order non-autonomous difference equations that we will meticulously analyze in Chapter 2.

(i) $x_{n+1} = a_n x_n, \quad n = 0, 1, \ldots,$
(ii) $x_{n+1} = x_n + b_n, \quad n = 0, 1, \ldots,$
(iii) $x_{n+1} = a_n x_n + b_n, \quad n = 0, 1, \ldots,$

where $\{a_n\}_{n=0}^{\infty}$ and $\{b_n\}_{n=0}^{\infty}$ are either sequences of real numbers or periodic sequences. In (i), each term of the sequence $\{a_n\}_{n=0}^{\infty}$ is multiplied by x_n during each iteration for all $n \geq 0$. In (ii), on the other hand, each term of the sequence $\{b_n\}_{n=0}^{\infty}$ is added to x_n during each iteration for all $n \geq 0$. In (iii), for all $n \geq 0$, b_n is added to $a_n x_n$. Therefore, there are three possibilities to express a first order non-autonomous Δ.E.:

$$x_{n+1} = a_n \cdot [f(x_n)], \quad n = 0, 1, \ldots, \tag{1.2}$$

$$x_{n+1} = f(x_n) + b_n, \quad n = 0, 1, \ldots, \tag{1.3}$$

or

$$x_{n+1} = a_n \cdot [f(x_n)] + b_n, \quad n = 0, 1, \ldots, \tag{1.4}$$

where $\{a_n\}_{n=0}^{\infty}$ and $\{b_n\}_{n=0}^{\infty}$ are either sequences of real numbers or periodic sequences. In addition, these are examples of non-autonomous Riccati Difference Equations that we will study in Chapter 3:

(i) $x_{n+1} = \frac{a_n}{x_n}, \quad n = 0, 1, \ldots,$
(ii) $x_{n+1} = \frac{a_n x_n}{x_{n-1}}, \quad n = 0, 1, \ldots.$

When we explicitly solve Eq. (1.3) and (1.4), we will see convoluted patterns that will be discussed in the next section.

1.2.2. *Convolution*

Our plan is to study sequences and sums that arise in convoluted patterns. For instance, the **Binomial Expansion Formula**:

$$(x + y)^n = \sum_{k=0}^{n} \binom{n}{k} x^{n-k} y^k$$

is described in the convoluted pattern as powers of x decrease, the powers of y increase and the sum of the powers of x and y is always n for all $k = 0, 1, \ldots, n$.

Definition 1. The following sequence:

$$\{a_i b_{n-i}\}_{i=0}^{n} = a_0 b_n, \ a_1 b_{n-1}, \ a_2 b_{n-2}, \ldots, a_{n-1} b_1, \ a_n b_0$$

is a **Convoluted Sequence** as the sum of the indices of a_i and b_{n-i} is always constant for all $i = 0, 1, \ldots, n$.

Definition 2. The following summation:

$$\sum_{i=0}^{n} a_i b_{n-i} = a_0 b_n + a_1 b_{n-1} + a_2 b_{n-2} + \ldots + a_{n-1} b_1 + a_n b_0$$

is a **Convoluted Summation** as the sum of the indices of a_i and b_{n-i} is always constant for all $i = 0, 1, \ldots, n$.

In the next example we will distinguish a convoluted pattern as a solution to a non-autonomous difference equation.

Example 9. Determine the **explicit solution** to the following Δ.E.:

$$x_{n+1} = a x_n + b_n, \quad n = 0, 1, \ldots,$$

where $a \neq 0$ and $\{b_n\}_{n=0}^{\infty}$ is a sequence of real numbers.

Solution: Observe:

$$x_0,$$
$$x_1 = a x_0 + b_0,$$
$$x_2 = a x_1 + b_1 = a \cdot [a x_0 + b_0] + b_1 = a^2 x_0 + a b_0 + b_1,$$
$$x_3 = a x_2 + b_2 = a \cdot \left[a^2 x_0 + a b_0 + b_1\right] + b_2 = a^3 x_0 + a^2 b_0 + a b_1 + b_2,$$
$$x_4 = a x_3 + b_3 = a \cdot \left[a^3 x_0 + a^2 b_0 + a b_1 + b_2\right]$$
$$+ b_3 = a^4 x_0 + a^3 b_0 + a^2 b_1 + a b_2 + b_3,$$

$$\vdots$$

Hence for all $n \in \mathbb{N}$:

$$x_n = a^n x_0 + \sum_{i=0}^{n-1} a^{n-1-i} b_i.$$

This is a solution with a convoluted pattern to a first order linear nonhomogeneous and non-autonomous Δ.E. that we will investigate thoroughly in Chapter 2. Furthermore, we will see the implementation of this convoluted pattern with applications in Signal Processing in Chapters 2, 4, and 6.

Next we will consider a second order Δ.E. in the form:

$$x_{n+2} = f(x_{n+1}, x_n), \quad n = 0, 1, \dots . \tag{1.5}$$

Notice that this is a **second order Δ.E.** as we have two initial conditions x_0 and x_1 and x_{n+2} depends on x_{n+1} and x_n. In addition, the function $f(x, y)$ describes Eq. (1.5) on an interval (domain) $I \times I$. If $f : I \times I \to I \times I$ and $x_0, x_1 \in I$, then $x_n \in I$ for all $n \geq 0$.

Analogous to Eq. (1.1), the solution to Eq. (1.5) is a sequence $\{x_n\}_{n=0}^{\infty}$. From Eq. (1.1) and Eq. (1.5) we extend to the kth ($k \in \mathbb{N}$) order Δ.E. in the form:

$$x_{n+k} = f(x_{n+k-1}, x_{n+k-2}, \dots, x_n), \quad n = 0, 1, \dots , \tag{1.6}$$

with k initial conditions $x_0, x_1, \dots, x_{k-1}$, whose solution is a sequence $\{x_n\}_{n=0}^{\infty}$.

It is our goal to investigate the **long term behavior** of solutions to difference equations. It is of paramount interest and importance to address the following three primary questions throughout this book:

- Does every solution have a limit?
- Do periodic solutions exist?
- Is every solution bounded?

Our aims of this textbook are to address the following questions. Does the limit exist? Is the limit monotonic or oscillatory? If the limit does not exist, are solutions bounded and periodic or perhaps chaotic? If an unbounded solution exists, does it diverge monotonically or does a particular sub-sequence diverge? In addition, our intents are to ascertain the existence of periodic solutions and patterns of periodic solutions. Now we will resume with **Equilibrium Point(s)** of a Δ.E.

1.3. Equilibrium Points

In this section we will focus on the existence of equilibrium points of difference equations analytically and graphically.

Definition 3. We define $\bar{x}$ is an **equilibrium point** or a **trivial solution** of Eq. (1.1) provided that

$$\bar{x} = f(\bar{x}).$$

If $x_0 = \bar{x}$, then $x_n = \bar{x}$ for all $n \geq 0$.

The following examples determine the existence of equilibrium points of Eq. (1.1).

Example 10. Consider the following Δ.E.:

$$x_{n+1} = \frac{2x_n}{1 + x_n}, \quad n = 0, 1, \ldots.$$

Verify that if $x_0 = 1$, then $x_n = 1$ for all $n \in \mathbb{N}$.

Solution: Notice:

$$x_0 = 1,$$
$$x_1 = \frac{2x_0}{1 + x_0} = \frac{2 \cdot 1}{1 + 1} = 1,$$
$$x_2 = \frac{2x_1}{1 + x_1} = \frac{2 \cdot 1}{1 + 1} = 1,$$
$$x_3 = \frac{2x_2}{1 + x_2} = \frac{2 \cdot 1}{1 + 1} = 1,$$
$$\vdots$$

The result follows.

Example 11. Determine the **equilibrium point(s)** of:

$$x_{n+1} = 4x_n(1 - x_n), \quad n = 0, 1, \ldots. \tag{1.7}$$

Solution: First set

$$\bar{x} = 4\bar{x}(1 - \bar{x}).\qquad(1.8)$$

Eq. (1.8) describes the intersection between the functions $y = x$ and $y = 4x(1 - x)$ and is depicted by the following graph:

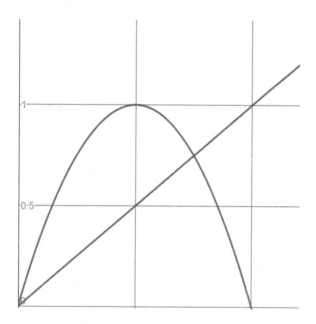

Therefore $\bar{x} = 0$ and $\bar{x} = \frac{3}{4}$ are the only equilibrium points of Eq. (1.7). This is a special case of the **Logistic Δ.E.** that we will study in Chapter 3. The diagram above will direct us to the **Cobweb Method** in Chapter 3. The Logistic Δ.E. has various applications in population dynamics and has been studied in ([9, 10] and [54]).

Example 12. Determine the **equilibrium point(s)** of:

$$x_{n+1} = 3x_n e^{-x_{n-1}}, \quad n = 0, 1, \dots.\qquad(1.9)$$

Solution: First set

$$\bar{x} = 3\bar{x}e^{-\bar{x}}.\qquad(1.10)$$

Eq. (1.10) describes the intersection between the functions $y = x$ and $y = 3xe^{-x}$ and is evoked by the following graph:

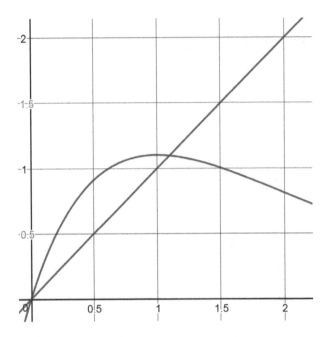

Note that $\bar{x} = 0$ and $\bar{x} = Ln(3)$ are the only equilibrium points of Eq. (1.9). This is a special case of a **Δ.E. in Exponential Form** that we will study in Chapters 3 and 5.

Moreover, in Chapters 3 and 5, we will study the stability character of equilibrium points. The following theorem relates the limit of a solution of Eq. (1.1) to an equilibrium point.

Theorem 1. *Let* $\{x_n\}_{n=0}^{\infty}$ *be a solution of Eq. (1.1). Suppose that:*

(i) $f(x)$ *is a continuous function.*
(ii) *There exists L such that:*

$$\lim_{n \to \infty} x_n = L.$$

Then $L = \bar{x}.$

Proof.   First of all,

$$\lim_{n \to \infty} x_{n+1} = L.$$

Second of all, as we assumed that $f(x)$ is continuous, then we obtain

$$L = \lim_{n \to \infty} x_{n+1} = \lim_{n \to \infty} [f(x_n)] = f\left(\lim_{n \to \infty} x_n\right) = f(L).$$

Thus $L = \bar{x}$. $\qquad\qquad\qquad\qquad\qquad\qquad\qquad\qquad\qquad\qquad\qquad$ □

In Chapters 2 and 4, we will examine examples of difference equations where the function $f(x)$ is not continuous, there are no equilibrium points, and yet the limit exists. Now we will focus on **convergent sequences**.

1.4. Convergent Sequences (Solutions)

In this section we will examine convergent sequences. In fact we will render examples of a sequence converging **monotonically** to the limit, sub-sequences converging monotonically to the limit and **oscillatory** convergence in different sub-sequences.

Definition 4. $\{x_{n_k}\}_{k=0}^{\infty}$ is a **sub-sequence** of $\{x_n\}_{n=0}^{\infty}$.

The following are examples of sub-sequences.

Example 13. $\{2n\}_{n=1}^{\infty}$ is a **sub-sequence** of $\{n\}_{n=1}^{\infty}$ and shown below as:

$$1, \mathbf{2}, 3, \mathbf{4}, 5, \mathbf{6}, 7, \mathbf{8}, 9, \mathbf{10}, \ldots.$$

Example 14. $\{4^n\}_{n=0}^{\infty}$ is a **sub-sequence** of $\{2^n\}_{n=0}^{\infty}$ and expressed below as:

$$\mathbf{1}, 2, \mathbf{4}, 8, \mathbf{16}, 32, \mathbf{64}, 128, \mathbf{256}, \ldots.$$

Now we will direct our analysis on monotonic properties of sequences with the following definitions and examples.

Definition 5. The sequence $\{x_n\}_{n=0}^{\infty}$ is **monotonic** if one of the following holds true:

(i) $x_n < x_{n+1}$ for all $n \geq 0$, (**monotonically increasing**).
(ii) $x_{n+1} < x_n$ for all $n \geq 0$, (**monotonically decreasing**).

Example 15. The sequence:

$$x_n = \left(\frac{1}{2}\right)^n, \quad n = 0, 1, \ldots,$$

is resembled by the following graph:

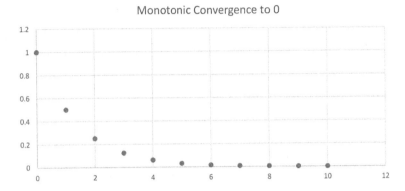

Monotonic Convergence to 0

This evokes a **monotonically decreasing** sequence that converges to 0 from above. Also notice:

(i) $x_{n+1} < x_n$ for all $n \geq 0$,

(ii) $\lim_{n \to \infty} x_n = 0$.

In Population Dynamics convergence to 0 would imply extinction and convergence to a positive equilibrium would imply survival. Examples of Population Dynamics Models have been studied in [9, 10, 68, 69]. Next we will probe non-monotonic sequences.

Definition 6. The sequence $\{x_n\}_{n=0}^{\infty}$ is **oscillatory** about the equilibrium $\bar{x}$ if for all $n \geq 0$ and some $k \in \mathbb{N}$ one of the followings holds true:

(i) $x_n, x_{n+1}, \ldots, x_{n+k-1} < \bar{x} < x_{n+k}$,

(ii) $x_n < \bar{x} < x_{n+1}, x_{n+2} \ldots, x_{n+k}$.

In part (i), the sequence $\{x_n\}_{n=0}^{\infty}$ oscillates with **negative semi-cycles** of length k. In part (ii), the sequence $\{x_n\}_{n=0}^{\infty}$ oscillates with **positive semi-cycles** of length k.

Example 16. The sequence:

$$x_n = \left(-\frac{4}{5}\right)^n, \quad n = 0, 1, \ldots,$$

is portrayed by the following graph:

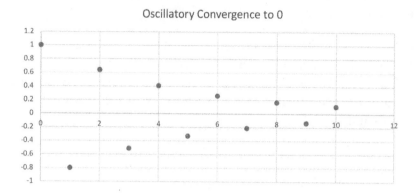

Now the sequence converges to 0 in two sub-sequences. In fact, one sub-sequence (even-indexed sub-sequence) converges to 0 from above and the other sub-sequence (odd-indexed sequence) converges to 0 from below. Furthermore, this is an **oscillatory** sequence that oscillates about 0 with semi-cycles of length 1. In addition we acquire:

(i) $x_{2n+2} < x_{2n}$ for all $n \geq 0$,

(ii) $x_{2n+1} < x_{2n+3}$ for all $n \geq 0$,

(iii) $\lim_{n \to \infty} x_{2n} = 0$ and $\lim_{n \to \infty} x_{2n+1} = 0$.

Example 17. The graph below:

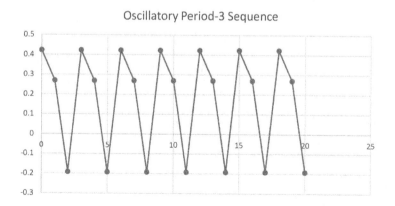

depicts an **oscillatory** period-3 cycle. Two terms of the cycle are positive and one term of the cycle is negative portraying a positive semi-cycle with length 2 and a negative semi-cycle with length 1.

Oscillatory behavior has very crucial applications in Biological Sciences, in Economics and in Engineering Sciences (vibrations, resonance, and signal processing [25]). Applications of oscillations in population dynamics have been studied by Jim Cushing in [23, 24]. Oscillations in the Logistic Model have been studied in [54].

Example 18. The sequence:

$$
x_n = \begin{cases} \left(\dfrac{1}{2}\right)^n & \text{if } n \text{ is even,} \\[2ex] \left(\dfrac{2}{3}\right)^n & \text{if } n \text{ is odd,} \end{cases} \qquad n = 0, 1, \ldots,
$$

is characterized by the following graph:

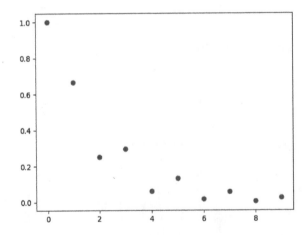

The sequence converges to 0 in two **monotonically converging** sub-sequences to 0 from above. Furthermore:

(i) $x_{2n+2} < x_{2n}$ for all $n \geq 0$,
(ii) $x_{2n+3} < x_{2n+1}$ for all $n \geq 0$,
(iii) $\lim_{n \to \infty} x_{2n} = 0$ and $\lim_{n \to \infty} x_{2n+1} = 0$.

Example 19. The sequence:

$$x_n = \begin{cases} \left(\dfrac{1}{2}\right)^n & \text{if } n \text{ is even,} \\[2ex] \dfrac{n}{n+1} & \text{if } n \text{ is odd,} \end{cases} \quad n = 0, 1, \ldots,$$

is described by the following graph:

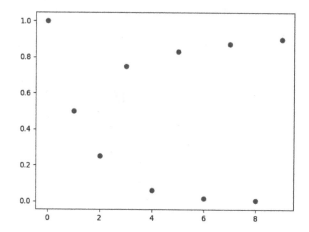

Observe that the sequence does not converge (does not have a limit) as

$$\lim_{n \to \infty} x_{2n} = 0 \neq 1 = \lim_{n \to \infty} x_{2n+1}.$$

Furthermore, the even-indexed sub-sequence is **monotonically decreasing** to 0 and the odd-indexed sub-sequence is **monotonically increasing** to 1, resembled analytically as:

(i) $x_{2n+2} < x_{2n}$ for all $n \geq 0$,
(ii) $x_{2n+1} < x_{2n+3}$ for all $n \geq 0$,
(iii) $\lim_{n \to \infty} x_{2n} = 0$ and $\lim_{n \to \infty} x_{2n+1} = 1$.

Now we will shift our probe on **periodic sequences** and their patterns.

1.5. Periodic Sequences (Solutions)

Our next aim is to recognize periodic traits and patterns graphically and analytically. In Pre-calculus, we studied periodic functions such as $y = \sin(x)$, $y = \cos(x)$, and Piecewise Functions such as $y = |x|$. The graph below sketches four cycles of $y = sin\left(\frac{\pi x}{2}\right)$ with period-4:

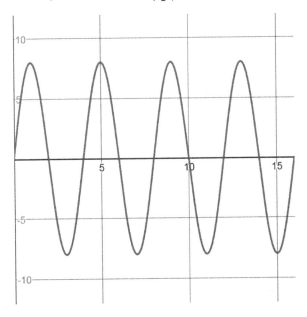

Observe that $y = sin\left(\frac{\pi x}{2}\right)$ oscillates about 0.

Definition 7. The sequence $\{x_n\}_{n=0}^{\infty}$ is periodic with **minimal period-p,** $(p \geq 2)$, provided that

$$x_{n+p} = x_n \quad \text{for all } n = 0, 1, \ldots.$$

We will illustrate two graphical examples of a period-4 cycle and a period-5 cycle:

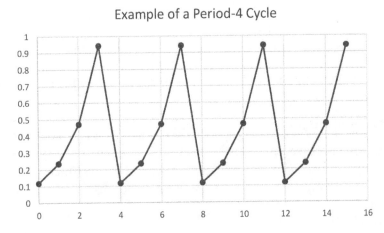

Example of a Period-4 Cycle

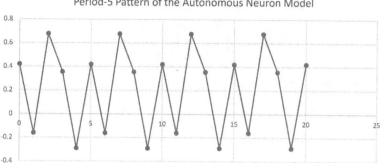

Period-5 Pattern of the Autonomous Neuron Model

The upcoming examples will describe patterns of assorted periodic cycles analytically by solving the given **Initial Value Problem**.

Example 20. Solve the **Initial Value Problem** explicitly and determine the period.

$$\begin{cases} x_{n+2} = -x_{n+1} - x_n, & n = 0, 1, \ldots, \\ x_0 = 4, \\ x_1 = 1. \end{cases}$$

Solution: Notice:

$$\begin{aligned} x_0 &= 4, \\ x_1 &= 1, \\ x_2 &= -x_1 - x_0 = -4 - 1 = -5, \\ x_3 &= -x_2 - x_1 = 5 - 1 = 4 = x_0, \\ x_4 &= -x_3 - x_2 = -4 + 5 = 1 = x_1. \end{aligned}$$

Hence we procure a period-3 cycle and for all $n \geq 0$:

$$\begin{cases} x_{3n} = x_0 = 4, \\ x_{3n+1} = x_1 = 1, \\ x_{3n+2} = x_2 = -5. \end{cases}$$

Example 21. Solve the **Initial Value Problem** explicitly and determine the period.

$$\begin{cases} x_{n+1} = x_n + a_n, & n = 0, 1, \ldots, \\ x_0 = 1, \end{cases}$$

where $\{a_n\}_{n=0}^{\infty}$ is a period-2 sequence defined as:

$$a_n = \begin{cases} a_0 & \text{if } n \text{ is even,} \\ a_1 & \text{if } n \text{ is odd,} \end{cases}$$

and assume $a_0 + a_1 = 0$.

Solution: Observe:

$$
\begin{aligned}
x_0 &= 1, \\
x_1 &= x_0 + a_0 = 1 + a_0, \\
x_2 &= x_1 + a_1 = 1 + a_0 + a_1 = 1 = x_0, \\
x_3 &= x_2 + a_0 = 1 + a_0 = x_1.
\end{aligned}
$$

Hence we acquire a period-2 cycle and for all $n \geq 0$:

$$
\begin{cases}
x_{2n} = x_0 = 1, \\
x_{2n+1} = x_1 = 1 + a_0.
\end{cases}
$$

This is an example of a periodic cycle of a **Non-autonomous Δ.E.** that we will study in Chapters 2, 3, 4, and 5.

1.6. Complex Numbers and Periodic Cycles

We define a complex number in **rectangular coordinates** as:

$$z = x + yi, \tag{1.11}$$

where $Re(z) = x$, $Im(z) = y$, and $i = \sqrt{-1}$. In addition, $|z| = \sqrt{x^2 + y^2}$ and $\theta = arg(z)$ as shown in the diagram below:

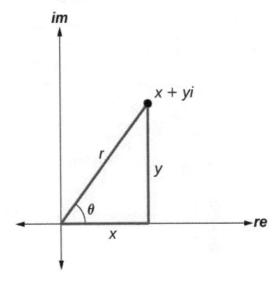

Eq. (1.11) is expressed in **rectangular coordinates** and we can write Eq. (1.11) in **polar coordinates**:

$$z = |z|e^{i\theta} = |z|\left[cos(\theta) + isin(\theta)\right].$$

Our next goal is to examine periodicity of the following sequence of complex numbers:

$$\{z_n\}_{n=0}^{\infty} = (x + yi)^n = \left[|z|e^{i\theta}\right]^n = |z|^n e^{ni\theta}$$
$$= |z|^n \left[cos(n\theta) + isin(n\theta)\right].$$

This is also called **De Moivre's Formula**. The following examples will illustrate assorted periods.

Example 22. The sequence of complex numbers:

$$\{z_n\}_{n=0}^{\infty} = (i)^n = \left[e^{i\left(\frac{\pi}{2}\right)}\right]^n = e^{ni\left(\frac{\pi}{2}\right)} = 1, i, -1, -i, \ldots$$

is periodic with **period-4** ($\theta = arg(i) = \frac{\pi}{2}$) and is evoked by the following diagram:

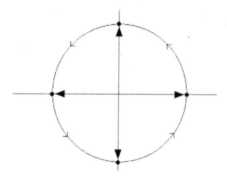

A period-4 cycle with argument $\frac{\pi}{2}$. This diagram was designed by Olga A. Orlova (doctoral student at Munich Technical University).

Example 23. The sequence of complex numbers:

$$\{z_n\}_{n=0}^{\infty} = \left(-\frac{1}{2} + i\frac{\sqrt{3}}{2}\right)^n = \left[e^{i\left(\frac{2\pi}{3}\right)}\right]^n$$
$$= e^{ni\left(\frac{2\pi}{3}\right)} = 1, -\frac{1}{2} + i\frac{\sqrt{3}}{2}, -\frac{1}{2} - i\frac{\sqrt{3}}{2}, \ldots$$

is periodic with **period-3**; $\theta = arg\left(-\frac{1}{2} + i\frac{\sqrt{3}}{2}\right) = \frac{2\pi}{3}$ is evoked by the following diagram:

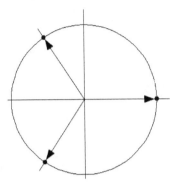

A period-3 cycle with argument $\frac{2\pi}{3}$. This diagram was designed by Olga A. Orlova (doctoral student at Munich Technical University).

Therefore, it follows from the previous two examples that the sequence

$$\{z_n\}_{n=0}^{\infty} = (x + yi)^n = |z|^n e^{ni\theta}, \quad n = 0, 1, \ldots$$

is periodic with period $p \geq 3$ and expressed in the form:

$$z = e^{i\left(\frac{2\pi}{p}\right)} = \cos\left(\frac{2\pi}{p}\right) + \sin\left(\frac{2\pi}{p}\right)i.$$

Furthermore, it follows that:

(1) $|z| = \sqrt{x^2 + y^2} = 1$.
(2) $\arg(x + yi)$ is a rational multiple of π.

In Chapter 4 we will apply this principle when the characteristic polynomial

$$\lambda^2 + p\lambda + q = 0$$

has complex roots and the corresponding second order linear Δ.E. will exhibit periodic solutions corresponding to the argument of one of the complex roots.

1.7. Specific Patterns of Periodic Cycles

Our aim is to ascertain specific patterns of periodic cycles. In fact, how do we detect the pattern(s) when we transition from one neighbor of the periodic cycle to the next?

Definition 8. The sequence $\{x_n\}_{n=0}^{\infty}$ is an **alternating sequence** if for some $k \in \mathbb{N}$, $x_n = -x_{n+k}$ for all $n \geq 0$.

Example 24. The sequence $\{x_n\}_{n=0}^{\infty} = (-1)^n$ is an alternating period-2 sequence described as:

$$1, \ -1, \ 1, \ -1, \ldots.$$

Note that $x_n = -x_{n+1}$ for all $n \geq 0$.

Example 25. The sequence $\{x_n\}_{n=0}^{\infty} = (-i)^n$ is an alternating period-4 sequence resembled as:

$$1, \ i, \ -1, \ -i, \ 1, \ i, \ -1, \ -i, \ldots.$$

Note that $x_n = -x_{n+2}$ for all $n \geq 0$.

Notice in Examples 24 and 25 both sequences are of even order. Therefore an alternating periodic sequence must be of even order. The following examples will manifest different patterns with shift of indices and switch of negative signs.

Example 26. In the period-2 pattern

$$\frac{A_0 - A_1}{A_0 A_1 + 1}, \ \frac{A_1 - A_0}{A_0 A_1 + 1}, \ldots,$$

from neighbor to neighbor the indices of the period-2 sequence $\{A_n\}_{n=0}^{\infty}$ shift by 1 under modulo 2 arithmetic and their signs switch in the numerator, yet the indices do not change in the denominator. This is also an example of an oscillatory and alternating period-2 cycle.

Example 27. In the period-4 pattern

$$\frac{A_0}{A_0 A_1 + 1}, \ \frac{A_1}{A_0 A_1 + 1}, \ \frac{-A_0}{A_0 A_1 + 1}, \ \frac{-A_1}{A_0 A_1 + 1}, \ldots,$$

from neighbor to neighbor the indices of the period-2 sequence $\{A_n\}_{n=0}^{\infty}$ shift by 1 under modulo 2 arithmetic, and their signs switch in the numerator and the negative sign alternates two terms later. The indices do not change in the denominator. This is also an example of an oscillatory and alternating period-4 cycle.

Example 28. In the period-2 pattern

$$\frac{A_1 B_0 + A_1}{1 - A_0 A_1}, \quad \frac{A_0 B_1 + A_0}{1 - A_0 A_1}, \dots,$$

the indices of the period-2 sequences $\{A_n\}_{n=0}^{\infty}$ and $\{B_n\}_{n=0}^{\infty}$ in the denominator stay the same from neighbor to neighbor. However, in the numerator the indices rotate by 1 under modulo 2 arithmetic.

More detailed examples of periodic patterns and alternating periodic patterns can be found in the **Appendix Chapter**.

1.8. Eventually Constant Sequences (Solutions)

In this section we will discuss **eventually constant sequences**.

Definition 9. The sequence $\{x_n\}_{n=0}^{\infty}$ is **eventually constant** if there exists $N \in \mathbb{N}$ such that

$$x_{n+N} = x_n = C \quad \text{for all } n = 0, 1, \dots,$$

for some constant $C \in \Re$. In this case, we have N **transient terms**.

Example 29. The graph below illustrates an eventually constant solution with constant $C = 0$ with four transient terms:

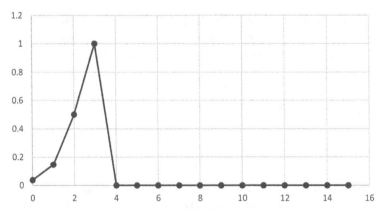

Eventually Constant with Four Transient Terms

Graph of an eventually constant solution with four increasing transient terms. Also $x_4 = x_5$. This graph is an example of a **Logistic Difference Equation** that we will analyze in Chapter 3.

Example 30. The graph below illustrates an eventually constant solution with constant $C = 1$ with nine transient terms:

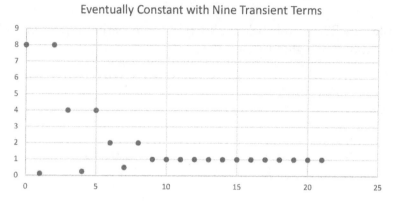

Eventually Constant with Nine Transient Terms

Graph of an eventually constant solution with nine transient terms that are clustered in three different groups compared to the pattern of increasing transient terms in the previous example. In addition $x_9 = x_{10}$. This graph is an example of a **Max-Type Difference Equation** that we will analyze in Chapter 5.

1.9. Eventually Periodic Sequences (Solutions)

In this section we will focus on **eventually periodic sequences**.

Definition 10. The sequence $\{x_n\}_{n=0}^{\infty}$ is **Eventually Periodic** with minimal period $p \geq 2$, if there exists $N \geq 1$ such that

$$x_{n+N+p} = x_{n+N} \quad \text{for all } n = 0, 1, \ldots.$$

In this case, we have N **transient terms**.

We will illustrate three examples of eventually periodic solutions that exhibit transient terms or transient behavior.

Example 31. The sequence below is eventually periodic with period-2 with three transient terms:

$$[\mathbf{16, \ 8, \ 4}], \ 2, \ 1, \ 2, \ 1, \ldots.$$

The three transient terms $x_0 - x_2$ are in square brackets and $x_5 = x_3$. This is an example of **3x + 1 Conjecture** that we will study in Chapter 3.

Now we will inspect some graphical examples of eventually periodic solutions of various periods and with different numbers of transient terms and the patterns of the transient terms.

Example 32. The graph below illustrates an eventually periodic solution with period-3 with eight transient terms:

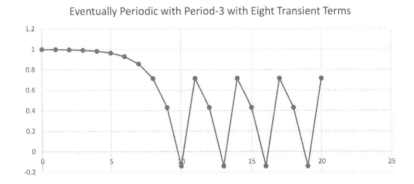

Graph of a period-3 cycle with eight decreasing transient terms. Also $x_{11} = x_8$. This graph is an example of a **Piecewise Difference Equation** that we will analyze in Chapter 3.

Example 33. The graph below demonstrates an eventually periodic solution with period-4 with thirteen transient terms:

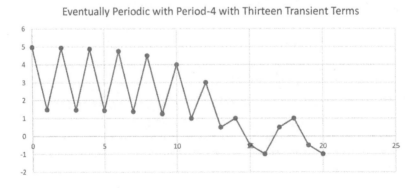

Graph of a period-4 cycle with thirteen transient terms that decrease in the pattern of two sub-sequences. In addition $x_{17} = x_{13}$. This graph is an example of a **Piecewise Difference Equation** that we will analyze in Chapter 3.

Example 34. The graph below demonstrates an eventually periodic solution with period-2 with six transient terms:

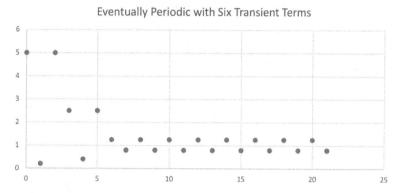

Eventually Periodic with Six Transient Terms

Graph of a period-2 cycle with six transient terms that are clustered in three different groups. Also note that $x_8 = x_6$. This graph is an example of a **Max-Type Δ.E.** that we will analyze in Chapter 5.

More attributes to the existence of eventually periodic solutions will be exhibited with the Logistic Difference Equation and the Piecewise Difference Equations in Chapter 3 and with Max-Type Difference Equations in Chapter 5.

1.10. Additional Examples of Periodic and Eventually Periodic Solutions

Now we will analyze additional graphical examples of periodic traits. These examples can be found in the Rulkov Autonomous and Non-autonomous models [70]. First of all, in the graph below:

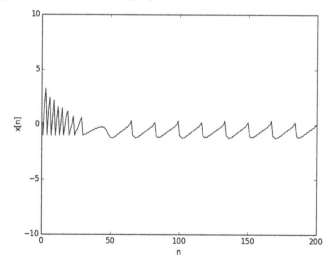

we can observe a pattern of transient terms with sharp spikes before the long and steady periodic solution emerges. Second of all:

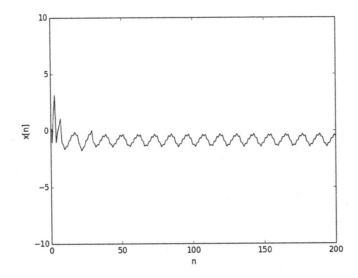

we see more spikes in the pattern of periodic solutions. In addition, by observing the next graph:

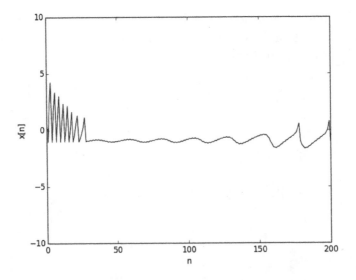

we can notice two different patterns of transient terms that we have not seen in any of the previous examples. Furthermore, by examining the dynamics of the following graph:

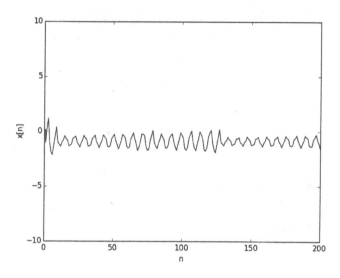

we can see that there is no distinct pattern in the transient terms. In this case, we have **chaotic behavior**. We will study more about Chaos in Chapter 3.

1.11. Divergent (Unbounded) Sequences (Solutions)

In this section we will focus on **divergent (unbounded)** sequences.

Definition 11. The sequence $\{x_n\}_{n=0}^{\infty}$ is **bounded** if for all $n \geq 0$:

$$-\infty < m \leq x_n \leq M < +\infty.$$

Definition 12. The sequence $\{x_n\}_{n=0}^{\infty}$ is **unbounded** if one of the following holds true:

(i) $x_n < x_{n+1}$ for all $n \geq 0$ and $\lim_{n \to \infty} x_n = +\infty$,

(ii) $x_{n+1} < x_n$ for all $n \geq 0$ and $\lim_{n \to \infty} x_n = -\infty$,

(iii) There exists a sub-sequence $\{x_{n_k}\}_{k=0}^{\infty}$ of $\{x_n\}_{n=0}^{\infty}$ such that either $\lim_{k \to \infty} x_{n_k} = +\infty$ or $\lim_{k \to \infty} x_{n_k} = -\infty$.

Example 35. The sequence:

$$x_n = \left(\frac{3}{2}\right)^n, \quad n = 0, 1, \ldots,$$

is characterized by the following graph:

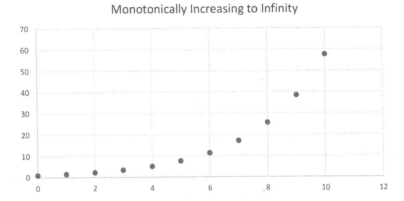

This depicts a **monotonically increasing** sequence diverging to $+\infty$ with the following properties:

(i) $x_n < x_{n+1}$ for all $n \geq 0$,
(ii) $\lim_{n \to \infty} x_n = \infty$.

Example 36. The sequence:

$$
x_n = \begin{cases} \left(\dfrac{1}{2}\right)^n & \text{if } n \text{ is even,} \\[3mm] \left(\dfrac{3}{2}\right)^n & \text{if } n \text{ is odd.} \end{cases} \qquad n = 0, 1, \ldots
$$

is depicted by the following graph:

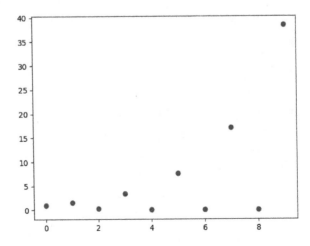

Also we see that:

(i) $x_{2n+2} < x_{2n}$ for all $n \geq 0$,
(ii) $x_{2n+1} < x_{2n+3}$ for all $n \geq 0$,
(iii) $\lim_{n \to \infty} x_{2n} = 0$ and $\lim_{n \to \infty} x_{2n+1} = \infty$.

Hence via (ii) and (iii), the even-indexed sub-sequence is monotonically converging to 0 and the odd-indexed sub-sequence is monotonically diverging to $+\infty$.

Boundedness of solutions is a vital property when applying difference equations in population modeling. For instance, the population model $x_{n+2} = \alpha + \beta x_n e^{-x_{n+1}}$ proposed by the Harvard School of Public Health in [34] has unbounded solutions when $\beta > e^\alpha$ and every solution is bounded when $\beta < e^\alpha$. Therefore, the second order Δ.E. in exponential form is a valid population model when $\beta < e^\alpha$.

1.12. Chapter 1 Exercises

In problems 1–6, write a **recursive formula (as an initial value problem)** of the following sequences:

1. 4, 9, 14, 19, 24, 29, 34, ...
2. 5, 17, 29, 41, 53, 65, 77, ...
3. 1, 3, 7, 13, 21, 31, 43, ...
4. 1, 4, 10, 19, 31, 46, 64, ...
5. 1, 2, 5, 10, 17, 26, 37, ...
6. 1, 4, 13, 28, 49, 76, 109, ...

In problems 7–15, write a **recursive formula (as an initial value problem)** of the following sequences:

7. 3, 12, 48, 192, 768, 3072, ...
8. 108, 36, 12, 4, $\dfrac{4}{3}$, $\dfrac{4}{9}$, ...
9. 64, 48, 36, 27, $\dfrac{81}{4}$, $\dfrac{343}{16}$, ...
10. 1, 2, 8, 48, 384, 3840, ...
11. 1, 3, 15, 105, 945, 10395, ...
12. 1, 5, 45, 585, 9945, ...
13. $1 \cdot 2$, $2 \cdot 3$, $3 \cdot 4$, $4 \cdot 5$, $5 \cdot 6$, ...
14. $1 \cdot 3$, $3 \cdot 5$, $5 \cdot 7$, $7 \cdot 9$, $9 \cdot 11$, ...

15. $2 \cdot 4, \ 4 \cdot 6, \ 6 \cdot 8, \ 8 \cdot 10, \ 10 \cdot 12, \ldots$.

In problems 16–20, write a **recursive formula (as an initial value problem)** of the following summations (series):

16. $\displaystyle\sum_{k=0}^{n} (2k+1)$.

17. $\displaystyle\sum_{k=0}^{n} (3k+2)$.

18. $\displaystyle\sum_{k=1}^{n} k^2$.

19. $\displaystyle\sum_{k=0}^{n} \left(\frac{1}{2}\right)^k$.

20. $\displaystyle\sum_{k=1}^{n} \left(\frac{1}{k}\right)^k$.

In problems 21–24, by iteration determine an **explicit solution** of each Δ.E.:

21. $x_{n+1} = 4x_n, \quad n = 0, 1, \ldots$.

22. $x_{n+1} = \dfrac{2x_n}{3}, \quad n = 0, 1, \ldots$.

23. $x_{n+1} + 2x_n = 0, \quad n = 0, 1, \ldots$.

24. $4x_{n+1} + 3x_n = 0, \quad n = 0, 1, \ldots$.

In problems 25–34, determine the **period** of each initial value problem inductively and discuss the **oscillatory character**:

25. $\begin{cases} x_{n+1} = \dfrac{1}{x_n}, \quad n = 0, 1, \ldots, \\ \\ x_0 = \dfrac{1}{3}. \end{cases}$

26. $\begin{cases} x_{n+1} = \dfrac{1+x_n}{x_n - 1}, \quad n = 0, 1, \ldots, \\ \\ x_0 = 3. \end{cases}$

27. $\begin{cases} x_{n+1} = x_n + (-1)^n, \quad n = 0, 1, \ldots, \\ \\ x_0 = 2. \end{cases}$

28. $\begin{cases} x_{n+1} = (-1)^n x_n + 2, & n = 0, 1, \ldots, \\ x_0 = 4. \end{cases}$

29. $\begin{cases} x_{n+1} = \dfrac{(-1)^n}{x_n}, & n = 0, 1, \ldots, \\ x_0 = 2. \end{cases}$

30. $\begin{cases} x_{n+2} = x_{n+1} - x_n, & n = 0, 1, \ldots, \\ x_0 = 1, \\ x_1 = 3. \end{cases}$

31. $\begin{cases} x_{n+2} = \sqrt{2}x_{n+1} - x_n, & n = 0, 1, \ldots, \\ x_0 = 3, \\ x_1 = 5. \end{cases}$

32. $\begin{cases} x_{n+2} = \dfrac{1}{x_n}, & n = 0, 1, \ldots, \\ x_0 = 2, \\ x_1 = 4. \end{cases}$

33. $\begin{cases} x_{n+2} = \dfrac{(-1)^n}{x_n}, & n = 0, 1, \ldots, \\ x_0 = 2, \\ x_1 = 4. \end{cases}$

34. $\begin{cases} x_{n+2} = \dfrac{x_{n+1}}{x_n}, & n = 0, 1, \ldots, \\ x_0 = 2, \\ x_1 = 6. \end{cases}$

In problems 35–39, determine if each given sequence is **periodic**. If not, explain why. If so, determine the period.

35. $x_n = \left(\dfrac{1}{\sqrt{2}} + \dfrac{1}{\sqrt{2}}i \right)^n, \quad n = 0, 1, \ldots.$

36. $x_n = \left(\dfrac{1}{2} + \dfrac{\sqrt{3}}{2}i \right)^n, \quad n = 0, 1, \ldots.$

37. $x_n = \left(\dfrac{\sqrt{3}}{2} + \dfrac{1}{2}i\right)^n$, $\quad n = 0, 1, \ldots$.

38. $x_n = \left(-\dfrac{1}{2}i\right)^n$, $\quad n = 0, 1, \ldots$.

39. $x_n = \left(\dfrac{5}{13} + \dfrac{12}{13}i\right)^n$, $\quad n = 0, 1, \ldots$.

In problems 40–44, determine the period and the **oscillatory character** from the following graphs:

40. Period of:

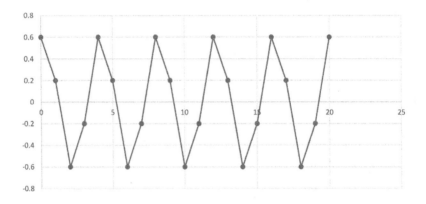

41. Period of:

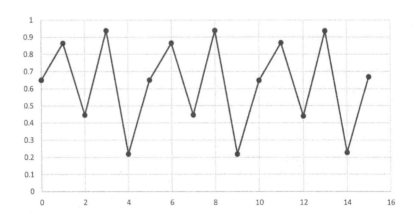

42. Period of:

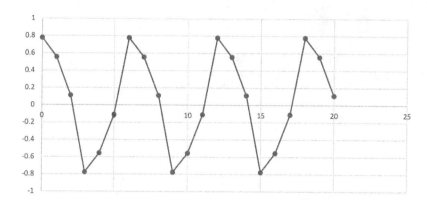

43. Period of:

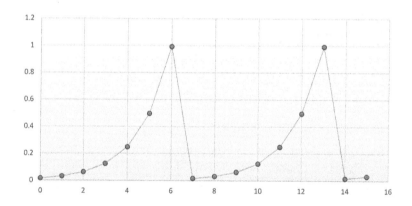

44. Period of:

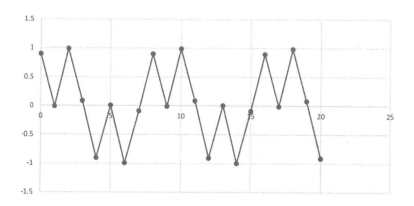

In problems 45–50, as in Examples 24–28, describe the pattern of the given periodic cycle:

45. $\dfrac{2}{17}, \dfrac{4}{17}, \dfrac{8}{17}, \dfrac{16}{17}, \ldots$

46. $\dfrac{b_0 + b_1 - b_2}{2}, \dfrac{b_0 - b_1 + b_2}{2}, \dfrac{-b_0 + b_1 + b_2}{2}, \ldots$

47. $\dfrac{a_0 + \sqrt{2}a_1 + a_2}{2}, \dfrac{a_1 + \sqrt{2}a_2 + a_3}{2},$

$\dfrac{a_2 + \sqrt{2}a_3 + a_0}{2}, \dfrac{a_3 + \sqrt{2}a_0 + a_1}{2}, \ldots$

48. $\dfrac{B_1 B_3 - 1}{1 + B_1}, 0, \dfrac{B_1 B_3 - 1}{1 + B_3}, 0, \ldots$

49. $\dfrac{b_0 b_1 b_2 b_3 + 1}{b_0 b_1 b_2 - b_0 b_1 + b_0 - 1}, \dfrac{b_0 b_1 b_2 b_3 + 1}{b_1 b_2 b_3 - b_1 b_2 + b_1 - 1},$

$\dfrac{b_0 b_1 b_2 b_3 + 1}{b_2 b_3 b_0 - b_2 b_3 + b_2 - 1}, \dfrac{b_0 b_1 b_2 b_3 + 1}{b_3 b_0 b_1 - b_3 b_0 + b_3 - 1}, \ldots$

50. $\dfrac{a_1 b_3 - b_1}{a_1 a_3 + 1}, \dfrac{a_2 b_0 - b_2}{a_0 a_2 + 1}, \dfrac{a_3 b_1 - b_3}{a_1 a_3 + 1}, \dfrac{a_0 b_2 - b_0}{a_0 a_2 + 1}, \ldots$

In problems 51–58, determine if each given sequence is **bounded**. If not, explain why. If so, determine if the limit exists. In either situation, determine the pattern of each sequence by breaking it up into proper sub-sequences if necessary.

51. $x_n = \begin{cases} \left(\dfrac{3}{4}\right)^n & \text{if } n \text{ is even,} \\ \dfrac{1}{n^2} & \text{if } n \text{ is odd.} \end{cases} \quad n = 1, 2, \ldots$

52. $x_n = \begin{cases} 1 + \left(\dfrac{1}{2}\right)^n & \text{if } n \text{ is even,} \\ \dfrac{n}{n+1} & \text{if } n \text{ is odd.} \end{cases} \quad n = 0, 1, \ldots$

53. $x_n = \begin{cases} 2 - \left(\dfrac{1}{2}\right)^n & \text{if } n \text{ is even,} \\ 1 + \left(\dfrac{1}{2}\right)^n & \text{if } n \text{ is odd.} \end{cases} \quad n = 0, 1, \ldots$

54. $x_n = \begin{cases} \dfrac{n-1}{n} & \text{if } n \text{ is even,} \\[2mm] \dfrac{n^2}{n+1} & \text{if } n \text{ is odd.} \end{cases} \qquad n = 1, 2, \ldots$

55. $x_n = \begin{cases} \left(\dfrac{1}{3}\right)^n & \text{if } n = 3k, \\[2mm] \left(\dfrac{3}{4}\right)^n & \text{if } n = 3k+1, \qquad n = 0, 1, \ldots \\[2mm] \dfrac{n^2}{n^2+1} & \text{if } n = 3k+2. \end{cases}$

56. $x_n = \left(-\dfrac{4}{5}\right)^n, \qquad n = 0, 1, \ldots.$

57. $x_n = \begin{cases} \left(\dfrac{5}{6}\right)^n & \text{if } n = 4k, \\[2mm] \left(\dfrac{8}{5}\right)^n & \text{if } n = 4k+1, \\[2mm] \dfrac{1}{1+4n} & \text{if } n = 4k+2, \qquad n = 0, 1, \ldots \\[2mm] \left(\dfrac{9}{4}\right)^n & \text{if } n = 4k+3. \end{cases}$

58. $x_n = \begin{cases} \left(\dfrac{2}{3}\right)^n & \text{if } n = 4k, \\[2mm] \left(\dfrac{4}{5}\right)^n & \text{if } n = 4k+1, \\[2mm] \dfrac{4n}{1+3n} & \text{if } n = 4k+2, \qquad n = 0, 1, \ldots \\[2mm] \dfrac{n^2}{1+(2n)^2} & \text{if } n = 4k+3. \end{cases}$

CHAPTER 2

FIRST ORDER LINEAR DIFFERENCE EQUATIONS

Our goal of this chapter is to solve first order linear difference equations explicitly (inductively), analyze convergence of solutions, evaluate the oscillatory character of solutions, study various applications in Population Dynamics, Finance and Signal Processing and examine the periodic traits and patterns of periodic cycles. We will commence with three examples of first order linear difference equations:

(i) (Homogeneous) $x_{n+1} = \frac{3x_n}{4}, \quad n = 0, 1, \ldots.$

(ii) (Nonhomogeneous) $x_{n+1} = 2x_n - 1, \quad n = 0, 1, \ldots.$

(iii) (Non-autonomous) $x_{n+1} = x_n + \left(\frac{1}{2}\right)^n, \quad n = 0, 1, \ldots.$

Our aim is to solve each linear Δ.E. explicitly, check the solution, and analyze the convergence nature of solutions and the periodic traits of solutions. In addition, our intent is to obtain an explicit solution to the linear Δ.E. in the form:

$$x_{n+1} = a_n x_n + b_n, \quad n = 0, 1, \ldots,$$

where $x_0 \in \Re$, and $\{a_n\}_{n=0}^{\infty}$ and $\{b_n\}_{n=0}^{\infty}$ are either infinite sequences or periodic sequences with the same period or with different periods. First we will launch off our investigation with the **Homogeneous First Order Δ.E.** in the form:

$$x_{n+1} = a x_n, \quad n = 0, 1, \ldots,$$

where $x_0 \in \Re$ and $a \neq 0$.

2.1. Homogeneous First Order Linear Difference Equations

The following are examples of first order linear homogeneous difference equations:

(i) $x_{n+1} = 4x_n, \quad n = 0, 1, \ldots.$
(ii) $x_{n+1} = \frac{4x_n}{5}, \quad n = 0, 1, \ldots.$
(iii) $x_{n+1} = -x_n, \quad n = 0, 1, \ldots.$

In (i), $a > 1$. In (ii), $0 < a < 1$. In (iii), $a = -1$. In this section, we will examine the first order $\Delta.$E. in the form:

$$x_{n+1} - ax_n = 0, \quad n = 0, 1, \ldots, \tag{2.12}$$

where the parameter $a \neq 0$ and the initial condition $x_0 \in \Re$. Let $\{x_n\}_{n=0}^{\infty}$ be a solution of Eq. (2.12). In Example 7 from Chapter 1 we derived the following solution to Eq. (2.12):

$$x_n = a^n x_0, \quad n = 0, 1, \ldots. \tag{2.13}$$

Note that $\bar{x} = 0$ is the only equilibrium point of Eq. (2.12) provided that $a \neq 1$. In fact if $a = 1$, then every initial condition x_0 is an equilibrium point of Eq. (2.12). The following statements hold true:

(i) When $|a| < 1$, then

$$\lim_{n \to \infty} x_n = \lim_{n \to \infty} a^n x_0 = 0.$$

(ii) When $a = 1$, then

$$\lim_{n \to \infty} x_n = \lim_{n \to \infty} x_0 = x_0.$$

(iii) When $a = -1$, then

$$x_n = (-1)^n x_0 = \begin{cases} x_0 & \text{if } n \text{ is even,} \\ -x_0 & \text{if } n \text{ is odd.} \end{cases}$$

In this case, we see that every non-trivial (non-equilibrium) solution of Eq. (2.12) is **oscillatory** and periodic with period-2.

(iv) When $a > 1$, then

$$\lim_{n \to \infty} x_n = \lim_{n \to \infty} a^n x_0 = \begin{cases} \infty & \text{if } x_0 > 0, \\ -\infty & \text{if } x_0 < 0. \end{cases}$$

(v) When $a < -1$, then we procure the following two cases:

— If $x_0 > 0$, then

$$\lim_{n \to \infty} x_{2n} = +\infty \quad \text{and} \quad \lim_{n \to \infty} x_{2n+1} = -\infty.$$

— If $x_0 < 0$, then

$$\lim_{n \to \infty} x_{2n} = -\infty \quad \text{and} \quad \lim_{n \to \infty} x_{2n+1} = +\infty.$$

From (iii), when $a = -1$, then every non-trivial (non-equilibrium) solution of Eq. (2.12) is **oscillatory** and periodic with the following alternating period-2 pattern:

$$x_0, -x_0, \ x_0, -x_0, \dots.$$

Furthermore, notice that the sum of two neighboring terms is always 0. Moreover, this is a frequent phenomena that will appear in other instances when periodic cycles exist. We will explore deeper analysis of periodicity properties in the section **Nonhomogeneous Case**. In next three examples, we will go through the details of solving the homogeneous first order linear difference equations and illustrate the monotonic behavior of solutions graphically.

Example 1. Solve the Initial Value Problem:

$$\begin{cases} x_{n+1} = \dfrac{3x_n}{4}, & n = 0, 1, \dots, \\[2mm] x_0 = \dfrac{3}{4}, \end{cases}$$

and:

(i) Determine

$$\lim_{n \to \infty} x_n.$$

(ii) Sketch the graph and describe the monotonic character.

Solution: Observe that from Eqs. (2.12) and (2.13), we get

$$x_n = x_0 \left(\frac{3}{4} \right)^n = \frac{3}{4} \left(\frac{3}{4} \right)^n = \left(\frac{3}{4} \right)^{n+1}.$$

So we see that

$$\lim_{n\to\infty} x_n = \lim_{n\to\infty} \left(\frac{3}{4}\right)^{n+1} = 0.$$

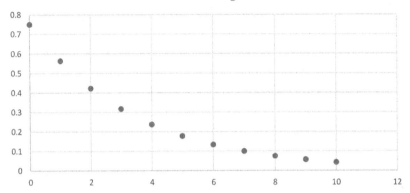

Notice that the solution is **monotonically decreasing** and converges to 0 from above.

Example 2. Solve the Initial Value Problem:

$$\begin{cases} x_{n+1} = \dfrac{-x_n}{2}, & n = 0, 1, \ldots, \\ x_0 = 4, \end{cases}$$

and:

(i) Determine

$$\lim_{n\to\infty} x_n.$$

(ii) Sketch the graph and describe the monotonic character.

Solution: Observe that from Eqs. (2.12) and (2.13), we get

$$x_n = x_0 \left(\frac{-1}{2}\right)^n = 4\left(\frac{-1}{2}\right)^n = \frac{(-1)^n}{2^{n-2}}.$$

So we see that

$$\lim_{n\to\infty} x_n = \frac{(-1)^n}{2^{n-2}} = 0.$$

Oscillatory Convergence to 0

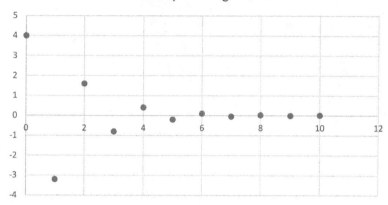

Note that the solution is an **oscillatory** convergent sequence; one sub-sequence converges to 0 from above and one sub-sequence converges to 0 from below.

Example 3. Solve the Initial Value Problem:

$$\begin{cases} x_{n+1} = \dfrac{3x_n}{2}, & n = 0, 1, \ldots, \\ x_0 = \dfrac{9}{4}, \end{cases}$$

and:

(i) Determine

$$\lim_{n \to \infty} x_n.$$

(ii) Sketch the graph and describe the monotonic character.

Solution: Observe that from Eqs. (2.12) and (2.13), we get

$$x_n = x_0 \left(\frac{3}{2}\right)^n = \frac{9}{4}\left(\frac{3}{2}\right)^n = \left(\frac{3}{2}\right)^{n+2}.$$

So we see that

$$\lim_{n \to \infty} x_n = \lim_{n \to \infty} \left(\frac{3}{2}\right)^{n+2} = +\infty.$$

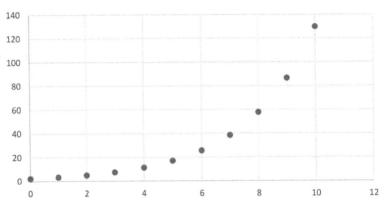

Observe that the solution is a **monotonically** divergent sequence that increases to $+\infty$.

In next two examples we will analytically verify the solution to the given **Initial Value Problem**.

Example 4. Solve the Initial Value Problem:

$$\begin{cases} 5x_{n+1} - 2x_n = 0, & n = 0, 1, \ldots, \\ x_0 = \dfrac{8}{125}, \end{cases}$$

and:

(i) Verify that the solution is correct.
(ii) Determine

$$\lim_{n \to \infty} x_n.$$

Solution: From Eqs. (2.12) and (2.13), we get

$$x_n = x_0 \left(\frac{2}{5}\right)^n = \frac{8}{125} \left(\frac{2}{5}\right)^n = \left(\frac{2}{5}\right)^{n+3}.$$

Now we see that

$$\lim_{n \to \infty} x_n = \lim_{n \to \infty} \left(\frac{2}{5}\right)^{n+3} = 0.$$

Furthermore, it follows that

$$5x_{n+1} - 2x_n = 5\left(\frac{2}{5}\right)^{n+4} - 2\left(\frac{2}{5}\right)^{n+3} = \frac{2^{n+4}}{5^{n+3}} - \frac{2^{n+4}}{5^{n+3}} = 0.$$

Example 5. Solve the Initial Value Problem:

$$\begin{cases} 6x_{n+1} + 10x_n = 0, \quad n = 0, 1, \ldots, \\ x_0 = \dfrac{9}{25}, \end{cases}$$

and:

(i) Verify that the solution is correct.
(ii) Determine

$$\lim_{n\to\infty} x_n.$$

Solution: From Eqs. (2.12) and (2.13), we get

$$x_n = x_0 \left(-\frac{5}{3}\right)^n = \frac{9}{25}\left(-\frac{5}{3}\right)^n = (-1)^n \left(\frac{5}{3}\right)^{n-2}.$$

Hence we see that

$$\lim_{n\to\infty} x_n = \lim_{n\to\infty} (-1)^n \left(\frac{5}{3}\right)^{n-2}$$

does not exist as

$$\lim_{n\to\infty} x_{2n} = +\infty \quad \text{and} \quad \lim_{n\to\infty} x_{2n+1} = -\infty.$$

Furthermore:

$$6x_{n+1} + 10x_n = 6(-1)^{n+1}\left(\frac{5}{3}\right)^{n-1} + 10(-1)^n\left(\frac{5}{3}\right)^{n-2}$$

$$= -2(-1)^n\frac{5^{n-1}}{3^{n-2}} + 2(-1)^n\frac{5^{n-1}}{3^{n-2}} = 0.$$

Now we will proceed with applications of first order linear homogeneous difference equations in biology and finance.

2.1.1. *Applications of first order linear difference equations in biology*

We will begin the discussion of applications of first order linear difference equations by examining the population of a species that either increases or decreases at a constant rate of $r\%$ per year. First, we define:

$$x_n = \text{the population at year } n,$$
$$x_{n+1} = \text{the population at year } n+1,$$
$$P_0 = \text{the initial population.}$$

Then we see that when the population **increases** at a constant rate of $r\%$ per year, we obtain the following initial value problem:

$$\begin{cases} x_{n+1} = x_n + \left(\dfrac{r}{100}\right) x_n, & n = 0, 1, \ldots, \\ x_0 = P_0. \end{cases}$$

Similarly, when the population **decreases** at a constant rate of $r\%$ per year, we obtain the following initial value problem:

$$\begin{cases} x_{n+1} = x_n - \left(\dfrac{r}{100}\right) x_n, & n = 0, 1, \ldots, \\ x_0 = P_0. \end{cases}$$

2.1.2. *Applications of first order linear difference equations in finance*

In this section, we will examine applications of first order linear difference equations in compound interest rates; in particular, the initial investment compounded a number of times per year and paying off the loans. Consider investing Q_0 dollars at a rate of $r\%$ per year compounded k times per year. Then we procure the following initial value problem:

$$\begin{cases} x_{n+1} = x_n + \left(\dfrac{r}{k}\right) x_n = \left(1 + \dfrac{r}{k}\right) x_n, & n = 0, 1, \ldots, \\ x_0 = P_0. \end{cases}$$

The following theorem describes the periodic payment required to pay off a loan with a constant interest rate.

Theorem 2. *Suppose that L dollars of loan is taken out. In addition, the loan pay off is divided into N periods at a constant rate of $i\%$ per year. Then the periodic payment P is*

$$P = \frac{iL}{1 - (1+i)^{-N}}.$$

Proof. Let x_n denote the amount owed immediately after the Nth payment. Then we obtain the following initial value problem:

$$\begin{cases} x_{n+1} = x_n + ix_n - P, & n = 0, 1, \ldots, N, \\ x_0 = L, \\ x_N = 0. \end{cases}$$

Therefore, we see that via (2.16), the solution of the above initial value problem is

$$x_n = L(1+i)^n + \left(\frac{P}{i}\right)\left[1 - (1+i)^n\right], \quad n = 0, 1, \ldots, N.$$

Now by setting $x_N = 0$ we get

$$L(1+i)^N + \left(\frac{P}{i}\right)\left[1 - (1+i)^N\right] = 0,$$

from which the result follows. $\square$

Now we will proceed with examining the **Linear Nonhomogeneous Δ.E.** in the form:

$$x_{n+1} = ax_n + b, \quad n = 0, 1, \ldots,$$

where $a \neq 0$, $b \neq 0$ and $x_0 \in \Re$.

2.2. Nonhomogeneous First Order Linear Difference Equations

The followings are examples of first order linear nonhomogeneous difference equations:

(i) $x_{n+1} = 5x_n - 8, \quad n = 0, 1, \ldots$.
(ii) $x_{n+1} = \frac{x_n}{5} - 2, \quad n = 0, 1, \ldots$.

In this section we will investigate the **Nonhomogeneous Δ.E.** in the form:

$$x_{n+1} - ax_n = b, \quad n = 0, 1, \ldots, \tag{2.14}$$

where $a \neq 0$, $b \neq 0$ and $x_0 \in \Re$. Notice that $\bar{x} = \frac{b}{1-a}$ is the only equilibrium point of Eq. (2.14) provided that $a \neq 1$. By solving Eq. (2.14) explicitly, we acquire the following cases:

(i) When $a = 1$, we procure:

$$x_0,$$
$$x_1 = x_0 + b,$$
$$x_2 = x_1 + b = x_0 + 2b,$$
$$x_3 = x_2 + b = x_0 + 3b,$$
$$\vdots$$

We see that for all $n \geq 0$:

$$x_n = x_0 + nb. \tag{2.15}$$

In this case Eq. (2.14) has no equilibrium point.

(ii) When $a = -1$, we obtain:

$$x_n = \begin{cases} x_0 & \text{if } n \text{ is even,} \\ -x_0 + b & \text{if } n \text{ is odd.} \end{cases}$$

In this case $\bar{x} = \frac{b}{2}$ and every non-trivial solution of Eq. (2.14) is periodic with period-2.

(iii) We will now consider all other cases when $a \neq -1, 0, 1$. In this case $\bar{x} = \frac{b}{1-a}$. In Example (8) from Chapter 1, we derived the following solution of Eq. (2.14):

$$x_n = a^n x_0 + b \left[\frac{1 - a^n}{1 - a} \right] = a^n \left[x_0 - \frac{b}{1-a} \right] + \frac{b}{1-a},$$

which can be rewritten as

$$x_n = a^n \left[x_0 - \bar{x} \right] + \bar{x}. \tag{2.16}$$

From (iii), when $a = -1$, then every non-trivial (non-equilibrium solution) solution of Eq. (2.14) is **oscillatory** and periodic with the following alternating period-2 pattern:

$$x_0, \ -x_0 + b, \ x_0, \ -x_0 + b, \ \ldots.$$

Moreover, the sum of two neighboring terms is always b. We will examine similar periodicity properties in the **Non-autonomous Case**. In the next three examples, we will solve the nonhomogeneous first order linear Δ.E. analytically and verify the solution.

Example 6. Solve the Initial Value Problem:

$$\begin{cases} 3x_{n+1} - x_n = 8, & n = 0, 1, \ldots, \\ x_0 = 10, \end{cases}$$

and:

(i) Determine

$$\lim_{n \to \infty} x_n.$$

(ii) Verify that the solution is correct.

Solution: Note that $\bar{x} = 4$ and from Eq. (2.14) we get

$$x_n = \left(\frac{1}{3}\right)^n [10 - 4] + 4 = 2\left(\frac{1}{3}\right)^{n-1} + 4.$$

Thus

$$\lim_{n \to \infty} x_n = \lim_{n \to \infty} 2\left(\frac{1}{3}\right)^{n-1} + 4 = 4.$$

Therefore:

$$3x_{n+1} - x_n = 3\left[2\left(\frac{1}{3}\right)^n + 4\right] - \left[2\left(\frac{1}{3}\right)^{n-1} + 4\right]$$

$$= \frac{2}{3^{n-1}} + 12 - \frac{2}{3^{n-1}} - 4 = 8.$$

Example 7. Solve the Initial Value Problem:

$$\begin{cases} 4x_{n+1} + 5x_n = 9, & n = 0, 1, \ldots, \\ x_0 = 5, \end{cases}$$

and:

(i) Determine

$$\lim_{n \to \infty} x_n.$$

(ii) Verify that the solution is correct.

Solution: Observe that $\bar{x} = 1$ and from Eqs. (2.14) and (2.16), we get

$$x_n = \left(\frac{-5}{4}\right)^n [5 - 1] + 1 = (-1)^n \frac{5^n}{4^{n-1}} + 1.$$

Now we see that

$$\lim_{n \to \infty} x_n = (-1)^n \frac{5^n}{4^{n-1}} + 1,$$

does not exist as

$$\lim_{n \to \infty} x_{2n} = +\infty \quad \text{and} \quad \lim_{n \to \infty} x_{2n+1} = -\infty.$$

Thus:

$$4x_{n+1} + 5x_n = 4\left[(-1)^{n+1}\frac{5^{n+1}}{4^n} + 1\right] + 5\left[(-1)^n \frac{5^n}{4^{n-1}}\right] + 1$$

$$= \frac{-(-1^n)5^{n+1}}{4^{n-1}} + 4 + \frac{(-1)^n 5^{n+1}}{4^{n-1}} + 5 = 9.$$

Example 8. Solve the Initial Value Problem:

$$\begin{cases} 4x_{n+1} - 4x_n = 1, & n = 0, 1, \ldots, \\ x_0 = 5, \end{cases}$$

and:

(i) Determine

$$\lim_{n \to \infty} x_n.$$

(ii) Verify that the solution is correct.

Solution: Observe $\bar{x}$ does not exist and from Eqs. (2.14) and (2.15), we get

$$x_n = 5 + \frac{n}{4}.$$

Thus, we see that

$$\lim_{n \to \infty} x_n = \lim_{n \to \infty} \left(5 + \frac{n}{4}\right) = +\infty.$$

Hence:

$$4x_{n+1} - 4x_n = 4\left[3 + \frac{n+1}{4}\right] - 4\left[3 + \frac{n}{4}\right]$$

$$= 12 + n + 1 - 12 - n = 1.$$

Our next aim to examine the Non-autonomous Δ.E. in the form:

$$x_{n+1} = a_n x_n + b_n, \quad n = 0, 1, \ldots,$$

where $x_0 \in \Re$, $\{a_n\}_{n=0}^{\infty}$ and $\{b_n\}_{n=0}^{\infty}$ are sequences of real numbers or periodic sequences with either the same period or with different periods.

2.3. Non-autonomous First Order Linear Difference Equations

The followings are examples of first order linear non-autonomous difference equations:

(i) $x_{n+1} = x_n + \frac{1}{n!}, \quad n = 0, 1, \ldots.$
(ii) $x_{n+1} = x_n + \frac{n}{4^n}, \quad n = 0, 1, \ldots.$
(iii) $x_{n+1} = 2^n x_n + \frac{3^n}{n!}, \quad n = 0, 1, \ldots.$

First we will examine the non-autonomous homogeneous Δ.E. in the form:

$$x_{n+1} = a_n x_n, \quad n = 0, 1, \ldots, \tag{2.17}$$

where either $\{a_n\}_{n=0}^{\infty}$ is a sequence of real numbers or $\{a_n\}_{n=0}^{\infty}$ is a periodic period-k sequence (where $k \geq 2$). Eq. (2.17) has only one equilibrium point $\bar{x} = 0$. Before deriving the general solution of Eq. (2.17), we will proclaim a specific example when $\{a_n\}_{n=0}^{\infty}$ is a period-3 sequence.

Example 9. Solve the following Δ.E.

$$x_{n+1} = a_n x_n, \quad n = 0, 1, \ldots,$$

where $\{a_n\}_{n=0}^{\infty}$ is a periodic period-3 sequence.

Solution: Observe:

$$x_0,$$
$$x_1 = a_0 x_0,$$
$$x_2 = a_1 x_1 = a_1 a_0 x_0,$$
$$x_3 = a_2 x_2 = [a_2 a_1 a_0] x_0,$$
$$x_4 = a_0 x_3 = a_2 a_1 a_0^2 x_0,$$
$$x_5 = a_1 x_4 = a_2 a_1^2 a_0^2 x_0,$$
$$x_6 = a_2 x_5 = [a_2 a_1 a_0]^2 x_0,$$
$$\vdots$$

Let $P = a_0 a_1 a_2$. Then for all $n \geq 0$ we get:

$$\begin{cases} x_{3n} = P^n x_0, \\ x_{3n+1} = a_0 P^n x_0, \\ x_{3n+2} = a_0 a_1 P^n x_0. \end{cases}$$

Then the following statements hold true:

(i) When $|P| < 1$, then

$$\lim_{n \to \infty} x_{3n} = \lim_{n \to \infty} x_{3n+1} = \lim_{n \to \infty} x_{3n+2} = 0.$$

(ii) When $P = 1$, then every non-trivial solution is periodic with period-3. More attributes will be discussed in Section 2.1.4.

(iii) When $P = -1$, then every non-trivial solution is periodic with period-6. More attributes will be discussed in Section 2.1.4.

(iv) When $P > 1$, and $a_0, a_1, a_2 > 0$, then:

— If $x_0 > 0$, then

$$\lim_{n \to \infty} x_{3n} = \lim_{n \to \infty} x_{3n+1} = \lim_{n \to \infty} x_{3n+2} = +\infty.$$

— If $x_0 < 0$, then

$$\lim_{n \to \infty} x_{3n} = \lim_{n \to \infty} x_{3n+1} = \lim_{n \to \infty} x_{3n+2} = -\infty.$$

(v) When $P < -1$, then the limits will vary depending on x_0, a_0, a_1 and a_2.

The graph below:

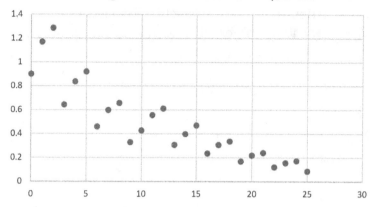

resembles monotonic convergence to 0 from above in three sub-sequences when $a_0 = 1.3$, $a_1 = 1.1$, $a_2 = 0.5$ and $x_0 = 0.9$. When either $P > 1$ or $P < -1$, then sub-sequence of the solutions of Eq. (2.17) will diverge to either $+\infty$ or $-\infty$ in three sub-sequences. When $P = 1$ then Eq. (2.17) will have period-3 cycles and when $P = -1$ then Eq. (2.17) will have period-6 cycles.

Now suppose that $\{a_n\}_{n=0}^{\infty}$ is a periodic period-k sequence (where $k \geq 2$) and let $P = \prod_{i=0}^{k-1} a_i$. Analogous to Example 9, we obtain the following solution to Eq. (2.17):

$$
\begin{cases}
x_{kn} = P^n x_0, \\[2mm]
x_{kn+1} = a_0 P^n x_0, \\[2mm]
x_{kn+2} = a_0 a_1 P^n x_0, \\[2mm]
\vdots \\[2mm]
x_{kn+k-2} = \left[\prod_{i=0}^{k-3} a_i \right] P^n x_0, \\[2mm]
x_{kn+k-1} = \left[\prod_{i=0}^{k-2} a_i \right] P^n x_0.
\end{cases}
$$

Then the following statements hold true:

(i) When $P < 1$, then for all $j = 0, 1, \ldots, k - 2$

$$
\lim_{n \to \infty} x_{kn+j} = 0.
$$

(ii) When $P = 1$, then every non-trivial solution is periodic with period-k. More attributes will be discussed in Section 2.1.4.

(iii) When $P = -1$, then every non-trivial solution is periodic with period-2k. More attributes will be discussed in Section 2.1.4.

(iv) When $P > 1$, and $a_i > 0$ for all $i = 0, 1, 2, \ldots, k - 2$, then

　— If $x_0 > 0$, then all $j = 0, 1, \ldots, k - 2$

$$\lim_{n \to \infty} x_{kn+j} = +\infty.$$

　— If $x_0 < 0$, then all $j = 0, 1, \ldots, k - 2$

$$\lim_{n \to \infty} x_{kn+j} = -\infty.$$

(v) When $P < -1$, then the limits will vary depending on x_0 and $a_0, a_1, \ldots, a_{k-1}$.

Next assume that $\{a_n\}_{n=0}^{\infty}$ is a sequence of real numbers. Then we acquire the following solution to Eq. (2.17):

$$x_n = \left[\prod_{i=0}^{n} a_i \right] x_0, \quad n = 1, 2, \ldots . \tag{2.18}$$

Example 10. Determine the **explicit solution** to the following Δ.E.:

$$x_{n+1} = \left(\frac{1}{2} \right)^{n+1} x_n, \quad n = 0, 1, \ldots,$$

where $x_0 \neq 0$.

Solution: By iteration we obtain:

$$x_0,$$

$$x_1 = \frac{1}{2} x_0,$$

$$x_2 = \left(\frac{1}{2} \right)^2 x_1 = \left(\frac{1}{2} \right)^{[1+2]} x_0,$$

$$x_3 = \left(\frac{1}{2} \right)^3 x_2 = \left(\frac{1}{2} \right)^{[1+2+3]} x_0,$$

$$x_4 = \left(\frac{1}{2}\right)^4 x_3 = \left(\frac{1}{2}\right)^{[1+2+3+4]} x_0,$$

$$x_5 = \left(\frac{1}{2}\right)^5 x_4 = \left(\frac{1}{2}\right)^{[1+2+3+4+5]} x_0.$$

$$\vdots$$

Thus for all $n \in \mathbb{N}$:

$$x_n = \left[\prod_{i=1}^{n}\left(\frac{1}{2}\right)^i\right] x_0 = \left(\frac{1}{2}\right)^{\left[\sum_{i=1}^{n} i\right]} x_0 = \left(\frac{1}{2}\right)^{\frac{n(n+1)}{2}} x_0.$$

Example 11. Determine the **explicit solution** to the following Δ.E.:

$$x_{n+1} = \frac{x_n}{n+1}, \quad n = 0, 1, \ldots,$$

where $x_0 \neq 0$.

Solution: By iteration we acquire:

$$x_0,$$

$$x_1 = \frac{x_0}{1},$$

$$x_2 = \frac{x_1}{2} = \frac{x_0}{1 \cdot 2},$$

$$x_3 = \frac{x_2}{3} = \frac{x_0}{1 \cdot 2 \cdot 3},$$

$$x_4 = \frac{x_3}{4} = \frac{x_0}{1 \cdot 2 \cdot 3 \cdot 4},$$

$$x_5 = \frac{x_4}{5} = \frac{x_0}{1 \cdot 2 \cdot 3 \cdot 4 \cdot 5},$$

$$\vdots$$

Hence for all $n \in \mathbb{N}$:

$$x_n = \left[\prod_{i=1}^{n}\frac{1}{i}\right] x_0 = \frac{x_0}{n!}.$$

Next we will examine the non-autonomous and nonhomogeneous A.E. in the form:

$$x_{n+1} = x_n + b_n, \quad n = 0, 1, \ldots, \tag{2.19}$$

where $\{b_n\}_{n=0}^{\infty}$ is a sequence of real numbers. By iteration and induction we obtain the following solution to Eq. (2.19):

$$x_n = x_0 + [b_0 + b_1 + \ldots + b_{n-1}] = x_0 + \sum_{k=0}^{n-1} b_k. \tag{2.20}$$

Eq. (2.19) has no equilibrium points. In addition:

$$\lim_{n \to \infty} x_n = \lim_{n \to \infty} \left[x_0 + \sum_{k=0}^{n-1} b_k \right] = x_0 + \lim_{n \to \infty} \sum_{k=0}^{n-1} b_k = x_0 + \sum_{n=0}^{\infty} b_n.$$

In the next two examples, we will work out the details in solving non-autonomous nonhomogeneous first order linear difference equations.

Example 12. Consider the following A.E.:

$$x_{n+1} - x_n = \frac{1}{3^{n+2}}, \quad n = 0, 1, \ldots.$$

(i) Solve the above A.E.
(ii) Determine $\lim_{n \to \infty} x_n$.

Solution: From Eqs. (2.19) and (2.20), we get

$$x_n = x_0 + \sum_{k=0}^{n-1} \frac{1}{3^{k+2}} = x_0 + \left[\frac{1}{9} + \frac{1}{27} + \frac{1}{81} + \ldots + \frac{1}{3^n} \right].$$

Then,

$$\lim_{n \to \infty} x_n = \lim_{n \to \infty} \left[x_0 + \sum_{k=0}^{n-1} \frac{1}{3^{k+2}} \right]$$

$$= x_0 + \sum_{n=0}^{\infty} \frac{1}{3^{n+2}} = x_0 + \frac{\frac{1}{9}}{1 - \frac{1}{3}} = x_0 + \frac{1}{6}.$$

Hence $\lim_{n \to \infty} x_n$ exists but it is not unique as it depends on the initial condition x_0.

Example 13. Consider the following A.E.:

$$x_{n+1} - x_n = \frac{(-1)^n}{n+1}, \quad n = 0, 1, \ldots.$$

(i) Solve the above Δ.E.

(ii) Determine $\lim_{n \to \infty} x_n$.

Solution: From Eqs. (2.19) and (2.20), we get

$$x_n = x_0 + \sum_{k=0}^{n-1} \frac{(-1)^k}{k+1}.$$

Furthermore,

$$\lim_{n \to \infty} x_n = \lim_{n \to \infty} \left[x_0 + \sum_{k=0}^{n-1} \frac{(-1)^k}{k+1} \right]$$

$$= x_0 + \sum_{n=0}^{\infty} \frac{(-1)^n}{n+1} = x_0 + Ln(2).$$

Thus $\lim_{n \to \infty} x_n$ exists but it is not unique as it depends on the initial condition x_0.

Example 14. Consider the following Δ.E.:

$$x_{n+1} + x_n = \left(\frac{1}{2} \right)^n, \quad n = 0, 1, \ldots .$$

(i) Solve the above Δ.E.

(ii) Determine $\lim_{n \to \infty} x_n$.

Solution: From Eqs. (2.19), (2.20), and by computation, we get

$$x_0,$$

$$x_1 = -x_0 + 1,$$

$$x_2 = -x_1 + \frac{1}{2} = x_0 - 1 + \frac{1}{2},$$

$$x_3 = -x_2 + \left(\frac{1}{2} \right)^2 = -x_0 + 1 - \frac{1}{2} + \left(\frac{1}{2} \right)^2,$$

$$x_4 = -x_2 + \left(\frac{1}{2} \right)^3 = x_0 - 1 + \frac{1}{2} - \left(\frac{1}{2} \right)^2 + \left(\frac{1}{2} \right)^3.$$

$$\vdots$$

Then for all $n \geq 1$,

$$x_n = (-1)^n x_0 + (-1)^{n+1} \sum_{k=0}^{n-1} \frac{(-1)^k}{2^k}.$$

Furthermore:

$$\lim_{n \to \infty} x_n = \begin{cases} x_0 - \displaystyle\sum_{n=0}^{\infty} \frac{(-1)^n}{2^n} = x_0 - \frac{2}{3} & \text{if } n \text{ is even,} \\[4mm] -x_0 + \displaystyle\sum_{n=0}^{\infty} \frac{(-1)^n}{2^n} = -x_0 + \frac{2}{3} & \text{if } n \text{ is odd.} \end{cases}$$

In this case, the solution $\{x_n\}_{n=0}^{\infty}$ converges to a period-2 solution and depends on the initial condition x_0.

Similar to Eq. (2.19), we consider the non-autonomous and nonhomogeneous A.E. in the form:

$$x_{n+1} = ax_n + b_n, \quad n = 0, 1, \ldots, \tag{2.21}$$

where $a \neq 0$ and $\{b_n\}_{n=0}^{\infty}$ is a sequence of real numbers. In Example 9 in Chapter 1, we procured the following solution to Eq. (2.21):

$$x_n = a^n x_0 + \sum_{i=0}^{n-1} a^{n-1-i} b_i.$$

This is an example of a **Convolution** which we will see in applications in Signal Processing in the next section.

Finally we will analyze the non-autonomous and nonhomogeneous A.E. in the form:

$$x_{n+1} = a_n x_n + b_n, \quad n = 0, 1, \ldots, \tag{2.22}$$

where $\{a_n\}_{n=0}^{\infty}$ and $\{b_n\}_{n=0}^{\infty}$ are sequences of real numbers. Let $\{x_n\}_{n=0}^{\infty}$ be a solution of Eq. (2.22). By iteration and induction we acquire:

$$x_0,$$
$$x_1 = a_0 x_0 + b_0,$$
$$x_2 = a_1 x_1 + b_1 = a_0 a_1 x_0 + a_1 b_0 + b_1,$$
$$x_3 = a_2 x_2 + b_2 = a_0 a_1 a_2 x_0 + a_1 a_2 b_0 + a_2 b_1 + b_2,$$
$$x_4 = a_3 x_3 + b_3 = a_0 a_1 a_2 a_3 x_0 + a_1 a_2 a_3 b_0 + a_2 a_3 b_1 + a_3 b_2 + b_3,$$
$$\vdots$$

Then for all $n \in \mathbb{N}$:

$$x_n = \prod_{i=0}^{n-1} a_i x_0 + \sum_{j=0}^{n-1} \left[\prod_{i=j+1}^{n-1} a_i b_j \right].$$

This is also an example of a **Convolution**. We will see applications of a Convolution in the next section in Signal Processing.

2.3.1. *Applications of non-autonomous first order linear difference equations in signal processing*

Our aim is to study the LTI (Linear and Time Invariance) of digital signal processing. We will emerge our study of the LTI Δ.E. with the following input and output signals:

(i) x_n is the input signal.
(ii) y_n and y_{n+1} are the output signals.

The input–output process is rendered by the following diagram:

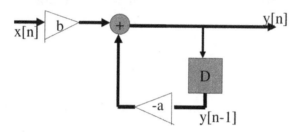

Then we write the following **LTI Δ.E.**:

$$bx_n - [y_{n+1} + ay_n] = 0, \tag{2.23}$$

where b is the **feed-forward coefficient** and a is the **feedback coefficient** that characterize the filter. Eq. (2.23) is applied for computing an output sample at time n based on the current and previous samples in the time domain. We can rewrite Eq. (2.23) as:

$$y_{n+1} = -ay_n + bx_n. \tag{2.24}$$

Now we acquire an explicit solution of Eq. (2.24):

$$y_0,$$
$$y_1 = -ay_0 + bx_0,$$
$$y_2 = -ay_1 + bx_1 = a^2 y_0 - abx_0 + bx_1,$$
$$y_3 = -ay_2 + bx_2 = -a^3 y_0 + a^2 bx_0 - abx_1 + bx_2,$$
$$y_4 = -ay_3 + bx_3 = a^4 y_0 - a^3 bx_0 + a^2 bx_1 - abx_2 + bx_3,$$
$$\vdots$$

Then for all $n \in \mathbb{N}$:

$$y_n = (-a)^n y_0 + \left[\sum_{i=0}^{n-1} (-a)^{n-(i+1)} b x_i \right].$$

The solution of Eq. (2.24) consists of two components where:

(i) $(-a)^n y_0$ is the **natural response** that depends on the initial condition x_0.
(ii) $\sum_{i=0}^{n-1} (-a)^{n-(i+1)} b x_i$ is the **forced response** that depends on the input signal x_n.

We can then extend Eq. (2.23) to the following LTI Δ.E.:

$$\left[\sum_{i=0}^{N-1} b_i x_{n+i} \right] - [y_{n+1} + a y_n] = 0, \tag{2.25}$$

where b_i are the **feed-forward coefficients** and a is the **feedback coefficient**. Acquiring the general solution of Eq. (2.25) will be left as an exercise at the end of the chapter. More details on the LTI Δ.E. will be discussed in Chapter 4 and in Chapter 6.

2.4. Periodic Traits of Non-autonomous First Order Linear Difference Equations

Our goal is to investigate the periodic traits of Non-autonomous First Order Linear Difference Equations and will encounter existence of unique periodic cycles in some instances. We will emerge with the periodic traits of the first order homogeneous non-autonomous Δ.E.:

$$x_{n+1} = a_n x_n, \quad n = 0, 1, \ldots, \tag{2.26}$$

where $x_0 \neq 0$ and $\{a_n\}_{n=0}^{\infty}$ is a periodic period-k sequence ($k \geq 2$). The next two examples will carefully examine the details in determining the necessary and sufficient conditions for the existence of periodic cycles and their patterns of Eq. (2.26).

Example 15. Suppose that $\{a_n\}_{n=0}^{\infty}$ is a periodic period-2 sequence. Determine the necessary and sufficient conditions for the existence of period-2 cycles of:

$$x_{n+1} = a_n x_n, \quad n = 0, 1, \ldots.$$

Solution: By iteration we get:

$$x_0,$$
$$x_1 = a_0 x_0,$$
$$x_2 = a_1 x_1 = a_1 [a_0 x_0] = x_0.$$

Note that $x_2 = x_0$ if and only if $a_0 a_1 = 1$ with the following period-2 pattern:

$$x_0, \; a_0 x_0, \; x_0, \; a_0 x_0, \ldots.$$

Unless $a_0 a_1 = 1$, the existence of period-2 solutions is not possible. We will see similar conditions for existence of periodic cycles in future examples. Also when $a_0 a_1 = -1$, then Eq. (2.26) will have alternating period-4 cycles.

Example 16. Suppose that $\{a_n\}_{n=0}^{\infty}$ is a periodic period-3 sequence. Determine the necessary and sufficient conditions for the existence of period-3 cycles of:

$$x_{n+1} = a_n x_n, \quad n = 0, 1, \ldots.$$

Solution: By iteration we get:

$$x_0,$$
$$x_1 = a_0 x_0,$$
$$x_2 = a_1 x_1 = a_1 [a_0 x_0],$$
$$x_3 = a_2 x_2 = a_2 [a_0 a_1 x_0] = x_0.$$

Note that $x_3 = x_0$ if and only if $a_0 a_1 a_2 = 1$ with the following period-3 pattern:

$$x_0, \; a_0 x_0, \; a_0 a_1 x_0, \ldots.$$

Unless $a_0 a_1 a_2 = 1$, the existence of period-3 solutions is not possible. When $a_0 a_1 a_2 = -1$, then Eq. (2.26) will exhibit alternating period-6 cycles.

From Examples 15 and 16, the following theorems describe the conclusions.

Theorem 3. *Suppose that $\{a_n\}_{n=0}^{\infty}$ is a period-k sequence $(k \geq 2)$. Then every solution of*

$$x_{n+1} = a_n x_n, \quad n = 0, 1, \ldots$$

is periodic with period-k if and only if:

$$\prod_{i=0}^{k-1} a_i = 1.$$

Proof. Similar to Example 12, we see that:

$$x_0,$$
$$x_1 = a_0 \, x_0,$$
$$x_2 = a_1 x_1 = [a_1 a_0] \, x_0,$$
$$x_3 = a_2 x_2 = [a_2 a_1 a_0] \, x_0,$$
$$x_4 = a_3 x_2 = [a_3 a_2 a_1 a_0] \, x_0,$$
$$x_5 = a_4 x_3 = [a_4 a_3 a_2 a_1 a_0] \, x_0,$$
$$\vdots$$

By induction for all $n \in \mathbb{N}$:

$$x_n = \left[\prod_{i=0}^{n-1} a_i \right] x_0.$$

□

Theorem 4. *Suppose that $\{a_n\}_{n=0}^{\infty}$ is a period-k sequence $(k \geq 2)$. Then every solution of*

$$x_{n+1} = a_n x_n, \quad n = 0, 1, \ldots$$

is periodic with period-2k if and only if:

$$\prod_{i=0}^{k-1} a_i = -1.$$

Proof. The proof is similar to the proof of Theorem 3 and will be omitted.

□

We will shift our focus on the periodic traits of:

$$x_{n+1} = x_n + a_n, \quad n = 0, 1, \ldots, \tag{2.27}$$

where $x_0 \in \Re$ and $\{a_n\}_{n=0}^{\infty}$ is a periodic period-k sequence ($k \geq 2$). The next two examples will analyze the details for existence of periodic cycles and their patterns of Eq. (2.27).

Example 17. Suppose that $\{a_n\}_{n=0}^{\infty}$ is a periodic period-2 sequence. Determine the necessary and sufficient conditions for the existence of period-2 cycles of:

$$x_{n+1} = x_n + a_n, \quad n = 0, 1, \ldots.$$

Solution: By iteration we get:

$$x_0,$$
$$x_1 = x_0 + a_0,$$
$$x_2 = x_1 + a_1 = [x_0 + a_0] + a_1 = x_0,$$
$$x_3 = x_2 + a_0 = x_0 + a_0 = x_1.$$

We see that $x_2 = x_0$ if and only if $a_0 + a_1 = 0$ with the following alternating period-2 pattern:

$$x_0, \ x_0 + a_0, \ x_0, \ x_0 + a_0, \ldots.$$

Example 18. Suppose that $\{a_n\}_{n=0}^{\infty}$ is a period-3 sequence. Determine the necessary and sufficient conditions for the existence of period-3 cycles of:

$$x_{n+1} = x_n + a_n, \quad n = 0, 1, \ldots.$$

Solution: Notice:

$$x_0,$$
$$x_1 = x_0 + a_0,$$
$$x_2 = x_1 + a_1 = [x_0 + a_0] + a_1,$$
$$x_3 = x_2 + a_2 = [x_0 + a_0 + a_1] + a_2 = x_0.$$

Hence $x_3 = x_0$ if and only if $a_0 + a_1 + a_2 = 0$ with the following period-3 pattern:

$$x_0, \ x_0 + a_0, \ x_0 + a_0 + a_1, x_0, \ x_0 + a_0, \ x_0 + a_0 + a_1, \ldots.$$

From Examples 17 and 18 the following theorem outlines the conclusions.

Theorem 5. *Suppose that $\{a_n\}_{n=0}^{\infty}$ is a period-k sequence $(k \geq 2)$. Then every solution of*

$$x_{n+1} = x_n + a_n, \quad n = 0, 1, \ldots$$

is periodic with period-k if and only if:

$$\sum_{i=0}^{k-1} a_i = 0.$$

Proof.   Similar to Example 13, we obtain:

$$x_0,$$
$$x_1 = x_0 + a_0,$$
$$x_2 = x_1 + a_1 = x_0 + a_0 + a_1,$$
$$x_3 = x_2 + a_2 = x_0 + a_0 + a_1 + a_2,$$
$$x_4 = x_3 + a_3 = x_0 + a_0 + a_1 + a_2 + a_3,$$
$$x_5 = x_4 + a_4 = x_0 + a_0 + a_1 + a_2 + a_3 + a_4,$$
$$\vdots$$

Then for all $n \in \mathbb{N}$:

$$x_n = x_0 + \left[\sum_{i=0}^{n-1} a_i \right].$$

$\square$

The following example will examine the periodic nature of the following non-autonomous Δ.E.:

$$x_{n+1} = a_n x_n + 1, \quad n = 0, 1, \ldots,$$

where $\{a_n\}_{n=0}^{\infty}$ is a period-k sequence $(k \geq 2)$.

Example 19. Suppose that $\{a_n\}_{n=0}^{\infty}$ is a period-2 sequence. Determine the necessary and sufficient conditions for the existence of period-4 cycles of:

$$x_{n+1} = a_n x_n + 1, \quad n = 0, 1, \ldots.$$

Solution: Observe that:

$$x_0,$$
$$x_1 = a_0 x_0 + 1,$$

$$x_2 = a_1 x_1 + 1 = a_1 [a_0 x_0 + 1] + 1,$$
$$= a_1 a_0 x_0 + a_1 + 1 = -x_0 + a_1 + 1,$$
$$x_3 = a_0 x_2 + 1 = a_0 [-x_0 + a_1 + 1] + 1$$
$$= -a_0 x_0 + a_0 a_1 + a_0 + 1 = -a_0 x_0 + a_0,$$
$$x_4 = a_1 x_3 + 1 = a_1 [-a_0 x_0 + a_0] + 1 = x_0.$$

Period-4 solutions are possible if and only if $a_0 a_1 = -1$ with the following period-4 pattern:

$$x_0, \quad a_0 x_0 + 1, \quad -x_0 + a_1 + 1, \quad -a_0 x_0 + a_0, \ldots.$$

Next we will transition to the periodicity nature of solutions of:

$$x_{n+1} = -x_n + a_n, \quad n = 0, 1, \ldots, \tag{2.28}$$

where $\{a_n\}_{n=0}^{\infty}$ is a period-k sequence $(k \geq 2)$. We will discover when $\{a_n\}_{n=0}^{\infty}$ is of odd order where Eq. (2.28) will have unique periodic solutions and when $\{a_n\}_{n=0}^{\infty}$ is of even order then every solution of Eq. (2.28) is periodic.

Example 20. Suppose that $\{a_n\}_{n=0}^{\infty}$ is a period-2 sequence. Show that:

$$x_{n+1} = -x_n + a_n, \quad n = 0, 1, \ldots$$

has no period-2 solutions and explain why.

Solution: Suppose that $x_2 = x_0$. Then:

$$x_0,$$
$$x_1 = -x_0 + a_0,$$
$$x_2 = -[x_1] + a_1 = x_0 - a_0 + a_1 = x_0.$$

Therefore $x_2 = x_0$ if an only if $a_0 = a_1$. This is a contradiction as we assumed that $\{a_n\}_{n=0}^{\infty}$ is a period-2 sequence.

Example 21. Suppose that $\{a_n\}_{n=0}^{\infty}$ is a period-3 sequence. Determine the necessary and sufficient conditions for the existence of period-3 cycles of:

$$x_{n+1} = -x_n + a_n, \quad n = 0, 1, \ldots.$$

Solution: Observe:

$$x_0,$$

$$x_1 = -x_0 + a_0,$$

$$x_2 = -[x_1] + a_1 = -[-x_0 + a_0] + a_1 = x_0 + a_1 - a_0,$$

$$x_3 = -[x_2] + a_2 = -[x_0 + a_1 - a_0] + a_2 = -x_0 + a_2 + a_0 - a_1 = x_0.$$

Therefore $x_0 = \frac{a_0 - a_1 + a_2}{2}$ and acquire the following **unique** period-3 pattern:

$$\frac{a_0 - a_1 + a_2}{2}, \quad \frac{a_0 + a_1 - a_2}{2}, \quad \frac{-a_0 + a_1 + a_2}{2}, \dots.$$

Note that from neighbor to neighbor the indices of the sequence $\{a_n\}_{n=0}^{\infty}$ do not change but the negative sign shifts from neighbor to neighbor in the numerator only.

Example 22. Suppose that $\{a_n\}_{n=0}^{\infty}$ is a period-4 sequence. Determine the necessary and sufficient conditions for the existence of period-4 cycles of:

$$x_{n+1} = -x_n + a_n, \quad n = 0, 1, \dots.$$

Solution: By iteration:

$$x_0,$$

$$x_1 = -x_0 + a_0,$$

$$x_2 = -[x_1] + a_1 = -[-x_0 + a_0] + a_1 = x_0 + a_1 - a_0,$$

$$x_3 = -[x_2] + a_2 = -[x_0 + a_1 - a_0] + a_2 = -x_0 + a_2 + a_0 - a_1,$$

$$x_4 = -[x_3] + a_3 = -[-x_0 + a_2 + a_0 - a_1] + a_3$$

$$= x_0 - [a_2 + a_0] + [a_1 + a_3] = x_0.$$

Period-4 solutions exist if and only if $a_1 + a_3 = a_0 + a_2$ with the following period-4 pattern:

$$x_0, \ -x_0 + a_0, \ x_0 + a_1 - a_0, \ -x_0 + a_2 + a_0 - a_1, \dots.$$

From Examples 21 and 22 we see quite a contrast of periodic traits of Eq. (2.28) when $\{a_n\}_{n=0}^{\infty}$ is an even ordered periodic sequence and when $\{a_n\}_{n=0}^{\infty}$ is an odd ordered periodic sequence. In Example 21 we have a unique periodic cycle when $\{a_n\}_{n=0}^{\infty}$ is an odd ordered periodic sequence. Contrarily, in Example 22 every solution of Eq. (2.28) is periodic when $\{a_n\}_{n=0}^{\infty}$ is an even ordered periodic sequence. The following two theorems generalize the conclusions.

Theorem 6. *Suppose that $\{a_n\}_{n=0}^{\infty}$ is a period-2k sequence ($k \geq 2$). Then every solution of*

$$x_{n+1} = -x_n + a_n, \quad n = 0, 1, \ldots$$

is periodic with period-2k if and only if:

$$\sum_{i=1}^{k} a_{2i-1} = \sum_{i=1}^{k} a_{2i-2}.$$

Proof. Similar to Example 12, we get:

$$x_0,$$
$$x_1 = -x_0 + a_0,$$
$$x_2 = -[x_1] + a_1 = x_0 + a_1 - a_0,$$
$$x_3 = -[x_2] + a_2 = -x_0 + a_2 + a_0 - a_1,$$
$$x_4 = -[x_3] + a_3 = x_0 - [a_2 + a_0] + [a_1 + a_3],$$
$$\vdots$$

$$x_{2k} = x_0 - \left[\sum_{i=1}^{k} a_{2i-2}\right] + \left[\sum_{i=1}^{k} a_{2i-1}\right]. \qquad \square$$

Theorem 7. *Suppose that $\{a_n\}_{n=0}^{\infty}$ is a period-$(2k+1)$ sequence ($k \in \mathbb{N}$). Then*

$$x_{n+1} = -x_n + a_n, \quad n = 0, 1, \ldots$$

has a unique periodic solution with period-$(2k+1)$ where

$$x_0 = \frac{\sum_{i=1}^{2k+1} (-1)^{i+1} a_{i-1}}{2}.$$

The proof of Theorem 7 will be left as an exercise at the end of the chapter.

2.5. Chapter 2 Exercises

In problems 1–6, show that the solution **satisfies** the given Δ.E.:

1. $x_n = \left(\dfrac{4}{3}\right)^{n+2}$ is a solution of $3x_{n+1} - 4x_n = 0$.

2. $x_n = \dfrac{8^{n-2}}{5^{n-1}}$ is a solution of $5x_{n+1} - 8x_n = 0$.

3. $x_n = \left(\dfrac{3}{5}\right)^{n+1} - 2$ is a solution of $5x_{n+1} - 3x_n = -4$.

4. $x_n = 3^{n+1} - 4$ is a solution of $2x_{n+1} - 6x_n = 16$.

5. $x_n = (-4)^{n-2} + 3$ is a solution of $x_{n+1} + 4x_n = 15$.

6. $x_n = 2n + 1$ is a solution of $x_{n+1} - x_n = 2$.

In problems 7–20, solve the given **Initial Value Problem** and check your answer.

7.
$$\begin{cases} 6x_{n+1} - 5x_n = 0, \quad n = 0, 1, \dots \\ x_0 = \dfrac{25}{36}. \end{cases}$$

8.
$$\begin{cases} 3x_{n+1} + 5x_n = 0, \quad n = 0, 1, \dots \\ x_0 = -\dfrac{27}{5}. \end{cases}$$

9.
$$\begin{cases} 2x_{n+1} + 7x_n = 18, \quad n = 0, 1, \dots \\ x_0 = 6. \end{cases}$$

10.
$$\begin{cases} 2x_{n+1} + 2x_n = \dfrac{7}{2}, \quad n = 0, 1, \dots \\ x_0 = \dfrac{3}{4}. \end{cases}$$

11.
$$\begin{cases} x_{n+1} - x_n = 3, \quad n = 0, 1, \dots \\ x_0 = -5. \end{cases}$$

12.
$$\begin{cases} 2x_{n+1} - 2x_n = -1, \quad n = 0, 1, \dots \\ x_0 = \dfrac{3}{2}. \end{cases}$$

13.
$$\begin{cases} x_{n+1} + x_n = 7, \quad n = 0, 1, \dots \\ x_0 = -2. \end{cases}$$

14.
$$\begin{cases} x_{n+1} - x_n = \left(\dfrac{2}{3}\right)^{n+2}, \quad n = 0, 1, \dots \\ x_0 = \dfrac{2}{3}. \end{cases}$$

15. $\begin{cases} x_{n+1} - x_n = (2n+1), & n = 0, 1, \ldots. \\ x_0 = 0. \end{cases}$

16. $\begin{cases} x_{n+1} + x_n = 2^{n+1}, & n = 0, 1, \ldots. \\ x_0 = 0. \end{cases}$

17. $\begin{cases} x_{n+1} = x_n + (n+1)^2, & n = 0, 1, \ldots. \\ x_0 = 0. \end{cases}$

18. $\begin{cases} x_{n+1} = x_n + 4n + 4, & n = 0, 1, \ldots. \\ x_0 = 0. \end{cases}$

19. $\begin{cases} x_{n+1} = x_n + 4n + 4 + 3^{n+2}, & n = 0, 1, \ldots. \\ x_0 = 3. \end{cases}$

20. $\begin{cases} x_{n+1} + x_n = n + 2, & n = 0, 1, \ldots. \\ x_0 = 1. \end{cases}$

In problems 21–30, determine the general solution to each Δ.E. In addition, determine if the limit of each solution exists. If so, determine if the limit is unique. If not, explain why.

21. $4x_{n+1} - x_n = 9, \quad n = 0, 1, \ldots.$
22. $5x_{n+1} - 2x_n = 6, \quad n = 0, 1, \ldots.$
23. $3x_{n+1} + 3x_n = 4, \quad n = 0, 1, \ldots.$
24. $2x_{n+1} + 7x_n = 0, \quad n = 0, 1, \ldots.$
25. $2x_{n+1} - 2x_n = 3, \quad n = 0, 1, \ldots.$
26. $3x_{n+1} + 5x_n = -4, \quad n = 0, 1, \ldots.$
27. $x_{n+1} - x_n = \frac{1}{(n+1)!}, \quad n = 0, 1, \ldots.$
28. $x_{n+1} - x_n = \frac{1}{(n+1)^2}, \quad n = 0, 1, \ldots.$
29. $x_{n+1} - x_n = \frac{2^n}{3^{n-1}}, \quad n = 0, 1, \ldots.$
30. $x_{n+1} - x_n = \frac{n}{2^n}, \quad n = 0, 1, \ldots.$

In problems 31–36, determine the general solution to each **LTI Δ.E.**

31. $y_{n+1} = ay_n + x_n + x_{n+1}.$
32. $y_{n+1} = ay_n + b_1 x_n + x_{n+1}.$
33. $y_{n+1} = ay_n + b_1 x_n + b_2 x_{n+1}.$
34. $y_{n+1} = ay_n + b_1 x_n + b_2 x_{n+1} + b_3 x_{n+2}.$

35. $y_{n+1} = a y_n + x_n + x_{n+1} + x_{n+2} + x_{n+3}.$

36. $y_{n+1} = a y_n + \left[\sum_{k=0}^{N-1} x_{n+k} \right].$

In problems 37–57, determine the necessary and sufficient conditions for existence of periodic solutions and the pattern of periodic solutions.

37. Existence and Pattern of Periodic Solutions of the Δ.E.:

$$x_{n+1} = (-1)^n x_n + 2, \quad n = 0, 1, \ldots.$$

38. Existence and Pattern of Periodic Solutions of the Δ.E.:

$$x_{n+1} = -a_n x_n + 1, \quad n = 0, 1, \ldots,$$

where $\{a_n\}_{n=0}^{\infty}$ is a period-2 sequence.

39. Existence and Pattern of Periodic Solutions of the Δ.E.:

$$x_{n+1} = a_n x_n - 1, \quad n = 0, 1, \ldots,$$

where $\{a_n\}_{n=0}^{\infty}$ is a period-4 sequence.

40. Existence and Pattern of Periodic Solutions of the Δ.E.:

$$x_{n+1} = x_n + a_n, \quad n = 0, 1, \ldots,$$

where $\{a_n\}_{n=0}^{\infty}$ is a period-8 sequence.

41. Existence and Pattern of Periodic Solutions of the Δ.E.:

$$x_{n+1} = x_n + a_n, \quad n = 0, 1, \ldots,$$

where $\{a_n\}_{n=0}^{\infty}$ is a period-k sequence $(k \geq 2)$.

42. Existence and Pattern of Periodic Solutions of the Δ.E.:

$$x_{n+1} = -x_n + a_n, \quad n = 0, 1, \ldots,$$

where $\{a_n\}_{n=0}^{\infty}$ is a period-5 sequence.

43. Existence and Pattern of Periodic Solutions of the Δ.E.:

$$x_{n+1} = -x_n + a_n, \quad n = 0, 1, \ldots,$$

where $\{a_n\}_{n=0}^{\infty}$ is a period-4 sequence.

44. Existence and Pattern of Periodic Solutions of the Δ.E.:

$$x_{n+1} = -x_n + a_n, \quad n = 0, 1, \ldots,$$

where $\{a_n\}_{n=0}^{\infty}$ is a period-2k sequence $(k \in \mathbb{N})$.

45. Existence and Pattern of Periodic Solutions of the Δ.E.:

$$x_{n+1} = -x_n + a_n, \quad n = 0, 1, \ldots,$$

where $\{a_n\}_{n=0}^{\infty}$ is a period-$(2k+1)$ sequence $(k \in \mathbb{N})$.

46. Existence and Pattern of Periodic Solutions of the Δ.E.:

$$x_{n+1} = a_n x_n + (-1)^{n+1}, \quad n = 0, 1, \ldots,$$

where $\{a_n\}_{n=0}^{\infty}$ is a period-2 sequence.

47. Existence and Pattern of Periodic Solutions of the Δ.E.:

$$x_{n+1} = a_n x_n + (-1)^{n+1}, \quad n = 0, 1, \ldots,$$

where $\{a_n\}_{n=0}^{\infty}$ is a period-4 sequence.

48. Existence and Pattern of Periodic Solutions of the Δ.E.:

$$x_{n+1} = -a_n x_n, \quad n = 0, 1, \ldots,$$

where $\{a_n\}_{n=0}^{\infty}$ is a period-k sequence $(k \geq 2)$.

49. Existence and Pattern of Period-4 Solutions of the Δ.E.:

$$x_{n+1} = a_n x_n + b_n, \quad n = 0, 1, \ldots,$$

where $\{a_n\}_{n=0}^{\infty}$ and $\{b_n\}_{n=0}^{\infty}$ are period-2 sequences.

50. Existence and Pattern of Period-5 Solutions of the Δ.E.:

$$x_{n+1} = a_n x_n + b_n, \quad n = 0, 1, \ldots,$$

where $\{a_n\}_{n=0}^{\infty}$ and $\{b_n\}_{n=0}^{\infty}$ are period-3 sequences.

51. Existence and Pattern of Period-k Solutions of the Δ.E.:

$$x_{n+1} = a_n x_n + b_n, \quad n = 0, 1, \ldots,$$

where $\{a_n\}_{n=0}^{\infty}$ and $\{b_n\}_{n=0}^{\infty}$ are period-k sequences $(k \geq 2)$.

52. Existence and Pattern of Periodic Solutions of the Δ.E.:

$$x_{n+1} = a_n x_n + b_n, \quad n = 0, 1, \ldots,$$

where $\{a_n\}_{n=0}^{\infty}$ is a period-2 sequence and $\{b_n\}_{n=0}^{\infty}$ is a period-4 sequence.

53. Existence and Pattern of Periodic Solutions of the Δ.E.:

$$x_{n+1} = a_n x_n + b_n, \quad n = 0, 1, \ldots,$$

where $\{a_n\}_{n=0}^{\infty}$ is a period-4 sequence and $\{b_n\}_{n=0}^{\infty}$ is a period-2 sequence.

54. Existence and Pattern of Periodic Solutions of the Δ.E.:

$$x_{n+1} = a_n x_n + b_n, \quad n = 0, 1, \ldots,$$

where $\{a_n\}_{n=0}^{\infty}$ is a period-2k sequence ($k \in \mathbb{N}$), $\{b_n\}_{n=0}^{\infty}$ is a period-2l sequence ($l \in \mathbb{N}$), and $k \neq l$.

55. Existence and Pattern of Periodic Solutions of the Δ.E.:

$$x_{n+1} = a_n x_n + b_n, \quad n = 0, 1, \ldots,$$

where $\{a_n\}_{n=0}^{\infty}$ is a period-2 sequence and $\{b_n\}_{n=0}^{\infty}$ is a period-3 sequence.

56. Existence and Pattern of Periodic Solutions of the Δ.E.:

$$x_{n+1} = a_n x_n + b_n, \quad n = 0, 1, \ldots,$$

where $\{a_n\}_{n=0}^{\infty}$ is a period-3 sequence and $\{b_n\}_{n=0}^{\infty}$ is a period-2 sequence.

57. Existence and Pattern of Periodic Solutions of the Δ.E.:

$$x_{n+1} = a_n x_n + b_n, \quad n = 0, 1, \ldots,$$

where $\{a_n\}_{n=0}^{\infty}$ is a period-k sequence (for $k \geq 2$), $\{b_n\}_{n=0}^{\infty}$ is a period-l sequence (for $l \geq 2$), and $k \neq l$.

Problems 58–61 are open-ended questions. Determine if periodic solutions exist. If so, then determine the pattern of the period. If not, then explain why. Either determine analytically or from computer observations.

58. Periodic Solutions of the Δ.E.:

$$x_{n+1} = (-1)^n x_n + a_n, \quad n = 0, 1, \ldots,$$

where $\{a_n\}_{n=0}^{\infty}$ is a period-2k sequence ($k \in \mathbb{N}$).

59. Periodic Solutions of the Δ.E.:

$$x_{n+1} = (-1)^n x_n + a_n, \quad n = 0, 1, \ldots,$$

where $\{a_n\}_{n=0}^{\infty}$ is a period-$(2k+1)$ sequence ($k \in \mathbb{N}$).

60. Periodic Solutions of the Δ.E.:

$$x_{n+1} = (-1)^n a_n x_n + b_n, \quad n = 0, 1, \ldots,$$

where $\{a_n\}_{n=0}^{\infty}$ and $\{b_n\}_{n=0}^{\infty}$ are period-k sequences (for $k \geq 2$).

61. Periodic Solutions of the Δ.E.:

$$x_{n+1} = (-1)^n a_n x_n + b_n, \quad n = 0, 1, \ldots,$$

where $\{a_n\}_{n=0}^{\infty}$ is a period-k sequence (for $k \geq 2$), $\{b_n\}_{n=0}^{\infty}$ is a period-l sequence (for $l \geq 2$), and $k \neq l$.

Problems 62–71 are open-ended questions. Using a computer, determine the periodic character of solutions to the following linear difference equations with **modulo arithmetic** and the initial condition $x_0 = 1$.

62. $x_{n+1} = 2x_n \, (Mod \, 3), \quad n = 0, 1, \ldots.$
63. $x_{n+1} = 2x_n \, (Mod \, 4), \quad n = 0, 1, \ldots.$
64. $x_{n+1} = 2x_n \, (Mod \, 5), \quad n = 0, 1, \ldots.$
65. $x_{n+1} = 2x_n \, (Mod \, 6), \quad n = 0, 1, \ldots.$
66. $x_{n+1} = 2x_n \, (Mod \, 7), \quad n = 0, 1, \ldots.$
67. $x_{n+1} = 3x_n \, (Mod \, 2), \quad n = 0, 1, \ldots.$
68. $x_{n+1} = 3x_n \, (Mod \, 4), \quad n = 0, 1, \ldots.$
69. $x_{n+1} = 3x_n \, (Mod \, 5), \quad n = 0, 1, \ldots.$
70. $x_{n+1} = 3x_n \, (Mod \, 6), \quad n = 0, 1, \ldots.$
71. $x_{n+1} = 3x_n \, (Mod \, 7), \quad n = 0, 1, \ldots.$

CHAPTER 3

FIRST ORDER NONLINEAR
DIFFERENCE EQUATIONS

The aims of this chapter are to study the local stability nature of equilibrium points, the global stability of equilibrium points, oscillatory nature of solutions, existence and patterns of periodic solutions, and existence of eventually periodic solutions of first order nonlinear difference equations. We will inquire various applications of first order nonlinear difference equations in population dynamics and in neural networking: the Logistic Model, the Beverton–Holt Model, the Ricker Model, Neural Networking Model, the Williamson Model and the West Nile Epidemics Model. We will commence with three examples of first order nonlinear difference equations:

(i) (Special Case of the **Riccati Δ.E.**)

$$x_{n+1} = \frac{x_n}{x_n - 1}, \quad n = 0, 1, \ldots.$$

(ii) (Special Case of the **Logistic Δ.E.**)

$$x_{n+1} = 4x_n(1 - x_n), \quad n = 0, 1, \ldots.$$

(iii) (Special Case of the Piecewise Difference Equations **Tent-Map**)

$$x_{n+1} = \begin{cases} 2x_n & \text{if } x_n < \dfrac{1}{2}, \\ 2(1 - x_n) & \text{if } x_n \geq \dfrac{1}{2}. \end{cases} \quad n = 0, 1, \ldots,$$

Now we will examine several graphical examples that address the convergence of solutions.

Example 1. The solution of the **Riccati Δ.E.**

$$x_{n+1} = \frac{2x_n}{x_n + 1},$$

where $x_0 = 2$, is described by the following graph:

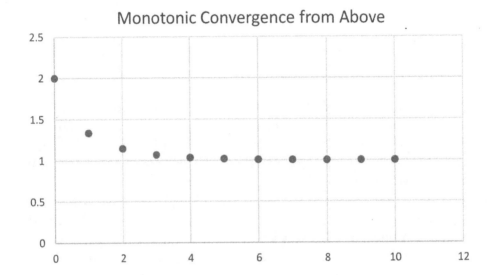

We obtain:

(i) $x_{n+1} < x_n$ for all $n \geq 0$,
(ii) $\lim_{n \to \infty} x_n = 1$.

This is a **monotonic** convergent solution that converges to $\bar{x} = 1$ from above.

Example 2. The solution of the Δ.E.

$$x_{n+1} = \frac{8}{\sqrt{x_n}},$$

where $x_0 = 12$, is portrayed by the following graph:

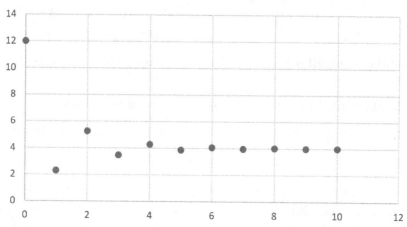

We acquire:

(i) $x_{2n+2} < x_{2n}$ and $x_{2n+1} < x_{2n+3}$ for all $n \geq 0$,
(ii) $\lim_{n\to\infty} x_n = 4$.

This is an **oscillatory** convergent solution as the even-indexed sub-sequence converges to $\bar{x} = 4$ from above and the odd-indexed sub-sequence converges to $\bar{x} = 4$ from below.

Example 3. The solution of the **Δ.E. in Exponential Form**

$$x_{n+1} = 9x_n e^{-x_n},$$

where $x_0 = 2$, is depicted by the following graph:

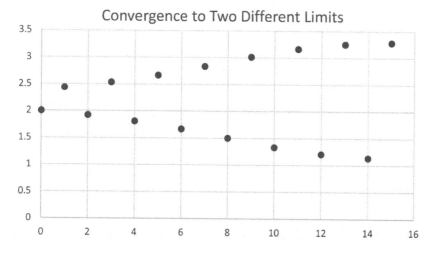

Now notice:

(i) $x_{2n+2} < x_{2n}$ and $x_{2n+1} < x_{2n+3}$ for all $n \geq 0$,
(ii) $\lim_{n \to \infty} x_{2n} = 1$ and $\lim_{n \to \infty} x_{2n+1} = 3.5$.

The solution is **oscillatory** about the positive equilibrium $\bar{x} = Ln(9)$.

3.1. Local Stability Character of Equilibrium Points

In Chapter 1 we commenced our studies of the first order Δ.E. in the form:

$$x_{n+1} = f(x_n), \quad n = 0, 1, \ldots. \tag{3.29}$$

This is a **first order** Δ.E. as we have one initial condition x_0 and as x_{n+1} depends on x_n. The function $y = f(x)$ describes Eq. (3.29) on an interval (domain) I. If $f : I \to I$ and $x_0 \in I$, then $x_n \in I$ for all $n \geq 0$. In addition, recall that $\bar{x}$ is an **equilibrium point** of Eq. (3.29) provided that

$$\bar{x} = f(\bar{x}).$$

This is where the function $f(x)$ crosses the bisector $y = x$ as we illustrated in Examples 10–12 of Chapter 1. Now we will introduce the following definitions:

Definition 13. The equilibrium $\bar{x}$ of Eq. (3.29) is **locally stable** if for every $\varepsilon > 0$, there exists $\delta > 0$ such that for all $x_0 \in I$ with $|x_0 - \bar{x}| < \delta$, we have

$$|x_n - \bar{x}| < \varepsilon \quad \text{for all } n \geq 0.$$

Definition 14. The equilibrium $\bar{x}$ of Eq. (3.29) is **locally asymptotically stable** if $\bar{x}$ is a locally stable solution of Eq. (3.29), and if there exists $\gamma > 0$ such that for all $x_0 \in I$ with $|x_0 - \bar{x}| < \gamma$, we have

$$\lim_{n \to \infty} x_n = \bar{x}.$$

Definition 15. The equilibrium $\bar{x}$ of Eq. (3.29) is a **global attractor** if for all $x_0 \in I$, we have

$$\lim_{n \to \infty} x_n = \bar{x}.$$

Definition 16. The equilibrium $\bar{x}$ of Eq. (3.29) is **globally asymptotically stable** if $\bar{x}$ is locally stable and $\bar{x}$ is also a global attractor of Eq. (3.29).

Definition 17. The equilibrium solution $\bar{x}$ of Eq. (3.29) is **unstable** if $\bar{x}$ is not locally stable.

Definition 18. The equilibrium $\bar{x}$ of Eq. (3.29) is a **source** if there exists $\rho > 0$ such that for all $x_0 \in I$ with $0 < |x_0 - \bar{x}| < \rho$, there exists $N \geq 1$ such that

$$|x_N - \bar{x}| > \rho.$$

Clearly a source is an unstable equilibrium of Eq. (3.29). The following theorem outlines the local stability nature of an equilibrium point $\bar{x}$ of Eq. (3.29).

Theorem 8. *Let $\bar{x}$ be an equilibrium point of Eq. (3.29), where $f(x)$ is continuously differentiable at $\bar{x}$. Then the following statements are true:*

(i) *If $|f'(\bar{x})| < 1$, then $\bar{x}$ is locally asymptotically stable.*
(ii) *If $|f'(\bar{x})| > 1$, then $\bar{x}$ is unstable.*

Proof. First we will prove part (i). Since we assumed that $f(x)$ is continuously differentiable and $f'(\bar{x}) < 1$, then there exist $r > 0$ and $\rho \in (0,1)$ such that $f'(x) \leq \rho$ for all $x \in (\bar{x} - r, \bar{x} + r)$. Then by the **Mean Value Theorem** for $x_0 \in (\bar{x} - r, \bar{x} + r)$ we acquire:

$$|x_1 - \bar{x}| = |f(x_0) - f(\bar{x})| = |f'(\eta)| \cdot |x_0 - \bar{x}| \leq \rho |x_0 - \bar{x}|,$$

where $\eta \in (\bar{x} - x_0, \bar{x} + x_0)$ and thus $\eta \in (\bar{x} - r, \bar{x} + r)$. Then it follows that $x_1 \in (\bar{x} - r, \bar{x} + r)$ as $\rho < 1$. Similarly we see that:

$$|x_2 - \bar{x}| \leq \rho |x_1 - \bar{x}| \leq \rho^2 |x_0 - \bar{x}|.$$

It follows by induction that for all $n \geq 1$:

$$|x_n - \bar{x}| \leq \rho^n |x_0 - \bar{x}|,$$

from which the result follows.

Now we will prove part(ii). In this case, there exist $r > 0$ and $R > 1$ such that $f'(x) \geq R$ for all $x \in (\bar{x} - r, \bar{x} + r)$. Then by the **Mean Value Theorem** and for $x_0 \in (\bar{x} - r, \bar{x} + r)$ we obtain:

$$|x_1 - \bar{x}| = |f(x_0) - f(\bar{x})| = |f'(x)| \cdot |x_0 - \bar{x}| \geq R |x_0 - \bar{x}|,$$

Inductively it follows that:

$$|x_k - \bar{x}| \geq R^k |x_0 - \bar{x}|,$$

for $x_k \in (\bar{x} - r, \bar{x} + r)$ from which the result follows. $\square$

Note that when $|f'(\bar{x})| = 1$ the test fails. We can find an alternative proof of this theorem by S. Elaydi (2005, 27–28) in [33]. The next series of examples will illustrate the use of Theorem 8 to determine the local stability character of equilibrium points.

Example 4. Determine all the equilibrium point(s) and their local stability character of the following **Riccati Δ.E.**:

$$x_{n+1} = \frac{rx_n}{1 + x_n}, \quad n = 0, 1, \ldots, \tag{3.30}$$

where $x_0, r > 0$.

Solution: Eq. (3.30) has two equilibrium points $\bar{x}_1 = 0$ and $\bar{x}_2 = r - 1$ (when $r > 1$). In addition:

$$f(x) = \frac{rx}{1 + x} \quad \text{and} \quad f'(x) = \frac{r}{(x + 1)^2}.$$

Then,

$$|f'(\bar{x}_1 = 0)| = r \quad \text{and} \quad |f'(\bar{x}_2 = r - 1)| = \frac{1}{r}.$$

Therefore, from Theorem 8 the following statements hold true:

(i) $\bar{x}_1 = 0$ is locally asymptotically stable if $r < 1$.
(ii) $\bar{x}_1 = 0$ is unstable if $r > 1$.
(iii) $\bar{x}_2 = r - 1$ is locally asymptotically stable if $r > 1$.

In Example 1 we observed convergence to $\bar{x} = 1$ from above when $r = 2$ and $x_0 = 2$. The first graph below depicts **monotonic convergence** to $\bar{x} = 0$ from above when $x_0 = 1$:

Monotonic Convergence to 0

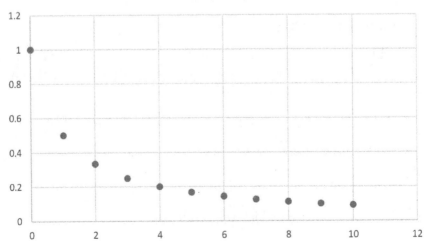

Observe that $x_{n+1} < x_n$ for all $n \geq 0$. The next graph below depicts **monotonic convergence** to $\bar{x} = 3$ from below when $x_0 = 0.5$:

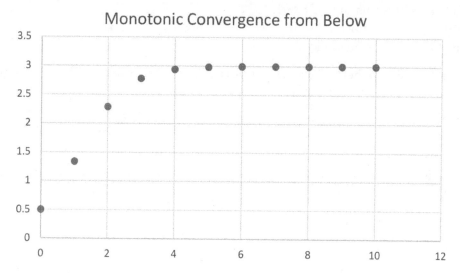

Monotonic Convergence from Below

Observe that $x_n < x_{n+1}$ for all $n \geq 0$. Furthermore, the **Riccati Δ.E.** has various applications in Nonlinear Physics and their computer algebra solutions, Newton's law of motion, and in Riemann Manifolds and Geodesic distributions. We will see the periodic traits of solutions of the **Riccati Δ.E.** in the later section of this chapter. We will see additional graphical examples that characterize the stability of the two equilibrium points in the **Cobweb Diagram Section**.

Example 5. Determine all the equilibrium point(s) and their local stability character of the following **Logistic Δ.E.**:

$$x_{n+1} = r x_n (1 - x_n), \quad n = 0, 1, \ldots, \tag{3.31}$$

where $x_0 \in (0, 1)$ and $r \in (0, 4]$.

Solution: Eq. (3.31) has two equilibrium points $\bar{x}_1 = 0$ and $\bar{x}_2 = \frac{r-1}{r}$ (when $1 < r \leq 4$). Also we have:

$$f(x) = rx - rx^2 \quad \text{and} \quad f'(x) = r - 2rx.$$

Then

$$\left| f'(\bar{x}_1 = 0) \right| = r \quad \text{and} \quad \left| f'\left(\bar{x}_2 = \frac{r-1}{r} \right) \right| = 3 - r.$$

Thus from Theorem 8 the following statements hold true:

  (i) $\bar{x}_1 = 0$ is locally asymptotically stable if $r < 1$.
  (ii) $\bar{x}_1 = 0$ is unstable if $r > 1$.
  (iii) $\bar{x}_2 = \frac{r-1}{r}$ is locally asymptotically stable if $1 < r < 3$.
  (iv) $\bar{x}_2 = \frac{r-1}{r}$ is unstable if $3 < r \le 4$.

The first graph below renders **monotonic convergence** to $\bar{x} = \frac{1}{2}$ from below when $r = 2$ and when $x_0 = 0.05$:

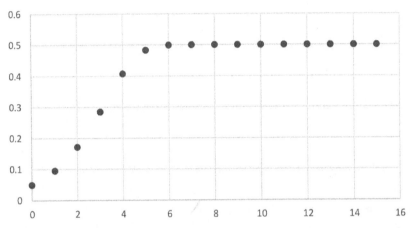

Monotonic Convergence from Below

The next graph below depicts **oscillatory convergence** to $\bar{x} = \frac{r-1}{r}$ when $r = 2.8$ and when $x_0 = 0.9$:

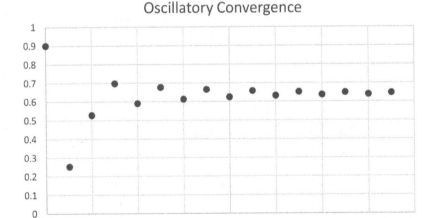

Oscillatory Convergence

The **Logistic Δ.E.** has various applications in Population Dynamics, Population Growth and Extinction, Harvesting, Cardiology, Archeology,

Pharmacodynamic analysis in vitro bactericidal kinetics, Predator-Prey Model, and as Forecast models in business and economics [9, 36, 53, 79, 81]. We will examine the periodic traits of solutions and chaotic behavior of the **Logistic Δ.E.** in the later section of this chapter. We will see additional graphical examples of the stability of the two equilibrium points in the **Cobweb Diagram Section**.

Example 6. Determine all the equilibrium point(s) and their local stability character of:

$$x_{n+1} = ax_n e^{-x_n}, \quad n = 0, 1, \ldots, \tag{3.32}$$

where x_0, $a > 0$.

Solution: Eq. (3.32) has two equilibrium points $\bar{x}_1 = 0$ and $\bar{x}_2 = Ln(a)$ (when $a > 1$). Moreover:

$$f(x) = axe^{-x} \quad \text{and} \quad f'(x) = ae^{-x}(1 - x).$$

Then

$$\left| f'(\bar{x}_1 = 0) \right| = a \quad \text{and} \quad \left| f'(\bar{x}_2 = Ln(a)) \right| = 1 - Ln(a).$$

Hence from Theorem 8 the following statements hold true:

(i) $\bar{x}_1 = 0$ is locally asymptotically stable if $a < 1$.
(ii) $\bar{x}_1 = 0$ is unstable if $a > 1$.
(iii) $\bar{x}_2 = Ln(a)$ is locally asymptotically stable if $1 < a < e^2$.
(iv) $\bar{x}_2 = Ln(a)$ is unstable if $a > e^2$.

The first graph below describes **monotonic convergence** to $\bar{x} = Ln(2)$ from below when $a = 2$ and when $x_0 = 0.05$:

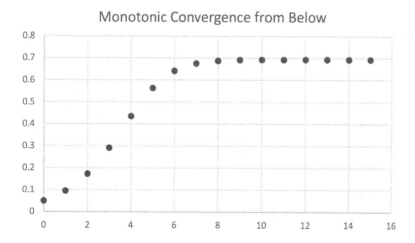

Monotonic Convergence from Below

The following graph below portrays **oscillatory convergence** to $\bar{x} = Ln(6)$ when $a = 6$ and when $x_0 = 3$:

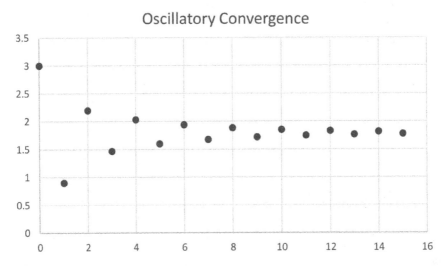

The following graph below describes convergence to two different limits when $a = 9$ and when $x_0 = 2$:

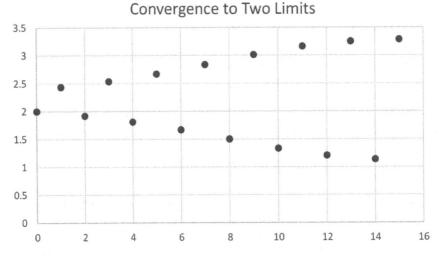

Difference Equations in **Exponential Form** have various applications in Population Dynamics and have been applied to study population growth by William Ricker [74, 75], by the Harvard School of Public Health [28, 34] and have been studied by several other authors [48, 65, 66]. We will examine additional graphical examples of the stability of the two equilibrium points in the **Cobweb Diagram Section.**

The upcoming two examples will focus on the existence of a positive equilibrium indirectly and determining its local stability character.

Example 7. Show that the Δ.E.:

$$x_{n+1} = 1 + x_n e^{-x_n}, \quad n = 0, 1, \ldots,$$

where $x_0 \geq 0$ has a **unique positive equilibrium point**.

Solution: First we set

$$\bar{x} = 1 + \bar{x} e^{-\bar{x}}. \tag{3.33}$$

Now notice that from the graph below Eq. (3.33) has a unique positive solution as the function $f(x) = 1 + xe^{-x}$ intersects the **bisector** $y = x$ exactly once.

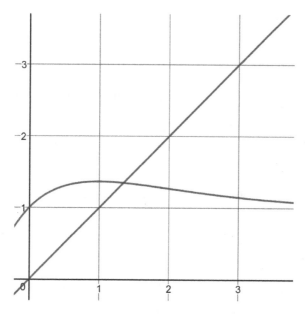

Now via (3.33), it suffices to consider the functions:

$$f(x) = 1 + xe^{-x} \quad \text{and} \quad y = x \text{ (bisector) for } x \geq 0.$$

Observe that

$$f'(x) = e^{-x}(1 - x).$$

Hence the point $(1, 1 + \frac{1}{e})$ is the absolute maximum of $f(x)$, and

$$\lim_{x \to \infty} f(x) = 1.$$

Thus the function $f(x) = 1 + xe^{-x}$ will cross the bisector $y = x$ exactly once. Also notice that $\bar{x} > 1$.

Example 8. Consider the Δ.E.:

$$x_{n+1} = 1 + x_n e^{-x_n}, \quad n = 0, 1, \ldots, \tag{3.34}$$

where $x_0 \geq 0$. Show that the unique positive equilibrium point is **locally asymptotically stable**.

Solution: From Example 7, Eq. (3.34) has a unique positive equilibrium point $\bar{x} > 1$.

In addition, from Example 7, we will consider the function:

$$f(x) = 1 + xe^{-x} \quad \text{for } x \geq 0.$$

Then

$$f'(x) = e^{-x}(1 - x).$$

To show that $\bar{x}$ is locally asymptotically stable, it suffices to show that

$$\left| f'(\bar{x}) \right| < 1.$$

Now we introduce the function

$$g(x) = e^{-x}(1 - x) \quad \text{for } x \geq 1.$$

Then

$$g'(x) = e^{-x}(x - 2).$$

The critical point $(2, \frac{-1}{e^2})$ is the absolute minimum of $g(x)$, and

$$\lim_{x \to \infty} g(x) = 0.$$

Hence for all $x \geq 0$,

$$|g(x)| \leq \frac{1}{e^2} < 1.$$

The result follows from Theorem 8.

Now we will examine some of the discrete biological models depicted by first order nonlinear difference equations.

3.1.1. *The Beverton–Holt Model*

The **Beverton–Holt Model** is a discrete population model resembled by the following Δ.E.:

$$n_{t+1} = \frac{R_0 n_t}{1 + \frac{n_t}{M}},$$

where $n_0, R_0, M > 0$ and:

(i) n_t is the expected number or density of individuals in generation t.
(ii) n_{t+1} is the expected number or density of individuals in generation $t+1$.
(iii) $K = (R_0 - 1)M$ is the carrying capacity of the environment.

The model was introduced in 1957 in [13] and also studied in [14]. First of all, notice that the **Beverton–Holt Model** resembles the same pattern as the Riccati Δ.E. with two equilibrium points $\bar{n} = 0$ and $\bar{n} = K = (R_0 - 1)M$ (when $R_0 > 1$). Second of all, we get:

(i) $\lim_{n \to \infty} n_t = 0$ if $R_0 \leq 1$. This would imply extinction.
(ii) $\lim_{n \to \infty} n_t = K$ if $R_0 > 1$. This would imply survival.

This will be left as an exercise at the end of the chapter to verify.

3.1.2. *The Logistic Models*

The **Logistic Model** was first introduced by Pierre-Francois Verhulst in 1838 [81]. It is a discrete population model described by the following Δ.E.:

$$P_{n+1} = P_n + rP_n \left(1 - \frac{P_n}{K}\right),$$

where $P_0, r, K > 0$ and:

(i) P_n is the population in year n.
(ii) P_{n+1} is the population in year $n + 1$.
(iii) r is the population growth rate.
(iv) K is the carrying capacity.

The model has two equilibrium points $\bar{P} = 0$ and $\bar{P} = \frac{rK}{1+r}$. By applying Theorem 8, we conclude that $\bar{P} = 0$ is unstable and the positive equilibrium $\bar{P} = \frac{rK}{1+r}$ is locally asymptotically stable when $r < 2$. This will be left as an exercise at the end of the chapter to verify. When $r > 2$, then periodic solutions exist as well as chaotic behavior. We will study further properties of the Logistic Δ.E. in Section 3.4.3.

The Logistic Δ.E. is also applied as the **Predator-Prey Model** in [36] as:

$$x_{n+1} = \mu x_n (1 - x_n),$$

where μ is the population growth rate. The dynamics is governed by μx_n which is proportional to the current population x_n in year n. The term $1 - x_n$ characterizes how far the system is from overcrowding. It generates an *inhibition phase* or a *contracting phase* throughout the dynamics. As we observed in Example 5, $0 < x_0 < 1$ and $0 < \mu \le 4$. In Chapter 6 we will proceed the study of this Predator-Prey Model as a system of logistic difference equations.

3.1.3. *The Ricker Model*

The **Ricker Model** is a discrete population model portrayed by the following Δ.E. in Exponential Form:

$$x_{n+1} = x_n e^{r\left(1 - \frac{x_n}{K}\right)},$$

where $x_0, r, K > 0$ and:

(i) x_n is the population at year n.
(ii) x_{n+1} is the population at year $n + 1$.
(iii) r is the population growth rate.
(iv) K is the carrying capacity.

This model was introduced by William Ricker in 1954 in the context of stock and recruitment in fisheries in [74]. The Model has two equilibrium points $\bar{x} = 0$ and $\bar{x} = K$. By seeking Theorem 8 we conclude that $\bar{x} = 0$ is unstable and the positive equilibrium $\bar{x} = K$ is locally asymptotically stable. This will be left as an exercise at the end of the chapter to verify.

3.1.4. *The Ricker Stock Recruitment Model*

The **Ricker Stock Recruitment Model** is a discrete population model represented by the following Δ.E. in Exponential Form:

$$x_{n+1} = \alpha x_n e^{-\beta x_n},$$

where $x_0, \alpha, \beta > 0$ and:

(i) x_n is the population at year n.
(ii) x_{n+1} is the population at year $n + 1$.

(iii) α is the population growth rate.

(iv) β is the population death rate.

This model introduced by William Ricker in 1954 in the context of some species of fish (salmon) exhibit cannibalism in [75]. The model has two equilibrium points $\bar{x} = 0$ and $\bar{x} = \frac{1}{\beta}Ln(\alpha)$ (exists when $\alpha > 1$). Via Theorem 8 we conclude:

(i) $\bar{x} = 0$ is locally asymptotically stable if $\alpha < 1$. This would apply extinction.

(ii) $\bar{x} = 0$ is unstable if $\alpha > 1$

(iii) $\bar{x} = \frac{1}{\beta}Ln(\alpha)$ is locally asymptotically stable if $1 < \alpha < e^2$.

(iv) $\bar{x} = \frac{1}{\beta}Ln(\alpha)$ is unstable if $\alpha > e^2$.

This will be left as an exercise at the end of the chapter to verify.

3.1.5. *The Hassell Model*

The **Ricker Model** is a special case of the **Hassell Model** characterized by the following Δ.E.:

$$N_{t+1} = \frac{k_1 N_t}{(1 + k_2 N_t)^c},$$

where $N_0, k_1, k_2, c > 0$. Notice when $c = 1$ then the **Hassell Model** simplifies to the **Beverton–Holt Model**.

3.2. The Cobweb Method

This section's goal is to apply the graphical method of determining if solutions of Eq. (3.29) converge. Recall that $\bar{x}$ is a point where the function $y = f(x)$ crosses the **bisector** $y = x$. To apply the **Cobweb Method** we will assume that either $x_0 > \bar{x}$ or $x_0 < \bar{x}$. Here are the following steps of the **Cobweb Method**:

1. Pick the initial condition x_0 on the <u>horizontal axis</u> of the graph such that either $x_0 > \bar{x}$ or $x_0 < \bar{x}$.
2. Then <u>vertically</u> trace to the *function* $y = f(x)$.
3. Then <u>horizontally</u> trace to the *bisector* $y = x$.
4. Then <u>vertically</u> trace to the *function* $y = f(x)$.
5. Then <u>horizontally</u> trace to the *bisector* $y = x$.

Proceed with the method several times or with several iterations. Then from the graph, determine if one of the following occurs:

- Does the solution approach an equilibrium point?
- Does the solution diverge either to ∞ or to $-\infty$?
- Does the solution fall in a periodic cycle?

The following examples will graphically illustrate the implementation of the method.

Example 9. Consider the following Initial Value Problem:

$$\begin{cases} x_{n+1} = x_n + 1, & n = 0, 1, \ldots, \\ x_0 = 0.5. \end{cases}$$

Using the Cobweb Method, determine $\lim_{n\to\infty} x_n$.

Solution: First construct the graph with the bisector $y = x$ (in red) and the function $f(x) = x + 1$ (in black):

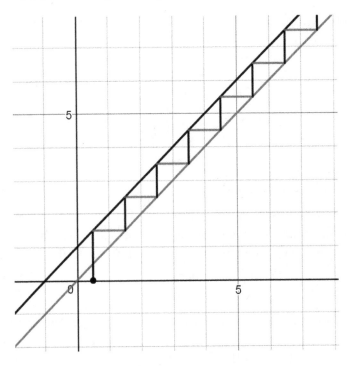

Then the following statements hold true:

(i) $x_n < x_{n+1}$ for all $n \geq 0$,

(ii) $\lim_{n\to\infty} x_n = +\infty$.

This is an example of a **Linear** Δ.E. depicting monotonic divergence to +∞.

Example 10. Consider the following Initial Value Problem:

$$\begin{cases} x_{n+1} = 6x_n e^{-x_n}, & n = 0, 1, \ldots, \\ x_0 = 0.8. \end{cases}$$

Using the Cobweb Method, determine $\lim_{n \to \infty} x_n$.

Solution: First construct the graph with the bisector $y = x$ (in red) and the function $f(x) = 6xe^{-x}$ (in black):

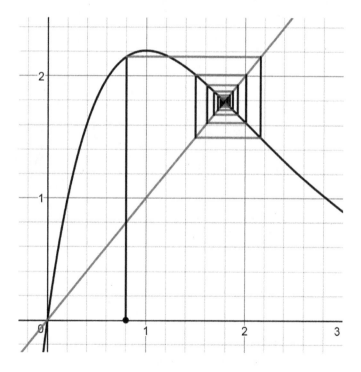

Furthermore:

(i) $x_{2n} < x_{2n+2}$ and $x_{2n+3} < x_{2n+1}$ for all $n \geq 0$,
(ii) $\lim_{n \to \infty} x_n = \bar{x} = Ln(6)$.

This is an example of the Δ.**E. in Exponential Form** with $a = 6$; depicting convergence to the positive equilibrium in two sub-sequences.

Example 11. Consider the following Initial Value Problem:

$$\begin{cases} x_{n+1} = 3.2x_n(1 - x_n), & n = 0, 1, \ldots, \\ x_0 = 0.4. \end{cases}$$

Using the Cobweb Method, determine $\lim_{n \to \infty} x_n$.

Solution: First construct the graph with the bisector $y = x$ (in red) and the function $f(x) = 3.2x(1 - x)$ (in black):

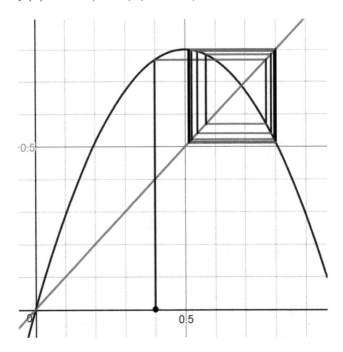

In addition:

(i) $\lim_{n \to \infty} x_{2n} = L_1$ and $\lim_{n \to \infty} x_{2n+1} = L_2$.
(ii) $L_1 \neq L_2$.

This is an example of the **Logistic Δ.E.** with $r = 3.2$ describing convergence to two different limits or convergence to a period-2 cycle.

3.3. Global Asymptotic Stability (Convergence)

Now we shift our intent to apply the monotonic properties of $f(x)$ to show global stability of either the zero equilibrium point or the positive equilibrium point of Eq. (3.29). In Chapter 1, the function $f(x)$ describes Eq. (3.29). We will assume that $f(x)$ is continuously differentiable on an interval (domain)

I and the initial condition $x_0 \in I$. In addition, we will assume that the following statements hold true:

(i) Either $f'(x) > 0$ or $f'(x) < 0$ on I.
(ii) $f''(x) < 0$ on I.

We will commence with analytical and graphical examples of global asymptotic stability.

Example 12. Consider the following A.E.:

$$x_{n+1} = \sqrt{x_n}, \quad n = 0, 1, \ldots, \tag{3.35}$$

with $x_0 > 0$. Show that

$$\lim_{n \to \infty} x_n = 1.$$

Solution: First of all, Eq. (3.35) has two equilibrium points $\bar{x}_1 = 0$ and $\bar{x}_2 = 1$. Second of all,

$$f'(\bar{x}_2 = 1) = \frac{1}{2} < 1.$$

Hence $\bar{x}_2 = 1$ is locally asymptotically stable. Also $f''(x) = \frac{-1}{2\sqrt{x^3}} < 0$ for all $x > 0$. Suppose that $x_0 \in (0, 1)$. The case when $x_0 > 1$ is similar and will be omitted. Let $x_0 = 0.01$ and we produce the following graph:

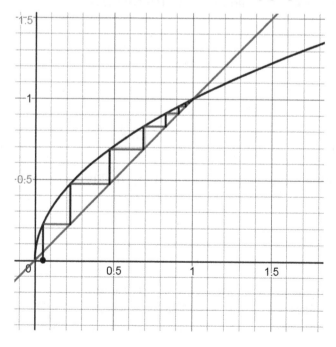

We see that the solution monotonically converges to $\bar{x}_2 = 1$ from below. Now by iterations we acquire:

$$x_0 < 1,$$
$$x_1 = \sqrt{x_0} > x_0,$$
$$x_2 = \sqrt{x_1} > x_1,$$
$$x_3 = \sqrt{x_2} > x_2,$$
$$x_4 = \sqrt{x_3} > x_3,$$
$$\vdots$$

Hence for all $n \geq 0$:

$$x_0 < x_1 < x_2 < \cdots x_n < x_{n+1} < \cdots < 1,$$

and

$$\lim_{n \to \infty} x_n = 1.$$

Example 13. Consider the following **Riccati** Δ.**E.**:

$$x_{n+1} = \frac{5x_n}{x_n + 1}, \quad n = 0, 1, \ldots, \tag{3.36}$$

with $x_0 > 0$. Show that

$$\lim_{n \to \infty} x_n = 4.$$

Solution: First of all, Eq. (3.36) has two equilibrium points $\bar{x}_1 = 0$ and $\bar{x}_2 = 4$. Also:

$$f'(\bar{x}_2 = 4) = \frac{1}{5} < 1.$$

Thus $\bar{x}_2 = 4$ is locally asymptotically stable. In addition, $f''(x) = \frac{-5}{(x+1)^2} < 0$ for all $x > 0$. Assume that $x_0 < 4$. The case when $x_0 > 4$ is similar and will be omitted. Consider $x_0 = 0.1$. Then we produce the following graph:

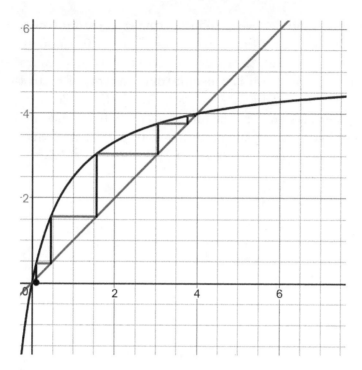

The solution monotonically converges to $\bar{x}_2 = 4$ from below. By iterations we acquire:

$$x_0 < 4,$$

$$x_1 = \frac{5x_0}{x_0 + 1} > x_0,$$

$$x_2 = \frac{5x_1}{x_1 + 1} > x_1,$$

$$x_3 = \frac{5x_2}{x_2 + 1} > x_2,$$

$$x_4 = \frac{5x_3}{x_3 + 1} > x_3,$$

$$\vdots$$

Hence for all $n \geq 0$:

$$x_0 < x_1 < x_2 < \cdots x_n < x_{n+1} < \cdots < 4.$$

Therefore

$$\lim_{n \to \infty} x_n = 4.$$

In Examples 12 and 13 every solution converges **monotonically** to the positive equilibrium as $f'(x) > 0$ and as $f''(x) < 0$. However, when one of these assumptions fail, then we will not see monotonic convergence. For instance, in Example 2 we had **oscillatory convergence** to the positive equilibrium as $f'(x) < 0$ and $f''(x) > 0$. Yet in Example 10 we discerned **oscillatory convergence** as the function $f(x) = 6xe^{-x}$ has a critical point and an inflection point on the interval $x > 0$. Similar phenomena occurred with the **Logistic Δ.E.** as the function $f(x) = rx(1-x)$ has a critical point on the interval $(0, 1)$.

Example 14. Consider the following Δ.E.:

$$x_{n+1} = \frac{1}{\sqrt{x_n}}, \quad n = 0, 1, \ldots, \tag{3.37}$$

with $x_0 > 0$. Show that

$$\lim_{n \to \infty} x_n = 1.$$

Solution: First of all, Eq. (3.37) has one positive equilibrium point $\bar{x} = 1$. Second of all,

$$|f'(\bar{x} = 1)| = \frac{1}{2} < 1$$

and $\bar{x} = 1$ is locally asymptotically stable. Also $f''(x) = \frac{3}{4\sqrt{x^5}} > 0$ for all $x > 0$. From Example 2 we observed oscillatory convergence. We will analytically show that the solution of Eq. (3.37) converges in two sub-sequences. Suppose that $x_0 > \bar{x}$. By iterations and induction we get:

$$x_0 > \bar{x} = 1,$$

$$x_1 = \frac{1}{\sqrt{x_0}} < \bar{x},$$

$$x_2 = \frac{1}{\sqrt{x_1}} > \bar{x},$$

$$x_3 = \frac{1}{\sqrt{x_2}} < \bar{x},$$

$$x_4 = \frac{1}{\sqrt{x_3}} > \bar{x},$$

$$\vdots$$

Hence for all $n \geq 0$:

$$x_{2n+1} < \bar{x} < x_{2n}.$$

Now observe:

$$x_0 > \bar{x} = 1,$$

$$x_2 = \frac{1}{\sqrt{x_1}} = \frac{1}{\sqrt{\frac{1}{\sqrt{x_0}}}} = \sqrt[4]{x_0} < x_0,$$

$$x_4 = \frac{1}{\sqrt{x_3}} = \frac{1}{\sqrt{\frac{1}{\sqrt{x_2}}}} = \sqrt[4]{x_2} < x_2,$$

$$\vdots$$

Thus for all $n \geq 0$:

$$\bar{x} < \cdots < x_{2n+2} < x_{2n}.$$

Similarly it follows for all $n \geq 0$:

$$x_{2n+1} < x_{2n+3} < \cdots < \bar{x}.$$

Therefore:

$$\lim_{n \to \infty} x_{2n} = 1 \quad \text{and} \quad \lim_{n \to \infty} x_{2n+1} = 1.$$

The case when $x_0 < \bar{x} = 1$ is similar and will be omitted. Notice that every non-trivial solution of Eq. (3.37) is oscillatory about the positive equilibrium $\bar{x}$.

From Examples 2, 3, 5, 6, 10, 11, and 14, the following theorem extends the result about the **oscillatory character** of non-trivial solutions of Eq. (3.29) about the positive equilibrium $\bar{x}$.

Theorem 9. *Let $\{x_n\}_{n=0}^{\infty}$ be a solution of Eq. (3.29). Suppose the following statements hold true:*

(i) *$f(x)$ is a continuously differentiable function.*
(ii) *$f'(x) < 0$.*
(iii) *Eq. (3.29) has exactly one positive equilibrium $\bar{x}$.*

Then every non-trivial solution of Eq. (3.29) is oscillatory.

Proof. First of all, suppose that $x_0 > \bar{x}$. Then we inductively obtain:

$$x_0 > \bar{x},$$
$$x_1 = f(x_0) < f(\bar{x}) = \bar{x},$$
$$x_2 = f(x_1) > f(\bar{x}) = \bar{x},$$
$$x_3 = f(x_2) < f(\bar{x}) = \bar{x},$$
$$x_4 = f(x_3) > f(\bar{x}) = \bar{x},$$
$$\vdots$$

Hence for all $n \geq 0$:

$$x_{2n+1} < \bar{x} < x_{2n}.$$

Thus the result follows. The case when $x_0 < \bar{x}$ is similar and will be omitted. $\square$

We will conclude this section with the following definition.

Definition 19. The function $f(x)$ satisfies the **negative feedback condition** on an interval J if:

(i) $\bar{x} \in J \subset I$,
(ii) $(f(x) - x)(x - \bar{x}) < 0$ for all $x \in J - \bar{x}$.

Notice that if $f(x)$ is a decreasing function on an interval I then it will satisfy the negative feedback condition. In fact, using the Cobweb Method, we can confirm that the functions in Examples 10 and 14 will satisfy the negative feedback condition. Furthermore, when $f(x)$ is an increasing function then it will not satisfy the negative feedback condition. For instance, using the Cobweb Method we can verify that $f(x)$ in Example 13 will not satisfy the negative feedback condition.

3.4. Periodic Traits of Solutions

From Chapter 1, the sequence $\{x_n\}_{n=0}^{\infty}$ is periodic with **minimal period-p** ($p \geq 2$), provided that

$$x_{n+p} = x_n \quad \text{for all } n = 0, 1, \ldots.$$

For instance, Eq. (3.29) has a period-2 cycle:

$$\alpha, \beta, \alpha, \beta, \ldots,$$

where $\alpha \neq \beta$ if either:

(i) $f[f(\alpha)] = \alpha$ and $f[f(\beta)] = \beta$,

(ii) $f(\alpha) = \beta$ and $f(\beta) = \alpha$.

In addition, Eq. (3.29) has period-p solutions $(p \geq 2)$ if:

$$f^p[\alpha] = \alpha.$$

Our plan is to analyze the existence and patterns of periodic solutions of the **Riccati Δ.E.**, the **Logistic Δ.E.** and **Piecewise Difference Equations**.

3.4.1. *Periodic solutions of the Riccati Difference Equation*

First we will commence with the **Riccati Δ.E.**:

$$x_{n+1} = \frac{ax_n + b}{cx_n + d}, \quad n = 0, 1, \ldots,$$

where the parameters $a, b, c, d \geq 0$ and $x_0 \geq 0$. Riccati Δ.E. has many applications in gravitational sciences and biological sciences. Observe that by setting:

$$\bar{x} = \frac{a\bar{x} + b}{c\bar{x} + d},$$

we obtain the following quadratic equation:

$$c\bar{x}^2 + (d - a)\bar{x} - b = 0,$$

with two solutions:

$$\bar{x}_1 = \frac{(a - d) + \sqrt{(a - d)^2 + 4bc}}{2c} \quad \text{and} \quad \bar{x}_2 = \frac{(a - d) - \sqrt{(a - d)^2 + 4bc}}{2c}.$$

Now we will examine the existence of period-2 solutions by setting $x_2 = x_0$:

$$x_0,$$

$$x_1 = \frac{ax_0 + b}{cx_0 + d},$$

$$x_2 = \frac{ax_1 + b}{cx_1 + d} = \frac{a\left[\frac{ax_0+b}{cx_0+d}\right] + b}{c\left[\frac{ax_0+b}{cx_0+d}\right] + d} = x_0,$$

which gives us:

$$\frac{a^2x_0 + ab + bcx_0 + bd}{acx_0 + bc + dcx_0 + d^2} = x_0,$$

and reduces to:

$$c(a + d)x_0^2 + (d^2 - a^2)x_0 - b(a + d) = 0,$$

with two solutions:

$$x_0 = \frac{(a - d) + \sqrt{(a - d)^2 + 4bc}}{2c} \quad \text{and} \quad x_0 = \frac{(a - d) - \sqrt{(a - d)^2 + 4bc}}{2c}.$$

The two solutions above are the equilibrium points $\bar{x}_1$ and $\bar{x}_2$. Then we proceed with studying periodic traits of two special cases of the Riccati A.E. where every non-trivial solution (non-equilibrium solution) is periodic with period-2:

$$x_{n+1} = \frac{1}{x_n}, \quad n = 0, 1, \ldots \tag{3.38}$$

and

$$x_{n+1} = \frac{x_n}{x_n - 1}, \quad n = 0, 1, \ldots \tag{3.39}$$

We will emerge with the periodic character of solutions of Eq. (3.38) and assume that $x_0 \neq 0$.

Example 15. Show that every non-trivial solution of

$$x_{n+1} = \frac{1}{x_n}, \quad n = 0, 1, \ldots$$

is periodic with period-2 and determine their pattern.

Solution: The two equilibrium points of Eq. (3.38) are $\bar{x}_1 = 1$ and $\bar{x}_2 = -1$. In addition $f(x) = \frac{1}{x}$ and

$$f'(\bar{x}_1 = 1) = f'(\bar{x}_2 = -1) = -1.$$

Thus the Linearized Stability Analysis fails at both equilibrium points. Now observe:

$$x_0,$$

$$x_1 = \frac{1}{x_0},$$

$$x_2 = \frac{1}{x_1} = \frac{1}{\left[\frac{1}{x_0}\right]} = x_0,$$

$$x_3 = \frac{1}{x_2} = \frac{1}{x_0} = x_1.$$

Hence we acquire the following period-2 pattern:

$$x_0, \frac{1}{x_0}, x_0, \frac{1}{x_0}, \ldots.$$

Notice that the product of two neighboring terms:

$$x_0 \cdot \frac{1}{x_0} = 1.$$

Using the Cobweb Method we see that the periodic solutions are on the hyperbolic curve $y = \frac{1}{x}$ with $x_0 = 0.5$ and $x_1 = 2$:

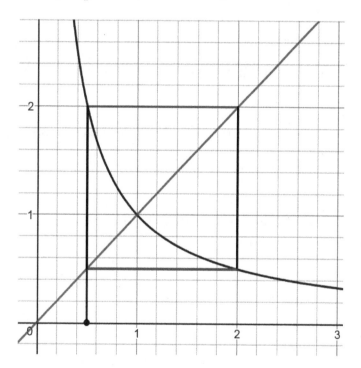

The period-2 cycles oscillate about the positive equilibrium $\bar{x} = 1$ with semi-cycles of length 1.

Now we proceed with the periodic nature of solutions of Eq. (3.39) and suppose that $x_0 \neq 1$.

Example 16. Show that every non-trivial solution of

$$x_{n+1} = \frac{x_n}{x_n - 1}, \quad n = 0, 1, \ldots$$

is periodic with period-2 and determine their pattern.

Solution: The two equilibrium points of Eq. (3.39) are $\bar{x}_1 = 0$ and $\bar{x}_2 = 2$. The Linearized Stability Analysis fails at both equilibrium points. Then we acquire:

$$x_0,$$

$$x_1 = \frac{x_0}{x_0 - 1},$$

$$x_2 = \frac{x_1}{x_1 - 1} = \frac{\left[\frac{x_0}{x_0-1}\right]}{\left[\frac{x_0}{x_0-1}\right] - 1} = \frac{x_0}{x_0 - (x_0 - 1)} = x_0,$$

$$x_3 = \frac{x_2}{x_2 - 1} = \frac{x_0}{x_0 - 1} = x_1.$$

We then procure the following period-2 pattern:

$$x_0, \frac{x_0}{x_0 - 1}, x_0, \frac{x_0}{x_0 - 1}, \ldots$$

Notice that the product and the sum of two neighboring terms are always equal:

$$x_0 \cdot \frac{x_0}{x_0 - 1} = \frac{(x_0)^2}{x_0 - 1} = x_0 + \frac{x_0}{x_0 - 1}.$$

Using the Cobweb Method we see that the periodic solutions are on the hyperbolic curve $y = \frac{x}{x-1}$ with $x_0 = 3$ and $x_1 = \frac{3}{2}$:

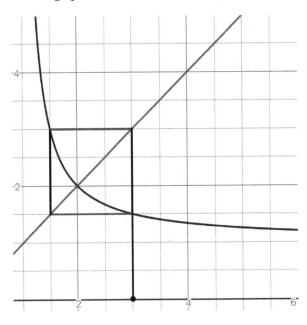

Period-2 cycles oscillate about the positive equilibrium $\bar{x} = 2$. Now we proceed with studying the periodic traits of the Non-autonomous Riccati Δ.E.

3.4.2. *Periodic solutions of Non-autonomous Riccati Difference Equations*

Our scheme of this section is to examine the existence, uniqueness and patterns of periodic cycles of the **Non-autonomous Riccati Difference Equations**:

$$x_{n+1} = \frac{a_n}{x_n}, \quad n = 0, 1, \ldots, \tag{3.40}$$

and

$$x_{n+1} = \frac{a_n x_n}{x_n - 1}, \quad n = 0, 1, \ldots, \tag{3.41}$$

where $\{a_n\}_{n=0}^{\infty}$ is a period-k sequence $(k \geq 2)$. We will start with Eq. (3.40) and assume that $x_0 \neq 0$. It is our goal to demonstrate various combinations of patterns of periodic cycles depending on the period of the period-k sequence $\{a_n\}_{n=0}^{\infty}$ and the relationship of the terms of the period-k sequence. We will show that sometimes the periodic cycles are unique and in other instances every solution is periodic. Now we will exhibit several examples of this phenomenon that we did not encounter in the autonomous case of Eq. (3.38).

Example 17. Suppose that $\{a_n\}_{n=0}^{\infty}$ is a period-2 sequence. Show that

$$x_{n+1} = \frac{a_n}{x_n}, \quad n = 0, 1, \ldots$$

has no period-2 solutions and explain why.

Solution: First we assume that $x_2 = x_0$ and we produce:

$$x_0,$$

$$x_1 = \frac{a_0}{x_0},$$

$$x_2 = \frac{a_1}{x_1} = \frac{a_1}{\left[\frac{a_0}{x_0}\right]} = \frac{a_1 x_0}{a_0} = x_0.$$

Hence we see that $x_2 = x_0$ if and only if $a_0 = a_1$. This contradicts that assumption that $\{a_n\}_{n=0}^{\infty}$ is a period-2 sequence where $a_0 \neq a_1$.

Example 18. Suppose that $\{a_n\}_{n=0}^{\infty}$ is a period-3 sequence. Determine the existence, uniqueness and the pattern of period-3 solutions of:

$$x_{n+1} = \frac{a_n}{x_n}, \quad n = 0, 1, \ldots.$$

Solution: Assume that $x_3 = x_0$ and we obtain:

$$x_0,$$

$$x_1 = \frac{a_0}{x_0},$$

$$x_2 = \frac{a_1}{x_1} = \frac{a_1}{\left[\frac{a_0}{x_0}\right]} = \frac{a_1 x_0}{a_0},$$

$$x_3 = \frac{a_2}{x_2} = \frac{a_2}{\left[\frac{a_1 x_0}{a_0}\right]} = \frac{a_2 a_0}{a_1 x_0} = x_0.$$

Now either $x_0 = \sqrt{\frac{a_2 a_0}{a_1}}$ or $x_0 = -\sqrt{\frac{a_2 a_0}{a_1}}$. We will verify the existence of a unique positive period-3 cycle:

$$x_0 = \sqrt{\frac{a_2 a_0}{a_1}},$$

$$x_1 = \frac{a_0}{x_0} = \frac{a_0}{\sqrt{\frac{a_2 a_0}{a_1}}} = \sqrt{\frac{a_0 a_1}{a_2}},$$

$$x_2 = \frac{a_1}{x_1} = \frac{a_1}{\sqrt{\frac{a_0 a_1}{a_2}}} = \sqrt{\frac{a_1 a_2}{a_0}},$$

$$x_3 = \frac{a_2}{x_2} = \frac{a_2}{\sqrt{\frac{a_1 a_2}{a_0}}} = \sqrt{\frac{a_2 a_0}{a_1}} = x_0.$$

So we obtain a unique positive period-3 cycle with the following pattern:

$$\sqrt{\frac{a_2 a_0}{a_1}}, \sqrt{\frac{a_0 a_1}{a_2}}, \sqrt{\frac{a_1 a_2}{a_0}}, \ldots.$$

Analogously it follows that there is a unique negative period-3 cycle with the following pattern:

$$-\sqrt{\frac{a_2 a_0}{a_1}}, -\sqrt{\frac{a_0 a_1}{a_2}}, -\sqrt{\frac{a_1 a_2}{a_0}}, \ldots.$$

Example 19. Suppose that $\{a_n\}_{n=0}^{\infty}$ is a period-4 sequence. Determine the existence, uniqueness and the pattern of period-4 solutions of:

$$x_{n+1} = \frac{a_n}{x_n}, \quad n = 0, 1, \dots.$$

Solution: Similar to previous examples, let $x_4 = x_0$ and we acquire:

$$x_0,$$

$$x_1 = \frac{a_0}{x_0},$$

$$x_2 = \frac{a_1}{x_1} = \frac{a_1}{\left[\frac{a_0}{x_0}\right]} = \frac{a_1 x_0}{a_0},$$

$$x_3 = \frac{a_2}{x_2} = \frac{a_2}{\left[\frac{a_1 x_0}{a_0}\right]} = \frac{a_2 a_0}{a_1 x_0},$$

$$x_4 = \frac{a_3}{x_3} = \frac{a_3}{\left[\frac{a_2 a_0}{a_1 x_0}\right]} = \frac{a_3 a_1 x_0}{a_2 a_0} = x_0.$$

Hence $x_4 = x_0$ if and only if $a_3 a_1 = a_2 a_0$. Therefore, every solution is periodic with the following period-4 pattern:

$$x_0, \frac{a_0}{x_0}, \frac{a_1 x_0}{a_0}, \frac{a_2 a_0}{a_1 x_0}, \dots.$$

On one hand, in Example 18, Eq. (3.40) has unique periodic cycles when $\{a_n\}_{n=0}^{\infty}$ is an odd ordered period. On the other hand, in Example 19 every solution of Eq. (3.40) is periodic when $\{a_n\}_{n=0}^{\infty}$ is an even ordered period. The following two theorems generalize the results from Examples 18 and 19.

Theorem 10. *Suppose that $\{a_n\}_{n=0}^{\infty}$ is a periodic sequence with period-$(2k+1)(k \in \mathbb{N})$. Then*

$$x_{n+1} = \frac{a_n}{x_n}, \quad n = 0, 1, \dots$$

has a unique period-$(2k+1)$ cycle where:

$$x_0 = \sqrt{\frac{\prod_{i=1}^{k+1} a_{2i-2}}{\prod_{i=1}^{k} a_{2i-1}}} \quad or \quad x_0 = -\sqrt{\frac{\prod_{i=1}^{k+1} a_{2i-2}}{\prod_{i=1}^{k} a_{2i-1}}}.$$

Proof. Similar to Example 18, by iteration we get:

$$x_0,$$

$$x_1 = \frac{a_0}{x_0},$$

$$x_2 = \frac{a_1}{x_1} = \frac{a_1 x_0}{a_0},$$

$$x_3 = \frac{a_2}{x_2} = \frac{a_0 a_2}{a_1 x_0},$$

$$x_4 = \frac{a_3}{x_3} = \frac{a_1 a_3 x_0}{a_0 a_2},$$

$$x_5 = \frac{a_4}{x_4} = \frac{a_0 a_2 a_4}{a_1 a_3 x_0},$$

$$x_6 = \frac{a_5}{x_5} = \frac{a_1 a_3 a_5 x_0}{a_0 a_2 a_4},$$

$$x_7 = \frac{a_6}{x_6} = \frac{a_0 a_2 a_4 a_6}{a_1 a_3 a_5 x_0},$$

$$\vdots$$

Then for all $n \geq 1$:

$$x_{2n+1} = \frac{\prod_{i=1}^{k+1} a_{2i-2}}{\left[\prod_{i=1}^{k} a_{2i-1} \right] x_0}.$$

The result follows. $\square$

Theorem 11. *Suppose that* $\{a_n\}_{n=0}^{\infty}$ *is a periodic sequence with period-2k* $(k \in \mathbb{N})$. *Then*

$$x_{n+1} = \frac{a_n}{x_n}, \quad n = 0, 1, \ldots$$

is periodic with period-2k if and only if:

$$\prod_{i=1}^{k} a_{2i-2} = \prod_{i=1}^{k} a_{2i-1}.$$

The proof of Theorem 11 will be left as an exercise at the end of the chapter. Now we will advance with deciphering the existence and patterns of periodic cycles of Eq. (3.41), where $\{a_n\}_{n=0}^{\infty}$ is a period-k sequence, $k \geq 2$ and $x_0 \neq 1$.

In the next two examples we will encounter unique periodic cycles and determine their patterns when $\{a_n\}_{n=0}^{\infty}$ is an even ordered periodic sequence. The case when $\{a_n\}_{n=0}^{\infty}$ is an odd ordered periodic sequence will be left as a conjecture and exercises at the end of the chapter.

Example 20. Suppose that $\{a_n\}_{n=0}^{\infty}$ is a period-2 sequence. Show that

$$x_{n+1} = \frac{a_n x_n}{x_n - 1}, \quad n = 0, 1, \ldots$$

has a unique period-2 cycle.

Solution: Suppose that $x_2 = x_0$ and we get:

$$x_0,$$

$$x_1 = \frac{a_0 x_0}{x_0 - 1},$$

$$x_2 = \frac{a_1 [x_1]}{[x_1] - 1} = \frac{a_1 \left[\frac{a_0 x_0}{x_0 - 1}\right]}{\left[\frac{a_0 x_0}{x_0 - 1}\right] - 1} = \frac{a_0 a_1 x_0}{a_0 x_0 - x_0 + 1} = x_0.$$

Solving for x_0 we get $x_0 = \frac{a_0 a_1 - 1}{a_0 - 1}$, where $a_0 a_1 \neq 1$ and $a_0 \neq 1$. By iteration we acquire:

$$x_0 = \frac{a_0 a_1 - 1}{a_0 - 1},$$

$$x_1 = \frac{a_0 [x_0]}{[x_0] - 1} = \frac{a_0 \left[\frac{a_0 a_1 - 1}{a_0 - 1}\right]}{\left[\frac{a_0 a_1 - 1}{a_0 - 1}\right] - 1} = \frac{a_0 a_1 - 1}{a_1 - 1},$$

$$x_2 = \frac{a_1 [x_1]}{[x_1] - 1} = \frac{a_0 \left[\frac{a_0 a_1 - 1}{a_1 - 1}\right]}{\left[\frac{a_0 a_1 - 1}{a_1 - 1}\right] - 1} = \frac{a_0 a_1 - 1}{a_0 - 1} = x_0.$$

Notice that $a_0, a_1 \neq 1$ and we obtain the following unique period-2 pattern:

$$\frac{a_0 a_1 - 1}{a_0 - 1}, \frac{a_0 a_1 - 1}{a_1 - 1}, \frac{a_0 a_1 - 1}{a_0 - 1}, \frac{a_0 a_1 - 1}{a_1 - 1}, \ldots$$

First of all, the pattern of the numerator does not change from term to term, whereas the pattern of the denominator changes from term to term. In future examples we will discover the opposite phenomenon. Second of all, in comparison with Example 16, Eq. (3.41) has a unique period-2 cycle.

From Example 20, the following theorem describes the result when $\{a_n\}_{n=0}^{\infty}$ is an even ordered periodic sequence.

Theorem 12. *Suppose that $\{a_n\}_{n=0}^{\infty}$ is a periodic sequence with period-2k $(k \in \mathbb{N})$. Then*

$$x_{n+1} = \frac{a_n x_n}{x_n - 1}, \quad n = 0, 1, \ldots$$

has a unique period-2k cycle where:

$$x_0 = \frac{\prod_{i=1}^{2k} a_{i-1} - 1}{\prod_{i=1}^{2k-1} a_{i-1} - \prod_{i=1}^{2k-2} a_{i-1} + \cdots + a_0 - 1}.$$

The proof of Theorem 12 and the case when $\{a_n\}_{n=0}^{\infty}$ is an odd ordered periodic sequence will be left as exercises at the end of the chapter.

3.4.3. *The periodic solutions of the Logistic Difference Equation*

Our next plan is to analyze the periodic character of the **Logistic** Δ.E. in the form:

$$x_{n+1} = r x_n (1 - x_n), \quad n = 0, 1, \ldots, \tag{3.42}$$

where $r \in (0, 4]$ and $x_0 \in [0, 1)$. Eq. (3.42) has many applications in population dynamics, cardiology and other biological and medical sciences [9, 10, 54]. By setting:

$$\bar{x} = r\bar{x}(1 - \bar{x}),$$

we obtain two equilibrium solutions:

$$\bar{x}_1 = 0 \quad \text{and} \quad \bar{x}_2 = \frac{r-1}{r} \quad (\text{when } r > 1).$$

Now we will examine the existence and patterns of periodic cycles. In fact, when $r \in (3, 4]$, Eq. (3.42) has periodic cycles of any period-p $(p \geq 2)$. We will introduce periodic traits of Eq. (3.42) together with some graphical examples.

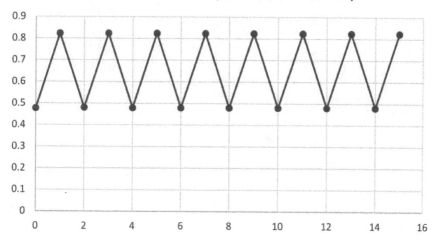

We procure a period-2 cycle when $r = 3.3$ and $x_0 = 0.476866736$.

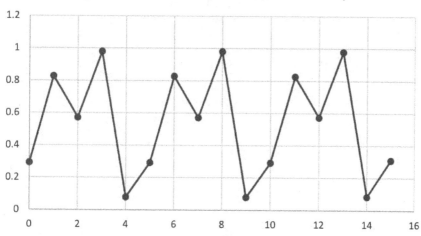

We obtain a period-5 cycle when $r = 4$ and $x_0 = 0.292292$.

Our next objective is to analytically determine the existence and patterns of periodic solutions of Eq. (3.42). We will emerge with the existence and patterns of period-2 cycles.

Example 21. Determine the necessary and sufficient conditions for the existence of period-2 cycles of:

$$x_{n+1} = rx_n(1 - x_n), \quad n = 0, 1, \ldots.$$

Solution: Suppose that Eq. (3.42) has a minimal period-2 solution,

$$\alpha, \ \beta, \ \alpha, \ \beta, \ldots,$$

where $\alpha \neq \beta$ and

$$\alpha = r\beta(1 - \beta) \quad \text{and} \quad \beta = r\alpha(1 - \alpha). \tag{3.43}$$

Now consider the following quadratic equation:

$$(x - \alpha)(x - \beta) = x^2 - x(\alpha + \beta) + \alpha\beta = 0. \tag{3.44}$$

It suffices to determine $\alpha + \beta$ and $\alpha\beta$ in terms of r. Via (3.43) we obtain:

$$\alpha + \beta = r\beta(1 - \beta) + r\alpha(1 - \alpha) = r(\alpha + \beta) - r(\alpha^2 + \beta^2), \tag{3.45}$$

and

$$\alpha - \beta = r\beta(1-\beta) - r\alpha(1-\alpha) = r(\beta-\alpha) - r(\beta^2 - \alpha^2) = r(\beta-\alpha) - r(\beta-\alpha)(\beta+\alpha). \tag{3.46}$$

As we assumed that $\alpha \neq \beta$, then via (3.46) we procure

$$1 = -r + r(\beta + \alpha). \tag{3.47}$$

Therefore, from (3.47) we obtain

$$\alpha + \beta = \frac{1 + r}{r}. \tag{3.48}$$

Also, via (3.43) we acquire:

$$\alpha\beta = r^2\alpha\beta(1 - \beta)(1 - \alpha),$$

which gives us

$$1 = r^2(1 - \beta)(1 - \alpha) = r^2[1 - (\alpha + \beta) + \alpha\beta]. \tag{3.49}$$

Then via (3.48) and (3.49):

$$\alpha\beta = \frac{1 + r}{r^2}. \tag{3.50}$$

Notice that by substituting (3.48) and (3.50) into (3.44) we assemble the following quadratic equation:

$$x^2 - x(\alpha + \beta) + \alpha\beta = x^2 - x\left(\frac{1 + r}{r}\right) + \frac{1 + r}{r^2} = 0. \tag{3.51}$$

Provided that $3 < r \leq 4$, the two distinct solutions of Eq. (3.51) are

$$x_1 = \frac{\frac{1+r}{r} + \sqrt{\left(\frac{1+r}{r}\right)^2 - 4\left(\frac{1+r}{r^2}\right)}}{2} \quad \text{and} \quad x_2 = \frac{\frac{1+r}{r} - \sqrt{\left(\frac{1+r}{r}\right)^2 - 4\left(\frac{1+r}{r^2}\right)}}{2},$$

which reduce to

$$x_1 = \frac{(1+r) + \sqrt{(r+1)(r-3)}}{2r} \quad \text{and} \quad x_2 = \frac{(1+r) - \sqrt{(r+1)(r-3)}}{2r}.$$

Since we assumed that $\alpha \neq \beta$, then $r \in (3, 4]$. Notice that if $r \leq 3$, we do not have two distinct real roots. Hence:

$$\alpha = \frac{(1+r) + \sqrt{(r+1)(r-3)}}{2r} \quad \text{and} \quad \beta = \frac{(1+r) - \sqrt{(r+1)(r-3)}}{2r}.$$

The next two examples will assume that $r = 4$ and will portray the existence of a period-3 cycle and a period-2 cycle of Eq. (3.42). Observe that when $r = 4$ then Eq. (3.42) has a positive equilibrium $\bar{x} = \frac{3}{4}$. In addition, we will address the oscillatory character of periodic cycles of Eq. (3.42).

Example 22. Determine the period of Eq. (3.42) by solving the Initial Value Problem:

$$\begin{cases} x_{n+1} = 4x_n(1 - x_n), & n = 0, 1, \ldots, \\ x_0 = sin^2\left(\frac{\pi}{7}\right). \end{cases}$$

Solution: By using the double angle identity $sin(2\theta) = 2sin(\theta)cos(\theta)$ and by iteration we procure:

$$x_0 = sin^2\left(\frac{\pi}{7}\right),$$

$$x_1 = 4x_0(1 - x_0) = 4sin^2\left(\frac{\pi}{7}\right)\left[1 - sin^2\left(\frac{\pi}{7}\right)\right]$$

$$= 4sin^2\left(\frac{2\pi}{7}\right)cos^2\left(\frac{\pi}{7}\right) = sin^2\left(\frac{2\pi}{7}\right),$$

$$x_2 = 4x_1(1 - x_1) = 4sin^2\left(\frac{2\pi}{7}\right)\left[1 - sin^2\left(\frac{2\pi}{7}\right)\right] = sin^2\left(\frac{4\pi}{7}\right),$$

$$x_3 = 4x_2(1 - x_2) = 4sin^2\left(\frac{4\pi}{7}\right)\left[1 - sin^2\left(\frac{4\pi}{7}\right)\right] = sin^2\left(\frac{8\pi}{7}\right)$$

$$= sin^2\left(\frac{\pi}{7}\right) = x_0.$$

We then acquire the following period-3 pattern:

$$\sin^2\left(\frac{\pi}{7}\right), \quad \sin^2\left(\frac{2\pi}{7}\right), \quad \sin^2\left(\frac{4\pi}{7}\right), \dots$$

Now applying the Cobweb Method:

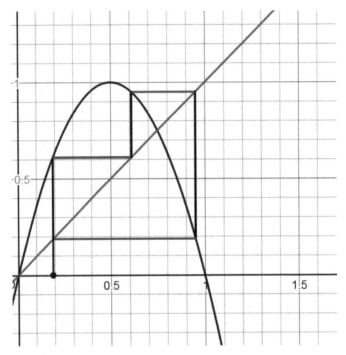

we see an oscillatory period-3 cycle with one term above $\bar{x} = \frac{3}{4}$ and two terms below $\bar{x} = \frac{3}{4}$.

Example 23. Determine the period of Eq. (3.42) by solving the Initial Value Problem:

$$\begin{cases} x_{n+1} = 4x_n(1 - x_n), & n = 0, 1, \dots, \\ x_0 = \sin^2\left(\frac{\pi}{5}\right). \end{cases}$$

Solution: Applying the double angle identity $\sin(2\theta) = 2\sin(\theta)\cos(\theta)$ gives us:

$$x_0 = \sin^2\left(\frac{\pi}{5}\right),$$

$$x_1 = 4x_0(1 - x_0) = 4\sin^2\left(\frac{\pi}{5}\right)\left[1 - \sin^2\left(\frac{\pi}{5}\right)\right] = \sin^2\left(\frac{2\pi}{5}\right),$$

$$x_2 = 4x_1(1 - x_1) = 4sin^2\left(\frac{2\pi}{5}\right)\left[1 - sin^2\left(\frac{2\pi}{5}\right)\right]$$

$$= sin^2\left(\frac{4\pi}{5}\right) = sin^2\left(\frac{\pi}{5}\right) = x_0.$$

We then attain the following period-2 pattern:

$$sin^2\left(\frac{\pi}{5}\right), sin^2\left(\frac{2\pi}{5}\right), sin^2\left(\frac{\pi}{5}\right), sin^2\left(\frac{2\pi}{5}\right), \ldots.$$

We can verify that x_0 is above $\bar{x} = \frac{3}{4}$ and x_1 is below $\bar{x} = \frac{3}{4}$.

From Examples 22 and 23 we can suggest the following **Open Problem**:

Open Problem 1. Let $k \in \mathbb{N}$. Then the solution to the Initial Value Problem:

$$\begin{cases} x_{n+1} = 4x_n(1 - x_n), & n = 0, 1, \ldots, \\ x_0 = sin^2\left(\dfrac{2\pi}{2k+1}\right), \end{cases}$$

is periodic with some period-p $(p \geq 2)$.

The next pertinent question to address: what is the period of Eq. (3.42) depending on the value of k? We will leave this question at the end of the chapter as exercises. We can then generalize that Eq. (3.42) has periodic solutions with period-p $(p \geq 2)$ when $r \in (3, 4]$. Furthermore, Eq. (3.42) has eventually periodic solutions as illustrated in the graph below:

Logistic Difference Equation ; Eventually Periodic
with Period-3 with Four Transient Terms

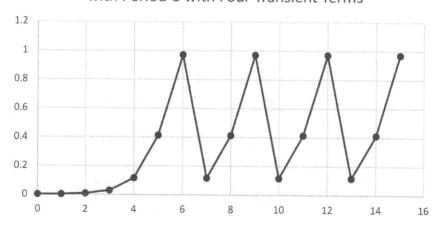

We acquire an eventually period-3 cycle with four transient terms with $r = 4$ and $x_0 = sin^2(\frac{\pi}{144})$.

Moreover, Eq. (3.42) has eventually constant solutions as shown in the diagram below:

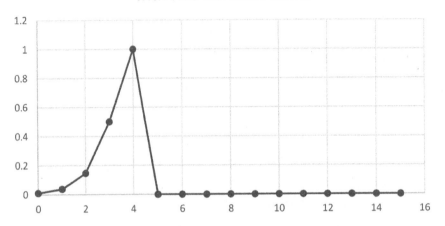

Logistic Difference Equation ; Eventually Constant with Five Transient Terms

We procure an eventually constant solution $\bar{x} = 0$ with five transient terms with $r = 4$ and $x_0 = sin^2(\frac{\pi}{32})$. More questions on eventually constant solutions of Eq. (3.42) will be addressed at the end of the chapter as exercises. This guides us to the following theorem.

Theorem 13. *The* **Logistic Δ.E.***:*

$$x_{n+1} = 4x_n(1 - x_n), \quad n = 0, 1, \ldots,$$

has an eventually constant solution $\bar{x} = 0$ with N transient terms $(N \in \mathbb{N})$ if

$$x_0 = sin^2\left(\frac{\pi}{2^N}\right).$$

The proof of Theorem 13 will be left as an exercise at the end of the chapter.

Further studies on the periodic and oscillatory character of Eq. (3.42) were studied in [54]. From Examples 22 and 23, we manifest sensitivity to initial conditions or dependency on the initial conditions. That is, the periodic character of solutions will depend on the initial condition that we choose. This is the first step leading to understanding **Chaos**.

3.4.4. *Chaos and Chaotic orbits*

Chaotic behavior of solutions have been studied by many authors such as Edward Lorenz, Benoit Mandelbrot, Tien-Yien Li and James Yorke. Edward Lorenz was an American mathematician, meteorologist, and a pioneer of chaos theory. In fact, he introduced the strange attractor notion and coined the term butterfly effect [62, 63]. Tien-Yien Li and James Yorke studied chaos on first order difference equations and are the pioneers in the definition and theorem "Period-3 Implies Chaos" [61]. Now we will define chaos as dependency on initial conditions or sensitivity to initial conditions and chaos in the sense of Li and Yorke.

Definition 20. Let I be an interval of real numbers and let $f : I \longrightarrow I$. Then f is **Chaotic** if it has sensitivity dependence on the initial conditions on I.

Definition 21. Let I be an interval of real numbers and let $f : I \longrightarrow I$ be a continuous function. Then f is **chaotic in the sense of Li and Yorke** if there exists a point $a \in I$ of minimal period-3.

We will now exhibit an example of chaotic behavior of Eq. (3.42). The graph below depicts irregular periodic behavior when $r = 4$ and $x_0 = 0.6114$, in comparison with Example 22 when we have a regular period-3 cycle when $r = 4$ and $x_0 = sin^2 \left(\frac{\pi}{7} \right)$.

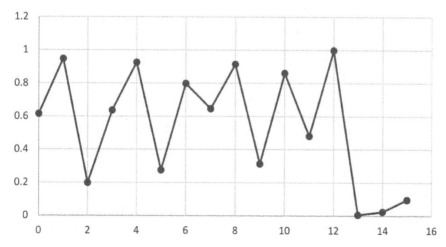

Logistic Difference Equation ; Chaotic Orbit

The next graph evokes chaos as period doubling:

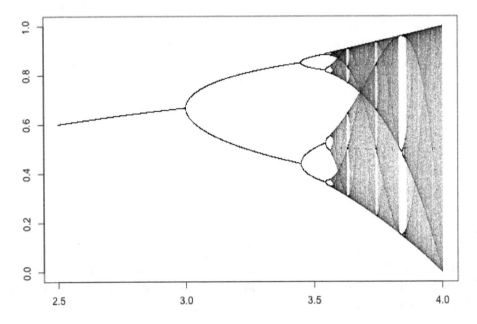

More material on chaos and period-doubling can be found in [7] and [8]. In the next three sections we will examine examples of periodic solutions, eventually periodic solutions, eventually constant solutions and chaotic behavior of **Piecewise Difference Equations**.

3.4.5. *The Tent-Map*

In this section we will study the existence of periodic solutions and eventually periodic solutions of the **Tent-Map**, which is a specific type of **Piecewise Δ.E.** in the form:

$$
x_{n+1} = \begin{cases} 2x_n & \text{if } x_n < \dfrac{1}{2}, \\[2mm] 2(1-x_n) & \text{if } x_n \geq \dfrac{1}{2}, \end{cases} \quad n = 0, 1, \ldots, \tag{3.52}
$$

where $x_0 \in (0,1)$. We classify these types of difference equations as **Piecewise Difference Equations** as they are composed of two or more pieces defined on a specific interval as piecewise functions are defined on a particular interval. Eq. (3.52) has two equilibrium points $\bar{x}_1 = 0$ and $\bar{x}_2 = \frac{2}{3}$.

The next three examples will examine the existence, uniqueness and patterns of the period-2, period-3, period-4 cycles and their oscillatory characters.

Example 24. Determine the period-2 cycle of:

$$x_{n+1} = \begin{cases} 2x_n & \text{if } x_n < \dfrac{1}{2}, \\ 2(1-x_n) & \text{if } x_n \geq \dfrac{1}{2}. \end{cases} \quad n = 0, 1, \ldots,$$

Solution: Set $x_2 = x_0$ and we acquire:

$$x_0,$$
$$x_1 = 2x_0,$$
$$x_2 = 2(1 - x_1) = 2(1 - 2x_0) = 2 - 4x_0 = x_0.$$

We get $x_0 = \frac{2}{5}$ and the following period-2 pattern:

$$\frac{2}{5}, \frac{4}{5}, \frac{2}{5}, \frac{4}{5}, \ldots$$

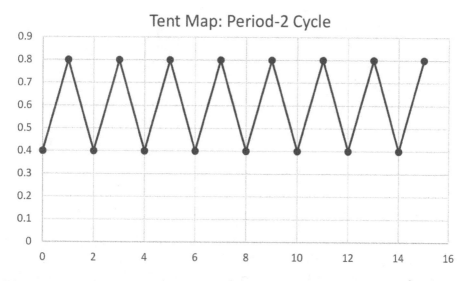

Tent Map: Period-2 Cycle

This is an oscillatory period-2 cycle with one term above $\bar{x}_2 = \frac{2}{3}$ and one term below $\bar{x}_2 = \frac{2}{3}$.

Example 25. Determine a period-3 cycle of:

$$x_{n+1} = \begin{cases} 2x_n & \text{if } x_n < \dfrac{1}{2}, \\ 2(1 - x_n) & \text{if } x_n \geq \dfrac{1}{2}. \end{cases} \quad n = 0, 1, \ldots,$$

Solution: Similarly, set $x_3 = x_0$ and we get:

$$x_0,$$
$$x_1 = 2x_0,$$
$$x_2 = 2x_1 = 2[2x_0] = 4x_0,$$
$$x_3 = 2(1 - x_2) = 2(1 - 4x_0) = 2 - 8x_0 = x_0.$$

Notice that $x_0 = \frac{2}{9}$ produces the following period-3 pattern:

$$\frac{2}{9}, \frac{4}{9}, \frac{8}{9}, \frac{2}{9}, \frac{4}{9}, \frac{8}{9}, \ldots$$

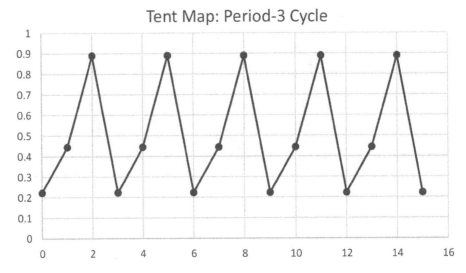

Tent Map: Period-3 Cycle

This is an oscillatory period-3 cycle with one term above $\bar{x}_2 = \frac{2}{3}$ and two terms below $\bar{x}_2 = \frac{2}{3}$. Furthermore, the existence of a period-3 cycle exhibits **Chaos in the sense of Li and Yorke** since Eq. (3.52) is resembled by a continuous piecewise function as stated in Definition 21.

Example 26. Determine a period-4 cycle of:

$$
x_{n+1} = \begin{cases} 2x_n & \text{if } x_n < \dfrac{1}{2}, \\[2mm] 2(1 - x_n) & \text{if } x_n \geq \dfrac{1}{2}. \end{cases} \quad n = 0, 1, \ldots,
$$

Solution: Set $x_4 = x_0$ and we procure:

$$
x_0,
$$
$$
x_1 = 2x_0,
$$
$$
x_2 = 2x_1 = 2[2x_0] = 4x_0,
$$
$$
x_3 = 2x_2 = 2[4x_0] = 8x_0,
$$
$$
x_4 = 2(1 - x_3) = 2(1 - 8x_0) = 2 - 16x_0 = x_0.
$$

Observe that $x_0 = \frac{2}{17}$, from which we obtain the following period-4 pattern:

$$
\frac{2}{17}, \frac{4}{17}, \frac{8}{17}, \frac{16}{17}, \frac{2}{17}, \frac{4}{17}, \frac{8}{17}, \frac{16}{17}, \ldots
$$

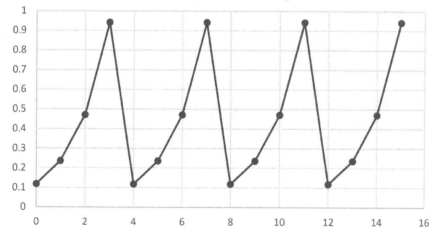

Tent Map: Period-4 Cycle

This is an oscillatory period-4 cycle with one term above $\bar{x}_2 = \frac{2}{3}$ and three terms below $\bar{x}_2 = \frac{2}{3}$.

From Examples 24–26, we can see that Eq. (3.52) has periodic solutions with period-p $(p \geq 2)$ and leads us to the following theorem.

Theorem 14. *The* **Tent-Map***:*

$$x_{n+1} = \begin{cases} 2x_n & \text{if } x_n < \dfrac{1}{2}, \\[2mm] 2(1 - x_n) & \text{if } x_n \geq \dfrac{1}{2}, \end{cases} \quad n = 0, 1, \ldots,$$

has period-p cycle $(p \geq 2)$*, where:*

$$x_0 = \frac{2}{2^p + 1}.$$

The proof of Theorem 14 will be left as an exercise at the end of the chapter. From Chapter 1, recall that $\{x_n\}_{n=0}^{\infty}$ is **eventually periodic** with minimal period-p $(p \geq 2)$ if there exists $N \in \mathbb{N}$ such that:

$$x_{n+N} = x_{(n+p)+N} \quad \text{for all} \quad n \geq 0.$$

In fact, $\{x_n\}_{n=0}^{\infty}$ is eventually periodic with **minimal period-2** if there exists $N \in \mathbb{N}$ such that:

$$x_{n+N} = x_{(n+2)+N} \quad \text{for all} \quad n \geq 0.$$

The consequent two examples will analytically and graphically exhibit the existence of N transient terms $(N \in \mathbb{N})$.

Example 27. Solve the Initial Value Problem:

$$x_{n+1} = \begin{cases} 2x_n & \text{if } x_n < \dfrac{1}{2}, \\[2mm] 2(1 - x_n) & \text{if } x_n \geq \dfrac{1}{2}, \quad n = 0, 1, \ldots, \\[2mm] x_0 = \dfrac{1}{20}, \end{cases}$$

and show that the solution is eventually periodic with period-2.

Solution: By iteration we get:

$$x_0 = \frac{1}{20},$$

$$x_1 = 2x_0 = \frac{1}{10},$$

$$x_2 = 2x_1 = \frac{1}{5},$$

$$x_3 = 2x_2 = \frac{2}{5},$$

$$x_4 = 2x_3 = \frac{4}{5},$$

$$x_5 = 2(1 - x_4) = \frac{2}{5} = x_3.$$

Now notice:

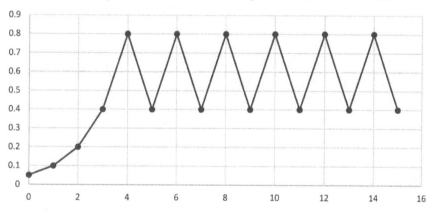

Eventually Periodic with Period-2 ; Three Transient Terms

we have three increasing transient terms from $x_0 - x_2$ and $x_5 = x_3$.

Example 28. Solve the Initial Value Problem:

$$x_{n+1} = \begin{cases} 2x_n & \text{if } x_n < \frac{1}{2}, \\ 2(1 - x_n) & \text{if } x_n \geq \frac{1}{2}, \quad n = 0, 1, \ldots, \\ x_0 = \frac{1}{72}, \end{cases}$$

and show that the solution is eventually periodic with period-3.

Solution: The graph below:

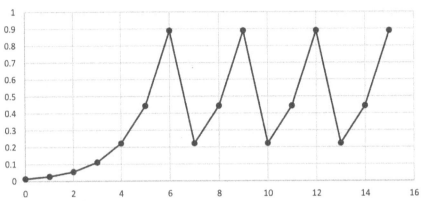

Eventually Periodic with Period-3 ; Four Transient Terms

describes four transient terms from $x_0 - x_3$ and $x_7 = x_4$.

Analogous to Examples 27 and 28, we can determine eventually periodic solutions with period-p $(p \geq 3)$. This will be left as an exercise at the end of the chapter.

Moreover, Eq. (3.52) has eventually constant solutions as illustrated in the graph below:

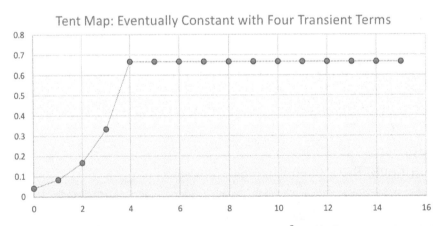

Tent Map: Eventually Constant with Four Transient Terms

We procure an eventually constant solution $\bar{x} = \frac{2}{3}$ with four transient terms when $x_0 = \frac{1}{24}$. More questions on eventually constant solutions of Eq. (3.52) will be addressed at the end of the chapter as exercises. Since Eq. (3.52) has two equilibrium points $\bar{x} = 0$ and $\bar{x} = \frac{2}{3}$, it is possible to determine the set of initial conditions that generate an eventually constant solution $\bar{x} = 0$ and this leads us to two theorems.

Theorem 15. *The* **Tent-Map:**

$$x_{n+1} = \begin{cases} 2x_n & \text{if } x_n < \dfrac{1}{2}, \\[2mm] 2(1 - x_n) & \text{if } x_n \geq \dfrac{1}{2}, \end{cases} \qquad n = 0, 1, \ldots,$$

has an eventually constant solution $\bar{x} = \frac{2}{3}$ *with N transient terms* $(N \in \mathbb{N})$ *if*

$$x_0 = \frac{1}{3 \cdot 2^N}.$$

The proof of Theorem 15 will be left as an exercise at the end of the chapter.

Theorem 16. *The* **Tent-Map:**

$$x_{n+1} = \begin{cases} 2x_n & \text{if } x_n < \dfrac{1}{2}, \\[2mm] 2(1 - x_n) & \text{if } x_n \geq \dfrac{1}{2}, \end{cases} \qquad n = 0, 1, \ldots,$$

has an eventually constant solution $\bar{x} = 0$ *with* $N+1$ *transient terms* $(N \geq 0)$ *if*

$$x_0 = \frac{1}{2^N}.$$

The proof of Theorem 16 will be left as an exercise at the end of the chapter.

Finally, observe that all the examples analyzing Eq. (3.52) lead to the existence of chaos as we portray very strong dependency on the initial conditions as stated in Definition 20. Now we will conclude this section with an example of a chaotic orbit. Let $x_0 = 0.222345$ and we depict the following graph:

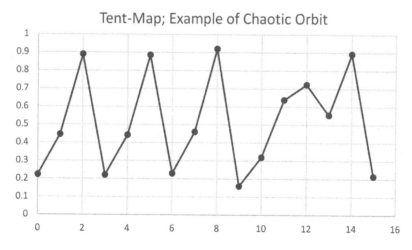

Tent-Map; Example of Chaotic Orbit

The graph resembles chaotic behavior or a chaotic orbit as we see no specific pattern compared to a period-3 cycle when $x_0 = \frac{2}{9}$ in Example 25.

3.4.6. *The 3X+1 Conjecture*

The **3X+1 Conjecture** also known as the **Collatz Conjecture** was introduced by Lothar Collatz in 1937 and was studied by several authors in [22, 56, 57]. Our intent is to explore the periodic solutions and eventually periodic solutions of the Piecewise Δ.E. known as the **3X+1 Conjecture** in the form:

$$x_{n+1} = \begin{cases} \dfrac{x_n}{2} & \text{if } x_n \text{ is even,} \\[2mm] \dfrac{3x_n + 1}{2} & \text{if } x_n \text{ is odd,} \end{cases} \qquad n = 0, 1, \ldots, \qquad (3.53)$$

where $x_0 \in \mathbb{N}$. First of all, $x_0 = 2$ produces the following period-2 pattern:

$$2, \ 1, \ 2, \ 1, \ldots.$$

Second of all, with $x_0 = 1$ we obtain:

$$1, \ 2, \ 1, \ 2, \ldots.$$

Conjecture 1. *Let $x_0 \in \mathbb{N}$. Then every solution of*

$$x_{n+1} = \begin{cases} \dfrac{x_n}{2} & \text{if } x_n \text{ is even,} \\[2mm] \dfrac{3x_n + 1}{2} & \text{if } x_n \text{ is odd,} \end{cases} \qquad n = 0, 1, \ldots$$

is eventually periodic with the following period-2 cycle:

$$2, \ 1, \ 2, \ 1, \ldots.$$

Now we will show a specific example how to implement the **3X+1 Conjecture**.

Example 29. Solve the Initial Value Problem:

$$x_{n+1} = \begin{cases} \dfrac{x_n}{2} & \text{if } x_n \text{ is even,} \\[2mm] \dfrac{3x_n + 1}{2} & \text{if } x_n \text{ is odd,} \quad n = 0, 1, \ldots, \\[2mm] x_0 = 15, \end{cases}$$

and show that the solution is eventually periodic with period-2.

Solution: Notice:

$$x_0 = 15,$$

$$x_1 = \frac{3 \cdot 15 + 1}{2} = 20,$$

$$x_2 = \frac{20}{2} = 10,$$

$$x_3 = \frac{10}{2} = 5,$$

$$x_4 = \frac{3 \cdot 5 + 1}{2} = 8,$$

$$x_5 = \frac{8}{2} = 4,$$

$$x_6 = \frac{4}{2} = 2,$$

$$x_7 = \frac{2}{2} = 1,$$

$$x_8 = \frac{3 \cdot 1 + 1}{2} = 2.$$

Observe that we have six transient terms from $x_0 - x_5$ and $x_8 = x_6$:

$$[15,\ 20,\ 10,\ 5,\ 8,\ 4],\ 2,\ 1,\ 2,\ 1, \ldots.$$

The transient terms are emphasized in square brackets.

The **3X+1 Conjecture** claims that every solution of Eq. (3.53) is eventually periodic with period-2. However, only special cases have been proved. We will advance our studies with periodic nature of solutions of another Piecewise Δ.E. that describes a neural networking model.

3.4.7. *Autonomous Piecewise difference equation as a Neuron model*

In this section our plan is to study the existence of periodic solutions and eventually periodic solutions of the Autonomous Piecewise Δ.E. (discrete-time network of a single neuron model) in the form:

$$x_{n+1} = \beta x_n - g(x_n), \quad n = 0, 1, 2, \ldots, \tag{3.54}$$

where $x_0 \in \Re$, $\beta > 0$ is an internal decay rate and g is a signal function. Eq. (3.54) is examined in several articles [4, 5, 16, 17] and is analyzed as a single neuron model, where a signal function g is the following piecewise constant with the **McCulloch–Pitts nonlinearity**:

$$g(x) = \begin{cases} 1 & \text{if } x \geq 0, \\ -1 & \text{if } x < 0. \end{cases}$$

Piecewise difference equations have been used as mathematical models in various applications including neurons [84–88]. We will manifest several examples that exhibit periodic cycles with various periods of Eq. (3.54).

Example 30. Determine the period-2 cycle of:

$$x_{n+1} = \beta x_n - g(x_n), \quad n = 0, 1, 2, \ldots,$$

where $x_0 \in \mathcal{R}$, $\beta > 0$ and

$$g(x) = \begin{cases} 1 & \text{if } x \geq 0, \\ -1 & \text{if } x < 0. \end{cases}$$

Solution: Assuming that $0 < x_0 < \frac{1}{\beta}$ and setting $x_2 = x_0$ gives us:

$$x_0 > 0,$$
$$x_1 = \beta x_0 - 1,$$
$$x_2 = \beta [x_1] + 1 = \beta [\beta x_0 - 1] + 1 = \beta^2 x_0 - \beta + 1 = x_0.$$

Hence $x_0 = \frac{1}{\beta+1}$ and produces the following period-2 pattern:

$$\frac{1}{\beta+1}, \quad -\frac{1}{\beta+1}, \quad \frac{1}{\beta+1}, \quad -\frac{1}{\beta+1}, \quad \ldots$$

Notice that two neighboring terms are of opposite signs. In addition we get:

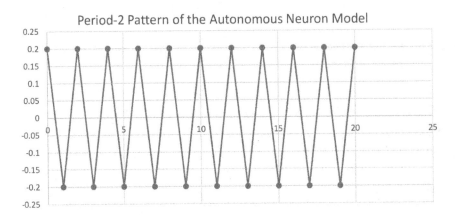

Period-2 Pattern of the Autonomous Neuron Model

a period-2 cycle where $\beta = 4$ and $x_0 = \frac{1}{5}$. Note that this is an oscillatory and alternating period-2 cycle with two neighboring terms that are of opposite signs. The sum of two neighboring terms is always 0.

Example 31. Determine a period-3 cycle of:

$$x_{n+1} = \beta x_n - g(x_n), \quad n = 0, 1, 2, \dots,$$

where $x_0 \in \Re$, $\beta > 0$, and

$$g(x) = \begin{cases} 1 \ \text{ if } \ x \geq 0, \\ -1 \ \text{ if } \ x < 0. \end{cases}$$

Solution: Suppose $\frac{1}{\beta} < x_0 < \frac{\beta+1}{\beta^2}$ and $x_3 = x_0$. Then:

$$x_0 > 0,$$
$$x_1 = \beta x_0 - 1,$$
$$x_2 = \beta [x_1] - 1 = \beta [\beta x_0 - 1] - 1 = \beta^2 x_0 - \beta - 1,$$
$$x_3 = \beta [x_2] + 1 = \beta [\beta^2 x_0 - \beta - 1] + 1 = \beta^3 x_0 - \beta^2 - \beta + 1 = x_0.$$

Therefore $x_0 = \frac{\beta^2 + \beta - 1}{\beta^3 - 1}$ presents the following period-3 pattern:

$$\frac{\beta^2 + \beta - 1}{\beta^3 - 1}, \ \frac{\beta^2 - \beta + 1}{\beta^3 - 1}, \ \frac{-\beta^2 + \beta + 1}{\beta^3 - 1}, \dots$$

Notice that the signs of the $\beta^2, \beta, 1$ in the numerator switch from neighbor to neighbor and:

$$\left[\frac{\beta^2 + \beta - 1}{\beta^3 - 1} \right] + \left[\frac{\beta^2 - \beta + 1}{\beta^3 - 1} \right] + \left[\frac{-\beta^2 + \beta + 1}{\beta^3 - 1} \right]$$
$$= \frac{\beta^2 + \beta + 1}{(\beta - 1)(\beta^2 + \beta + 1)} = \frac{1}{\beta - 1} = \bar{x}.$$

Therefore, period-3 cycles exist provided that $\beta \neq 1$ (this is not the only period-3 cycle). Now observe:

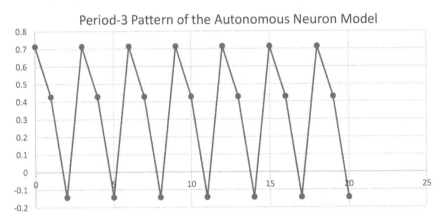

Period-3 Pattern of the Autonomous Neuron Model

a period-3 cycle where two terms of the cycle are positive and one term of the cycle is negative; $\beta = 2$ and $x_0 = \frac{5}{7}$. In the case, the existence of a period-3 cycles does not lead to chaos in the sense of Li and York as Eq. (3.54) is not resembled by a continuous function. However, dependency on initial conditions according to Definition 20 does lead to chaos. In fact, the next several examples will show the existence of multiple periodic solutions and eventually periodic solutions of Eq. (3.54).

Example 32. The graph below is an example of a period-4 cycle where $\beta = 2$ and $x_0 = 0.6$.

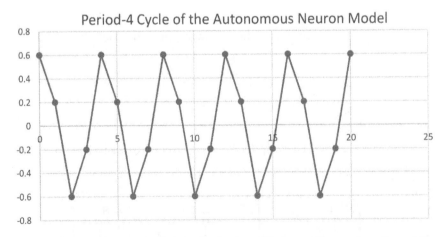

Period-4 Cycle of the Autonomous Neuron Model

This is an alternating period-4 cycle that oscillates with semi-cycles of length 2 about 0. This is not the only period-4 cycle and not all period-4 cycles oscillate with semi-cycles of length 2. In fact, some period-4 cycles may oscillate with positive semi-cycles of length 3 and negative semi-cycles of length 1 and vice versa.

From Examples 30 and 31 we can determine the pattern of even ordered cycles and odd ordered cycles of Eq. (3.54). Furthermore, must all the terms of the even ordered cycles of Eq. (3.54) add up to 0? The following **Open Problems** address these two questions.

Open Problem 2. The Δ.E.:

$$x_{n+1} = \beta x_n - g(x_n), \quad n = 0, 1, 2, \ldots,$$

where $x_0 \in \mathfrak{R}$, $\beta \neq 1$ and

$$g(x) = \begin{cases} 1 & \text{if } x \geq 0, \\ -1 & \text{if } x < 0, \end{cases}$$

has a period-2k solution $(k \in \mathbb{N})$ and

$$\sum_{i=1}^{2k} x_{i-1} = 0.$$

Notice that for some periodic cycles this may be true but not for others. First of all, how many periodic cycles exist with period-2k? Second of all, for which particular periodic cycles does this hold true? These are the vital questions to consider investigating.

The next **Open Problem** addresses the question if the sum of all the terms of the odd ordered periods adds up to $\bar{x} = \frac{1}{\beta - 1}$?

Open Problem 3. The Δ.E.:

$$x_{n+1} = \beta x_n - g(x_n), \quad n = 0, 1, 2, \ldots,$$

where $x_0 \in \mathfrak{R}$, $\beta \neq 1$ and

$$g(x) = \begin{cases} 1 & \text{if } x \geq 0, \\ -1 & \text{if } x < 0, \end{cases}$$

has a period-$(2k + 1)$ solution $(k \in \mathbb{N})$ and

$$\sum_{i=1}^{2k+1} x_{i-1} = \bar{x} = \frac{1}{\beta - 1}.$$

Notice that this may only hold for certain periodic cycles. How many periodic cycles exist with period-$(2k+1)$? For which particular periodic cycles does this hold true?

Now we will proceed with determining eventually periodic solutions with period-2 of Eq. (3.54). The next two examples will show how to procure N transient terms analytically $(N \in \mathbb{N})$.

Example 33. Determine the period-2 solution with two transient terms of:

$$x_{n+1} = \beta x_n - g(x_n), \quad n = 0, 1, 2, \ldots,$$

where $x_0 \in \mathbb{R}$, $\beta \neq 1$ and

$$g(x) = \begin{cases} 1 & \text{if } x \geq 0, \\ -1 & \text{if } x < 0. \end{cases}$$

Solution: Set $x_4 = x_2$ and suppose that $\frac{1+\beta+\beta^2}{\beta^3} < x_0 < \frac{1+\beta+\beta^2+\beta^3}{\beta^4}$. Then:

$$x_0 > 0,$$
$$x_1 = \beta x_0 - 1,$$
$$x_2 = \beta [x_1] - 1 = \beta [\beta x_0 - 1] - 1 = \beta^2 x_0 - \beta - 1,$$
$$x_3 = \beta [x_2] - 1 = \beta [\beta^2 x_0 - \beta - 1] - 1 = \beta^3 x_0 - \beta^2 - \beta - 1,$$
$$x_4 = \beta [x_3] + 1 = \beta [\beta^3 x_0 - \beta^2 - \beta - 1] + 1$$
$$\qquad = \beta^4 x_0 - \beta^3 - \beta^2 - \beta + 1 = x_2.$$

By solving for $x_0 = \frac{\beta^2(\beta+1)-2}{\beta^2(\beta^2-1)}$ we obtain:

$$x_0 = \frac{\beta^2(\beta+1) - 2}{\beta^2(\beta^2 - 1)},$$
$$x_1 = \beta [x_0] - 1 = \beta \left[\frac{\beta^2(\beta+1) - 2}{\beta^2(\beta^2 - 1)} \right] - 1 = \frac{\beta + 2}{\beta(\beta + 1)},$$
$$x_2 = \beta [x_1] - 1 = \beta \left[\frac{\beta + 2}{\beta(\beta + 1)} \right] - 1 = \frac{1}{\beta + 1},$$
$$x_3 = \beta [x_2] - 1 = \beta \left[\frac{1}{\beta + 1} \right] - 1 = \frac{-1}{\beta + 1},$$
$$x_4 = \beta [x_3] + 1 = \beta \left[\frac{-1}{\beta + 1} \right] + 1 = \frac{1}{\beta + 1} = x_2,$$

and generate the following pattern with two transient terms:

$$\left[\frac{\beta^2(\beta+1)-2}{\beta^2(\beta^2-1)}, \frac{\beta+2}{\beta(\beta+1)}\right], \frac{1}{\beta+1}, \frac{-1}{\beta+1}, \ldots$$

Furthermore we see:

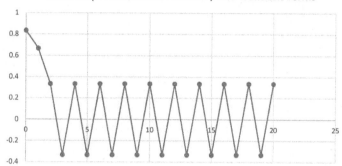

Eventually Periodic with Period-2 ; Two Transient Terms

an eventually periodic cycle with period-2 with two decreasing transient terms where $\beta = 2$ and $x_0 = \frac{5}{6}$.

Example 34. Determine the period-2 solution with four transient terms of:

$$x_{n+1} = \beta x_n - g(x_n), \quad n = 0, 1, 2, \ldots,$$

where $x_0 \in \mathbb{R}$, $\beta \neq 1$ and

$$g(x) = \begin{cases} 1 & \text{if } x \geq 0, \\ -1 & \text{if } x < 0. \end{cases}$$

Solution: Set $x_6 = x_4$ and assume that $\frac{1+\beta+\beta^2+\beta^3+\beta^4}{\beta^5} < x_0 < \frac{1+\beta+\beta^2+\beta^3+\beta^4+\beta^5}{\beta^6}$. Then:

$x_0 > 0,$

$x_1 = \beta x_0 - 1,$

$x_2 = \beta[x_1] - 1 = \beta[\beta x_0 - 1] - 1 = \beta^2 x_0 - \beta - 1,$

$x_3 = \beta[x_2] - 1 = \beta[\beta^2 x_0 - \beta - 1] - 1 = \beta^3 x_0 - \beta^2 - \beta - 1,$

$x_4 = \beta[x_3] - 1 = \beta[\beta^3 x_0 - \beta^2 - \beta - 1] - 1 = \beta^4 x_0 - \beta^3 - \beta^2 - \beta - 1,$

$x_5 = \beta[x_4] - 1 = \beta[\beta^4 x_0 - \beta^3 - \beta^2 - \beta - 1] - 1$
$\quad = \beta^5 x_0 - \beta^4 - \beta^3 - \beta^2 - \beta - 1,$

$x_6 = \beta[x_5] + 1 = \beta[\beta^5 x_0 - \beta^4 - \beta^3 - \beta^2 - \beta - 1] + 1$
$\quad = \beta^6 x_0 - \beta^5 - \beta^4 - \beta^3 - \beta^2 - \beta + 1 = x_4.$

Notice $x_0 = \frac{\beta^4(\beta+1)-2}{\beta^4(\beta^2-1)}$ produces the following pattern with four transient terms:

$$\left[\frac{\beta^4(\beta+1)-2}{\beta^4(\beta^2-1)}, \frac{\beta^3(\beta+1)-2}{\beta^3(\beta^2-1)}, \frac{\beta^2(\beta+1)-2}{\beta^2(\beta^2-1)}, \frac{\beta+2}{\beta(\beta+1)}\right],$$

$$\frac{1}{\beta+1}, \frac{-1}{\beta+1}, \dots$$

Now we see:

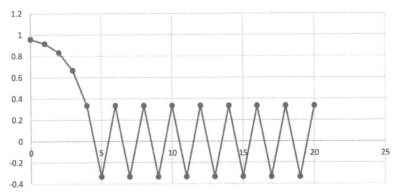

an eventually periodic cycle with period-2 with four decreasing transient terms where $\beta = 2$ and $x_0 = \frac{23}{24}$. This similar phenomenon occurred in Example 33.

The graph below depicts:

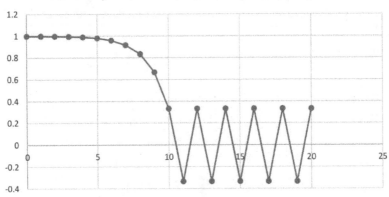

an eventually periodic cycle with period-2 with ten decreasing transient terms where $\beta = 2$ and $x_0 = \frac{1535}{1536}$.

From Examples 33 and 34 we can inductively determine the general pattern of the N transient terms ($N \in \mathbb{N}$). The following theorem characterizes the result and will be left as an exercise to prove.

Theorem 17. *The* $\Delta.E.$

$$x_{n+1} = \beta x_n - g(x_n), \quad n = 0, 1, 2, \ldots,$$

where $x_0 \in \mathbb{R}$, $\beta \neq 1$ *and*

$$g(x) = \begin{cases} 1 & \text{if } x \geq 0, \\ -1 & \text{if } x < 0, \end{cases}$$

is eventually periodic with period-2 with N transient terms ($N \in \mathbb{N}$) *when:*

$$x_0 = \frac{\beta^N(\beta+1) - 2}{\beta^N(\beta^2 - 1)}.$$

Notice that

$$\lim_{N \to \infty} \frac{\beta^N(\beta+1) - 2}{\beta^N(\beta^2 - 1)} = \frac{1}{\beta - 1}.$$

Similar to Examples 33 and 34, we can determine the existence of eventually periodic solutions with period-p ($p \geq 3$). This will be left as an exercise at the end of the chapter.

Can Eq. (3.54) exhibit an eventually constant solution? The answer is yes and the graph below verifies the answer:

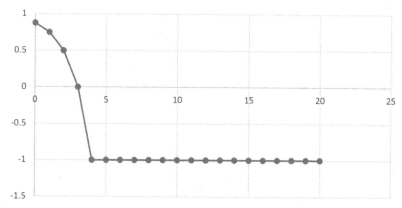

Eventually Constant with Four Transient Terms

This is eventually constant $\bar{x} = -1$ with four decreasing transient terms where $\beta = 2$ and $x_0 = \frac{7}{8}$. This leads to the following theorem.

Theorem 18. *The Δ.E.*

$$x_{n+1} = 2x_n - g(x_n), \quad n = 0, 1, 2, \ldots,$$

and

$$g(x) = \begin{cases} 1 & \text{if } x \geq 0, \\ -1 & \text{if } x < 0, \end{cases}$$

is eventually constant $\bar{x} = -1$ with $N + 1$ transient terms $(N \geq 0)$ when:

$$x_0 = \frac{2^N - 1}{2^N}.$$

Theorem 18 is proved by induction and will be left as an exercise at the end of the chapter. The next vital question to address: Do eventually constant solutions exist when $\beta > 2$ and when $1 < \beta < 2$? We will adjourn this section with an example of a chaotic orbit of Eq. (3.54). Let $\beta = 2$ and $x_0 = 0.600001$ with the following graph:

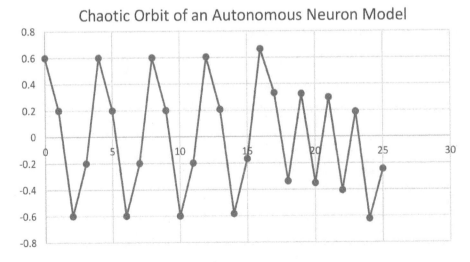

resembles chaotic behavior or a chaotic orbit as there is no specific pattern in comparison to a period-4 cycle when $\beta = 2$ and $x_0 = 0.6$ in Example 32.

3.4.8. *Autonomous Piecewise difference equation as a Neuron model when $\beta = 1$*

In this section our intent is to analyze the patterns of periodic solutions and eventually periodic solutions of the Autonomous Piecewise A.E.:

$$x_{n+1} = x_n - g(x_n), \quad n = 0, 1, 2, \ldots, \tag{3.55}$$

where $x_0 \in \Re$ and

$$g(x) = \begin{cases} 1 & \text{if } x \geq 0, \\ -1 & \text{if } x < 0. \end{cases}$$

Our plan is to show that Eq. (3.55) only has period-2 cycles. First of all, we will show that every solution Eq. (3.55) is either periodic with period-2 or eventually periodic with period-2. Second of all, we will not encounter unique period-2 solutions as we did with Eq. (3.54).

Example 35. Determine a period-2 solution of:

$$x_{n+1} = x_n - g(x_n), \quad n = 0, 1, 2, \ldots,$$

where $x_0 \in \Re$ and

$$g(x) = \begin{cases} 1 & \text{if } x \geq 0, \\ -1 & \text{if } x < 0. \end{cases}$$

Solution: Assume $0 < x_0 < 1$. Then:

$$x_0 > 0,$$

$$x_1 = x_0 - 1 < 0 \quad (\text{as } 0 < x_0 < 1),$$

$$x_2 = [x_1] + 1 = [x_0 - 1] + 1 = x_0.$$

If $0 < x_0 < 1$, then every solution of Eq. (3.55) is periodic with period-2. In addition, if $x_0 = 0$, then we obtain the following period-2 pattern:

$$0, \ -1, \ 0, \ -1, \ldots.$$

Similar pattern can be obtained by letting $x_0 = -1$. Now notice:

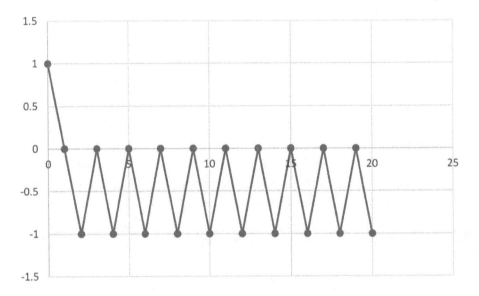

By setting $x_0 = 1$ we obtain exactly one transient term.

The immediate question to ask: is every solution either periodic or eventually periodic? The answer is yes and we will demonstrate several examples.

Example 36. Determine the pattern of eventually periodic solution of:

$$x_{n+1} = x_n - g(x_n), \quad n = 0, 1, 2, \ldots,$$

when $x_0 = 6$ and

$$g(x) = \begin{cases} 1 & \text{if } x \geq 0, \\ -1 & \text{if } x < 0. \end{cases}$$

Solution: By examining the graph below:

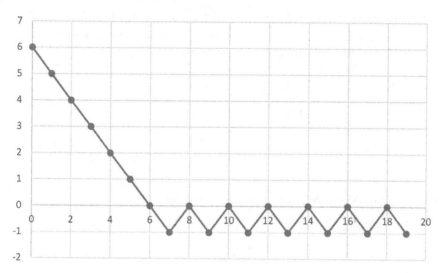

we see exactly six positive transient terms that are strictly decreasing. Furthermore, the transient terms are decreasing linearly in increments of one.

From Example 36, it follows that if x_0 is a positive integer $N \in \mathbb{N}$, then we will have N transient terms that are all decreasing in increments of 1. Similarly, if we let $x_0 = N$, where N is a negative integer, then we will have $N - 1$ negative increasing transient terms increasing in increments of 1. The transient terms of Eq. (3.55) either increase or decrease linearly in comparison with the pattern of transient terms in the previous section when $\beta \neq 1$.

More studies on Piecewise Difference Equations will be addressed in Chapter 6 and the following questions will be conveyed regarding the periodic character of solutions:

- When $\{\beta_n\}_{n=0}^{\infty}$ is a period-2 sequence, will periodic and eventually periodic solutions exist with only period-2N $(N \geq 1)$?
- When $\{\beta_n\}_{n=0}^{\infty}$ is a period-k sequence $(k \geq 3)$, will periodic and eventually periodic solutions exist with only period-3N $(N \geq 1)$?
- Systems of Piecewise Difference Equations.

Now we will conclude this chapter with additional models applied as Piecewise Difference Equations.

3.4.9. *The Williamson's Model*

The **Williamson's Model** was established by M. Williamson in 1974 [83] who studied age structured cases in a discrete population model resembled by the following Piecewise Δ.E.:

$$x_{n+1} = \begin{cases} \lambda_+ x_n & \text{if } x_n > 1, \\ \lambda_- x_n & \text{if } x_n < 1, \end{cases} \quad n = 0, 1, \ldots,$$

where $x_0 > 0$, $0 < \lambda_- < 1 < \lambda_+$; λ_+ and λ_- are the population growth rates.

3.4.10. *The West Nile Epidemics Model*

The **West Nile Epidemics Model** established by Vlajko Kocic in 2006 [49] is portrayed by the following Piecewise Δ.E.:

$$x_{n+1} = [a - bh(x_n - c)]\, x_n, \quad n = 0, 1, \ldots,$$

where h is the heaviside function defined as:

$$h(t) = \begin{cases} 0 & \text{if } t < 0, \\ 1 & \text{if } t \geq 0, \end{cases}$$

$x_0 \geq 0$, $0 < b < 1 < a < b+1$, $a - b \in (0, 1)$ and $c > 0$. This Piecewise Δ.E. appears as the discrete model of the West Nile Epidemics when spraying against mosquitoes is implemented only when the number of mosquitoes exceeds some predefined threshold level.

3.5. Chapter 3 Exercises

In problems 1–7, graphically show the existence of the **unique positive equilibrium point**; assume that $x_0 \geq 0$.

1. $x_{n+1} = \dfrac{2 + x_n}{3 + x_n}$, $\quad n = 0, 1, \ldots$

2. $x_{n+1} = \dfrac{1}{1 + x_n}$, $\quad n = 0, 1, \ldots$

3. $x_{n+1} = \dfrac{1}{x_n^2 + 1}$, $\quad n = 0, 1, \ldots$

4. $x_{n+1} = 8 - x_n^2$, $\quad n = 0, 1, \ldots$

5. $x_{n+1} = e^{-x_n}$, $\quad n = 0, 1, \ldots$

6. $x_{n+1} = 9x_n - x_n^3$, $\quad n = 0, 1, \ldots$

7. $x_{n+1} = x_n^4 - x_n^2$, $\quad n = 0, 1, \ldots$

In problems 8–18, determine the **local stability character** of all the non-negative equilibrium points; assume that $x_0 \geq 0$ and $a, b, c > 0$.

8. $x_{n+1} = x_n^2$, $\quad n = 0, 1, \ldots$

9. $x_{n+1} = \sqrt{x_n}$, $\quad n = 0, 1, \ldots$

10. $x_{n+1} = \dfrac{1}{x_n^2}$, $\quad n = 0, 1, \ldots$

11. $x_{n+1} = \dfrac{1}{\sqrt{x_n}}$, $\quad n = 0, 1, \ldots$

12. $x_{n+1} = (a+1)x_n(1 - \dfrac{x_n}{b})$, $\quad n = 0, 1, \ldots$

13. $x_{n+1} = \dfrac{ax_n}{1 + x_n^2}$, $\quad n = 0, 1, \ldots$

14. $x_{n+1} = \dfrac{ax_n^2}{1 + x_n^2}$, $\quad n = 0, 1, \ldots$

15. $x_{n+1} = \dfrac{a}{1 + x_n}$, $\quad n = 0, 1, \ldots$

16. $x_{n+1} = \dfrac{a}{1 + x_n^2}$, $\quad n = 0, 1, \ldots$

17. $x_{n+1} = x_n e^{a - \frac{x_n}{b}}$, $\quad n = 0, 1, \ldots$

18. $x_{n+1} = cx_n e^{a - \frac{x_n}{b}}$, $\quad n = 0, 1, \ldots$

In problems 19–28, using the **Cobweb Method**, determine the **global stability character** of all the non-negative equilibrium points; assume that $x_0 \geq 0$.

19. $x_{n+1} = \dfrac{1}{1 + x_n}$, $\quad n = 0, 1, \ldots$

20. $x_{n+1} = \dfrac{x_n + 1}{x_n - 1}$, $\quad n = 0, 1, \ldots$

21. $x_{n+1} = \dfrac{1}{1 + x_n^2}$, $\quad n = 0, 1, \ldots$

22. $x_{n+1} = \dfrac{x_n}{1 + x_n^2}$, $\quad n = 0, 1, \ldots$

23. $x_{n+1} = \dfrac{x_n^2}{1 + x_n^2}$, $\quad n = 0, 1, \ldots$

24. $x_{n+1} = 4x_n(1 - x_n)$, $\quad n = 0, 1, \ldots$

25. $x_{n+1} = e^{-x_n}, \quad n = 0, 1, \ldots$

26. $x_{n+1} = 8x_n e^{-x_n}, \quad n = 0, 1, \ldots$

27. $x_{n+1} = (1 - x_n)e^{-x_n}, \quad n = 0, 1, \ldots$

28. $x_{n+1} = x_n e^{-x_n} + 1, \quad n = 0, 1, \ldots$

In problems 29–31, suppose that $x_0 > 0$ and show that every positive solution is **monotonic** and converges monotonically.

29. $x_{n+1} = \dfrac{x_n}{1 + x_n^2}, \quad n = 0, 1, \ldots$

30. $x_{n+1} = \dfrac{x_n^2}{1 + x_n^2}, \quad n = 0, 1, \ldots$

31. $x_{n+1} = x_n e^{-x_n}, \quad n = 0, 1, \ldots$

In problems 32–34, suppose that $x_0 > 0$ and show that every positive solution is **oscillatory**.

32. $x_{n+1} = \dfrac{1}{1 + x_n}, \quad n = 0, 1, \ldots$

33. $x_{n+1} = \dfrac{1}{1 + x_n^2}, \quad n = 0, 1, \ldots$

34. $x_{n+1} = e^{-x_n}, \quad n = 0, 1, \ldots$

35. Consider the **Non-autonomous Riccati Δ.E.** in the form:

$$x_{n+1} = \frac{1}{x_n} + a_n, \quad n = 0, 1, \ldots,$$

where $\{a_n\}_{n=0}^{\infty}$ is a period-2 sequence. Show that there are two unique period-2 cycles and determine their patterns.

Consider the **Non-autonomous Riccati Δ.E.** in the form:

$$x_{n+1} = \frac{A_n}{x_n}, \quad n = 0, 1, \ldots,$$

where $\{A_n\}_{n=0}^{\infty}$ is a periodic sequence. In problems 36–42:

36. Show that there is no period-3 solution when $\{A_n\}_{n=0}^{\infty}$ is a period-2 sequence and explain why.

37. Show that there is no period-4 solution when $\{A_n\}_{n=0}^{\infty}$ is a period-2 sequence and explain why.

38. From Exercise 36 and 37, show that there is no period-k $(k \geq 2)$ solution when $\{A_n\}_{n=0}^{\infty}$ is a period-2 sequence and explain why.

39. Suppose that $\{A_n\}_{n=0}^{\infty}$ is a period-5 sequence. Determine the pattern of the periodic cycle.

40. Suppose that $\{A_n\}_{n=0}^{\infty}$ is a period-6 sequence. Determine the pattern of the periodic cycle.

41. Suppose that $\{A_n\}_{n=0}^{\infty}$ is a period-$(2k+1)$ sequence (for $k \in \mathbb{N}$). From Exercise 36, determine the pattern of the periodic cycle.

42. Suppose that $\{A_n\}_{n=0}^{\infty}$ is a period-$(2k)$ sequence for (for $k \geq 2$). From Exercise 37, determine the pattern of the periodic cycle.

Consider the **Non-autonomous Riccati Δ.E.** in the form:

$$x_{n+1} = \frac{A_n x_n}{x_n - 1}, \quad n = 0, 1, \dots,$$

where $\{A_n\}_{n=0}^{\infty}$ is a periodic sequence. In problems 43–50:

43. Suppose that $\{A_n\}_{n=0}^{\infty}$ is a period-4 sequence. Determine the pattern of the periodic cycle.

44. Suppose that $\{A_n\}_{n=0}^{\infty}$ is a period-6 sequence. Determine the pattern of the periodic cycle.

45. Suppose that $\{A_n\}_{n=0}^{\infty}$ is a period-8 sequence. Determine the pattern of the periodic cycle.

46. Suppose that $\{A_n\}_{n=0}^{\infty}$ is a period-2k sequence (for $k \geq 2$). From Exercise 43, 44 and 45, determine the pattern of the periodic cycle.

47. Suppose that $\{A_n\}_{n=0}^{\infty}$ is a period-3 sequence. Determine the pattern of the periodic cycle. **Hint:** set $x_6 = x_0$ and proceed with the algebra.

48. Suppose that $\{A_n\}_{n=0}^{\infty}$ is a period-5 sequence. Determine the pattern of the periodic cycle. **Hint:** set $x_{10} = x_0$ and proceed with the algebra.

49. Suppose that $\{A_n\}_{n=0}^{\infty}$ is a period-7 sequence. Determine the pattern of the periodic cycle. **Hint:** set $x_{14} = x_0$ and proceed with the algebra.

50. Suppose that $\{A_n\}_{n=0}^{\infty}$ is a period-$(2k+1)$ $(k \in \mathbb{N})$. From Exercise 47, 48 and 49, determine the pattern of the periodic cycle.

Consider the **Logistic Δ.E.**:

$$x_{n+1} = 4x_n (1 - x_n), \quad n = 0, 1, \dots.$$

In problems 51–58, using the double angle identity $sin(2t) = 2sin(t)cos(t)$:

51. Determine the periodic pattern when $x_0 = sin^2 \left(\frac{2\pi}{3} \right)$.

52. Determine the periodic pattern when $x_0 = sin^2 \left(\frac{2\pi}{9} \right)$.

53. Determine the periodic pattern when $x_0 = sin^2 \left(\dfrac{2\pi}{11} \right)$.

54. Determine the periodic pattern when $x_0 = sin^2 \left(\dfrac{2\pi}{13} \right)$.

55. Determine the periodic pattern when $x_0 = sin^2 \left(\dfrac{\pi}{12} \right)$.

56. Determine the periodic pattern when $x_0 = sin^2 \left(\dfrac{\pi}{96} \right)$.

57. Determine the periodic pattern when $x_0 = sin^2 \left(\dfrac{\pi}{160} \right)$.

58. Prove Theorem 13.

Consider the **Tent-Map** in the form:

$$x_{n+1} = \begin{cases} 2x_n & \text{if } x_n < \dfrac{1}{2}, \\ 2(1 - x_n) & \text{if } x_n \geq \dfrac{1}{2}, \end{cases} \quad n = 0, 1, \ldots,$$

where $0 < x_0 < 1$. In problems 59–66:

59. Determine a period-5 pattern.
60. Determine a period-6 pattern.
61. From Exercises 59–60, determine a period-k pattern (for $k \geq 2$).
62. Determine a period-6 pattern with three transient terms.
63. Determine a period-6 pattern with six transient terms.
64. From Exercises 62–63, determine a period-k pattern (for $k \geq 2$) with N transient terms $(N \in \mathbb{N})$.
65. Prove Theorem 15.
66. Prove Theorem 16.

Consider the **Tent-Map** in the form:

$$x_{n+1} = \begin{cases} Ax_n & \text{if } x_n < \dfrac{1}{2}, \\ A(1 - x_n) & \text{if } x_n \geq \dfrac{1}{2}, \end{cases} \quad n = 0, 1, \ldots,$$

where $0 < x_0 < 1$ and $A > 2$. In problems 67–75:

67. Determine a period-2 pattern.
68. Determine a period-3 pattern.
69. Determine a period-4 pattern.
70. From Exercises 67–69, determine a period-k pattern (for $k \geq 2$).
71. Determine a period-2 pattern with four transient terms.

72. Determine a period-4 pattern with eight transient terms.
73. From Exercises 71–72, determine a period-k pattern (for $k \geq 2$) with N transient terms $(N \in \mathbb{N})$.
74. Develop a Theorem similar to Theorem 15 and then prove it.
75. Develop a Theorem similar to Theorem 16 and then prove it.

Consider the **Piecewise** $\boldsymbol{\Delta}$**.E.** in the form:

$$x_{n+1} = \beta x_n - g(x_n), \quad n = 0, 1, 2, \ldots,$$

where $\beta > 0$ and

$$g(x) = \begin{cases} 1, & x \geq 0, \\ -1, & x < 0. \end{cases}$$

In problems 76–88:

76. Determine a period-4 pattern.
77. Determine a period-5 pattern.
78. From Exercise 76, determine a pattern of the period-2k cycle $(k \in \mathbb{N})$.
79. From Exercise 77, determine a pattern of the period-$(2k + 1)$ cycle $(k \in \mathbb{N})$.
80. Determine a period-2 pattern with 6 transient terms.
81. Determine a period-2 pattern with 9 transient terms.
82. From Exercises 80–81, determine a period-2 pattern with N transient terms $(N \in \mathbb{N})$.
83. Determine a period-3 pattern with 2 transient terms.
84. Determine a period-3 pattern with 3 transient terms.
85. From Exercises 83–84, determine a period-3 pattern with N transient terms $(N \in \mathbb{N})$.
86. From Exercise 78, determine a period-2k pattern $(k \in \mathbb{N})$ with N transient terms $(N \in \mathbb{N})$.
87. From Exercise 79, determine a period-$(2k + 1)$ pattern $(k \in \mathbb{N})$ with N transient terms $(N \in \mathbb{N})$.
88. Prove Theorem 18.

CHAPTER 4

SECOND ORDER LINEAR DIFFERENCE EQUATIONS

The aim of this chapter is to solve second order linear difference equations explicitly, to determine the necessary and sufficient conditions for convergence of solutions (asymptotic behavior), and to ascertain the periodic character and patterns of periodic cycles. We will explore various applications of second order linear difference equations in solving the Riccati Δ.E., the Fibonacci Sequence, the Gambler's Ruin Problem, the National Income, Signal Processing and Resonance. Here are three examples of second order linear difference equations:

(i) (Homogeneous) $x_{n+2} = 3x_{n+1} - x_n$, $n = 0, 1, \ldots$.
(ii) (Nonhomogeneous) $x_{n+2} = 4x_n + 3$, $n = 0, 1, \ldots$.
(iii) (Non-autonomous) $x_{n+2} = x_{n+1} + 4x_n - \left(\frac{2}{3}\right)^n$, $n = 0, 1, \ldots$.

In (i), we have a homogeneous second order linear Δ.E. In (ii), we have a nonhomogeneous second order linear Δ.E. In (iii), we have a non-autonomous second order linear Δ.E. We will solve each Δ.E. explicitly, check the solution, analyze the convergence nature of solutions and examine the existence and patterns of the periodic cycles. We will emerge our study with the **Second Order Linear Homogeneous Δ.E.** in the form:

$$x_{n+2} + px_{n+1} + qx_n = 0, \quad n = 0, 1, \ldots,$$

where $x_0, x_1, p \in \Re$ and $q \neq 0$.

4.1. Homogeneous Second Order Linear Difference Equations

The followings are examples of second order linear homogeneous difference equations:

(i) $x_{n+2} = x_{n+1} + x_n, \quad n = 0, 1, \ldots,$
(ii) $4x_{n+2} = x_n, \quad n = 0, 1, \ldots,$

which guide us to the study of second order homogeneous linear Δ.E. in the form:

$$x_{n+2} + px_{n+1} + qx_n = 0, \quad n = 0, 1, \ldots, \tag{4.56}$$

where $x_0, x_1, p \in \Re$ and $q \neq 0$. To obtain an explicit solution of Eq. (4.56), we set $x_n = \lambda^n$ and acquire the following quadratic **characteristic polynomial**:

$$\lambda^2 + p\lambda + q = 0, \tag{4.57}$$

whose roots (solutions) are

$$\lambda_1 = \frac{-p + \sqrt{p^2 - 4q}}{2} \quad \text{and} \quad \lambda_2 = \frac{-p - \sqrt{p^2 - 4q}}{2}.$$

Also let $D = p^2 - 4q$; either $D > 0$, $D = 0$ or $D < 0$, which lead us to the following three cases:

CASE 1. Suppose that $D > 0$. Then Eq. (4.57) has two distinct real roots $\lambda_1 \neq \lambda_2$ and we obtain the following solution to Eq. (4.56):

$$x_n = C_1(\lambda_1^n) + C_2(\lambda_2^n), \quad n = 0, 1, \ldots. \tag{4.58}$$

CASE 2. Suppose that $D = 0$. Then Eq. (4.57) has a repeated real root $\lambda_1 = \lambda_2$ and we acquire the following solution to Eq. (4.56):

$$x_n = C_1(\lambda_1^n) + C_2 n(\lambda_1^n), \quad n = 0, 1, \ldots. \tag{4.59}$$

CASE 3. Suppose that $D < 0$. Then Eq. (4.57) has two imaginary complex conjugate roots

$$\lambda_1 = A + Bi \quad \text{and} \quad \lambda_2 = A - Bi.$$

Now let

$$\Lambda = |A + Bi| = |A - Bi| \quad \text{and} \quad \theta = arg(\lambda_1).$$

Then we procure the following solution to Eq. (4.56):

$$x_n = (\Lambda)^n [C_1 sin(n\theta) + C_2 cos(n\theta)], \quad n = 0, 1, \ldots. \quad (4.60)$$

The following examples will demonstrate the implementation of the three cases.

Example 1. Solve the following Δ.E.:

$$x_{n+2} - 7x_{n+1} + 12x_n = 0, \quad n = 0, 1, \ldots, \quad (4.61)$$

and verify that the solution is correct.

Solution: The **characteristic polynomial** of Eq. (4.61) is:

$$\lambda^2 - 7\lambda + 12 = 0,$$

whose roots are $\lambda_1 = 3$ and $\lambda_2 = 4$. So via (4.58):

$$x_n = C_1 3^n + C_2 4^n, \quad n = 0, 1, \ldots. \quad (4.62)$$

To check our solution, via (4.62) we obtain:

$$x_{n+1} = C_1 3^{n+1} + C_2 4^{n+1} = 3C_1 3^n + 4C_2 4^n, \quad (4.63)$$

and

$$x_{n+2} = C_1 3^{n+2} + C_2 4^{n+2} = 9C_1 3^n + 16C_2 4^n. \quad (4.64)$$

By substituting (4.62), (4.63), and (4.64) into Eq. (4.61) we procure:

$$x_{n+2} - 7x_{n+1} + 12x_n$$
$$= [9C_1 3^n + 16C_2 4^n] - 7[3C_1 3^n + 4C_2 4^n] + 12[C_1 3^n + C_2 4^n]$$
$$= 9C_1 3^n + 16C_2 4^n - 21C_1 3^n - 28C_2 4^n + 12C_1 3^n + 12C_2 4^n = 0.$$

Example 2. Solve the following Δ.E.:

$$x_{n+2} - 8x_{n+1} + 16x_n = 0, \quad n = 0, 1, \ldots, \quad (4.65)$$

and verify that the solution is correct.

Solution: The **characteristic polynomial** of Eq. (4.65) is:

$$\lambda^2 - 8\lambda + 16 = 0$$

and has a repeated root $\lambda_1 = \lambda_2 = 4$. So via (4.59):

$$x_n = C_1 4^n + C_2 n 4^n, \quad n = 0, 1, \ldots . \tag{4.66}$$

To check our solution via (4.66) we acquire:

$$x_{n+1} = C_1 4^{n+1} + C_2(n+1)4^{n+1} = 4C_1 4^n + 4C_2(n+1)4^n, \tag{4.67}$$

and

$$x_{n+2} = C_1 4^{n+2} + C_2(n+2)4^{n+2} = 16C_1 4^n + 16C_2(n+2)4^n. \tag{4.68}$$

By substituting (4.66), (4.67) and (4.68) into Eq. (4.65) we get:

$$x_{n+2} - 8x_{n+1} + 16x_n$$
$$= [16C_1 4^n + 16C_2(n+2)4^n] - 8[4C_1 4^n + 4C_2(n+1)4^n]$$
$$+ 16[C_1 4^n + C_2 n 4^n]$$
$$= 0.$$

Example 3. Solve the following Δ.E.:

$$x_{n+2} + x_n = 0, \quad n = 0, 1, \ldots, \tag{4.69}$$

and verify that the solution is correct.

Solution: The **characteristic polynomial** of Eq. (4.69) is:

$$\lambda^2 + 1 = 0$$

and has two imaginary roots $\lambda_1 = i$ and $\lambda_2 = -i$. Also note that

$$\Lambda = |i| = |-i| = 1 \quad \text{and} \quad \theta = arg(i) = \frac{\pi}{2}.$$

Therefore via (4.60):

$$x_n = C_1 sin\left(\frac{n\pi}{2}\right) + C_2 cos\left(\frac{n\pi}{2}\right), \quad n = 0, 1, \ldots \quad (4.70)$$

To check our solution via (4.70) we procure:

$$x_{n+2} = C_1 sin\left(\frac{[n+2]\pi}{2}\right) + C_2 cos\left(\frac{[n+2]\pi}{2}\right). \quad (4.71)$$

Now by substituting (4.70) and (4.71) into Eq. (4.69) we procure:

$$x_{n+2} + x_n$$

$$= \left[C_1 sin\left(\frac{[n+2]\pi}{2}\right) + C_2 cos\left(\frac{[n+2]\pi}{2}\right)\right] + \left[C_1 sin\left(\frac{n\pi}{2}\right)\right.$$

$$\left. + C_2 cos\left(\frac{n\pi}{2}\right)\right]$$

$$= C_1 \left[sin\left(\frac{n\pi}{2}\right)cos(\pi) + sin(\pi)cos\left(\frac{n\pi}{2}\right)\right] + C_2 \left[cos\left(\frac{n\pi}{2}\right)cos(\pi)\right.$$

$$\left. - sin\left(\frac{n\pi}{2}\right)sin(\pi)\right] + \left[C_1 sin\left(\frac{n\pi}{2}\right) + C_2 cos\left(\frac{n\pi}{2}\right)\right]$$

$$= -C_1 sin\left(\frac{n\pi}{2}\right) - C_2 cos\left(\frac{n\pi}{2}\right) + C_1 sin\left(\frac{n\pi}{2}\right) + C_2 cos\left(\frac{n\pi}{2}\right) = 0.$$

Hence the result follows. Furthermore, we obtain period-4 cycles since $\theta = \frac{\pi}{2}$ as we can see in the diagram below.

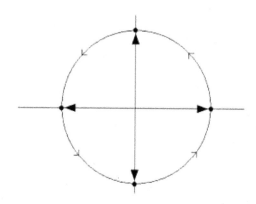

Example 4. Solve the Initial Value Problem:

$$\begin{cases} x_{n+2} - 4x_{n+1} + 3x_n = 0, & n = 0, 1, \ldots, \\ x_0 = 2, \\ x_1 = 4, \end{cases}$$

and verify that the solution is correct.

Solution: Via (4.58):

$$x_n = C_1 1^n + C_2 3^n = C_1 + C_2 3^n, \quad n = 0, 1, \ldots. \tag{4.72}$$

First we solve for C_1 and C_2. Applying (4.72) gives us:

$$x_0 = C_1 + C_2 = 2,$$
$$x_1 = C_1 + 3C_2 = 4.$$

Hence:

$$C_2 = 1 \quad \text{and} \quad C_1 = 1.$$

Therefore, via (4.72) the specific solution is

$$x_n = C_1 1^n + C_2 3^n = 1 + 3^n, \quad n = 0, 1, \ldots. \tag{4.73}$$

Now using (4.73) we obtain:

$$x_{n+1} = 1 + 3^{n+1} = 1 + 3(3^n), \tag{4.74}$$

and

$$x_{n+2} = 1 + 3^{n+2} = 1 + 9(3^n). \tag{4.75}$$

By substituting (4.73), (4.74) and (4.75) into the given Δ.E. we procure:

$$x_{n+2} - 4x_{n+1} + 3x_n$$
$$= [1 + 9(3^n)] - 4[1 + 3(3^n)] + 3[1 + 3^n]$$
$$= 1 + 9(3^n) - 4 - 12(3^n) + 3 + 3^n = 0.$$

Example 5. Solve the Initial Value Problem:

$$\begin{cases} x_{n+2} - 6x_{n+1} + 9x_n = 0, & n = 0, 1, \ldots, \\ x_0 = 1, \\ x_1 = 6, \end{cases}$$

and verify that the solution is correct.

Solution: The general solution is

$$x_n = C_1 3^n + C_2 n 3^n, \quad n = 0, 1, \ldots \tag{4.76}$$

To solve for C_1 and C_2, set:

$$x_0 = C_1 = 1,$$
$$x_1 = 3C_1 + 3C_2 = 6.$$

Note that

$$C_2 = 1 \quad \text{and} \quad C_1 = 1.$$

Therefore, via (4.76) the specific solution is

$$x_n = C_1 3^n + C_2 n 3^n = 3^n + n 3^n, \quad n = 0, 1, \ldots \tag{4.77}$$

Now we acquire:

$$x_{n+1} = 3^{n+1} + (n+1)3^{n+1} = 3 \cdot 3^n + 3(n+1)3^n, \tag{4.78}$$

and

$$x_{n+2} = 3^{n+2} + (n+2)3^{n+2} = 9 \cdot 3^n + 9(n+2)3^n. \tag{4.79}$$

By substituting (4.77), (4.78) and (4.79) into the given Δ.E., we get:

$$x_{n+2} - 6x_{n+1} + 9x_n$$
$$= [9(3^n) + 9(n+2)3^n] - 6[3(3^n) + 3(n+1)3^n] + 9[3^n + n3^n]$$
$$= 0.$$

From the previous examples we can pose the following Open Problems that address the convergence nature of solutions, the periodic character and the oscillatory character of solutions.

Open Problem 1. Solve the following Δ.E.:

$$8x_{n+2} - 6x_{n+1} + x_n = 0, \quad n = 0, 1, \ldots, \tag{4.80}$$

and determine the set of initial conditions for which:

(i) Every solution is monotonic.
(ii) Every solution is oscillatory.

The general solution of Eq. (4.80) is:

$$x_n = C_1 \left(\frac{1}{2}\right)^n + C_2 \left(\frac{1}{4}\right)^n, \quad n = 0, 1, \ldots.$$

Open Problem 2. Solve the following Δ.E.:

$$2x_{n+2} - x_{n+1} - x_n = 0, \quad n = 0, 1, \ldots, \tag{4.81}$$

and determine the set of initial conditions for which:

(i) Every solution is monotonic.
(ii) Every solution is periodic and oscillatory.

The general solution of Eq. (4.81) is:

$$x_n = C_1 \left(\frac{1}{2}\right)^n + C_2(-1)^n, \quad n = 0, 1, \ldots.$$

Open Problem 3. Solve the following Δ.E.:

$$2x_{n+2} - 5x_{n+1} + 2x_n = 0, \quad n = 0, 1, \ldots, \tag{4.82}$$

and determine the set of initial conditions for which:

(i) Every solution converges.
(ii) Every solution diverges to $+\infty$.
(iii) Every solution diverges to $-\infty$.

The general solution of Eq. (4.82) is:

$$x_n = C_1 2^n + C_2 \left(\frac{1}{2}\right)^n, \quad n = 0, 1, \ldots.$$

Now we will focus on some applications of second order homogeneous linear difference equations.

4.1.1. *The Fibonacci Sequence*

Our goal is to write a Fibonacci Sequence as an Initial Value Problem of a Second Order Linear Δ.E. We define the **Fibonacci Sequence** as:

$$\{x_n\}_{n=0}^{\infty} = 1, 1, 2, 3, 5, 8, 13, 21, \ldots$$

Our next aim is to show:

$$\lim_{n \to \infty} \frac{x_{n+1}}{x_n} = \phi = \frac{1 + \sqrt{5}}{2}.$$

First set:

$$x_0 = 1,$$
$$x_1 = 1.$$

Then:

$$x_2 = 1 + 1 = x_1 + x_0 = 2,$$
$$x_3 = 2 + 1 = x_2 + x_1 = 3,$$
$$x_4 = 3 + 2 = x_3 + x_2 = 5.$$

Now we obtain the following Initial Value Problem:

$$\begin{cases} x_{n+2} = x_{n+1} + x_n, & n = 0, 1, \ldots, \\ x_0 = 1, \\ x_1 = 1, \end{cases}$$

whose **characteristic polynomial** is

$$\lambda^2 - \lambda - 1 = 0$$

with two distinct real roots

$$\lambda_1 = \frac{1 + \sqrt{5}}{2} \quad \text{and} \quad \lambda_2 = \frac{1 - \sqrt{5}}{2}.$$

Thus the general solution is

$$x_n = C_1 \lambda_1^n + C_2 \lambda_2^n, \quad n = 0, 1, \ldots$$

Now notice:

$$\lim_{n \to \infty} \frac{x_{n+1}}{x_n} = \lim_{n \to \infty} \frac{C_1 \lambda_1^{n+1} + C_2 \lambda_2^{n+1}}{C_1 \lambda_1^n + C_2 \lambda_2^n}$$

$$= \lim_{n \to \infty} \frac{C_1 \frac{\lambda_1^{n+1}}{\lambda_1^n} + C_2 \frac{\lambda_2^{n+1}}{\lambda_1^n}}{C_1 \frac{\lambda_1^n}{\lambda_1^n} + C_2 \frac{\lambda_2^n}{\lambda_1^n}} = \lambda_1 = \frac{1 + \sqrt{5}}{2} = \phi.$$

Hence the result follows. Our next application is the transformation of a Riccati Δ.E. to a second order linear Δ.E.

4.1.2. *The Riccati Difference Equation as a second order linear difference equation*

In this section we will transform a first order nonlinear Riccati Δ.E. to a homogeneous second order linear Δ.E. In Chapter 3 we studied the following *Riccati Difference Equation*:

$$x_{n+1} = \frac{a + bx_n}{c + dx_n}, \quad n = 0, 1, \ldots . \tag{4.83}$$

First assume that $ad \neq bc$. Otherwise, Eq. (4.83) reduces to

$$x_{n+1} = \frac{b}{d}, \quad n = 0, 1, \ldots .$$

Also when $d = 0$, Eq. (4.83) reduces to the following linear Δ.E.:

$$x_{n+1} = \frac{a}{c} + \frac{b}{c}x_n, \quad n = 0, 1, \ldots .$$

Now we perform the following **change of variables** by setting:

$$\frac{y_{n+1}}{y_n} = c + dx_n, \quad n = 0, 1, \ldots , \tag{4.84}$$

with $y_0 = 1$ which gives us $y_1 = c + dx_0$ and

$$x_n = \frac{1}{d}\frac{y_{n+1}}{y_n} - \frac{c}{d}, \quad n = 0, 1, \ldots , \tag{4.85}$$

which reduces to:

$$x_{n+1} = \frac{1}{d}\frac{y_{n+2}}{y_{n+1}} - \frac{c}{d}, \quad n = 0, 1, \ldots . \tag{4.86}$$

Therefore, by substituting (4.84), (4.85) and (4.86) into Eq. (4.83) we obtain:

$$\frac{1}{d}\frac{y_{n+2}}{y_{n+1}} - \frac{c}{d} = \frac{y_n}{y_{n+1}}\left[a + b\left(\frac{1}{d}\frac{y_{n+1}}{y_n} - \frac{c}{d}\right)\right], \quad n = 0, 1, \ldots ,$$

which simplifies to the following second order linear homogeneous Δ.E.:

$$y_{n+2} + Ay_{n+1} + By_n = 0, \quad n = 0, 1, \ldots ,$$

where $A = -(b + c)$ and $B = bc - ad$. Furthermore:

$$\lim_{n \to \infty}\left[\frac{y_{n+1}}{y_n}\right] = \lim_{n \to \infty}\left[c + dx_n\right].$$

Example 6. Let $\{x_n\}_{n=0}^{\infty}$ be a solution of:

$$x_{n+1} = \frac{2 + x_n}{1 + x_n}, \quad n = 0, 1, \ldots, \tag{4.87}$$

where $x_0 \geq 0$. Show that

$$\lim_{n \to \infty} x_n = \sqrt{2}.$$

Solution: Observe that $\bar{x} = \sqrt{2}$ is the only positive equilibrium point of Eq. (4.87). Then via (4.84) set:

$$\frac{y_{n+1}}{y_n} = 1 + x_n, \quad n = 0, 1, \ldots.$$

We then obtain:

$$x_n = \frac{y_{n+1}}{y_n} - 1, \quad n = 0, 1, \ldots, \tag{4.88}$$

and

$$x_{n+1} = \frac{y_{n+2}}{y_{n+1}} - 1, \quad n = 0, 1, \ldots. \tag{4.89}$$

By substituting (4.88) and (4.89) into Eq. (4.87) we acquire:

$$\frac{y_{n+2}}{y_{n+1}} - 1 = \frac{y_n}{y_{n+1}} \left[2 + \left(\frac{y_{n+1}}{y_n} - 1 \right) \right], \quad n = 0, 1, \ldots,$$

which reduces to the following second order linear homogeneous Δ.E.:

$$y_{n+2} - 2y_{n+1} - y_n = 0, \quad n = 0, 1, \ldots,$$

whose solution is

$$y_n = c_1 (\lambda_1)^n + c_2 (\lambda_2)^n, \quad n = 0, 1, \ldots,$$

where

$$\lambda_1 = 1 + \sqrt{2} \quad \text{and} \quad \lambda_2 = 1 - \sqrt{2}.$$

Also notice:

$$\lim_{n \to \infty} \left[\frac{y_{n+1}}{y_n} \right] = \lambda_1 = 1 + \sqrt{2}.$$

Thus

$$\lim_{n \to \infty} x_n = \lim_{n \to \infty} \left[\frac{y_{n+1}}{y_n} - 1 \right] = \sqrt{2}.$$

Our next aim is to study applications of second order linear homogeneous difference equations in the **Gambler's Ruin Problem**.

4.1.3. *The Gambler's Ruin Problem*

Suppose a gambler plays a sequence of games against his or her opponent. The probability of winning \$1 in any game is q $(0 \le q \le 1)$ and the probability of losing \$1 is $1 - q$. The gambler will stop if he or she either loses all the money or achieves \$N. The gambler is then ruined if he or she runs out of money. Now let p_n be the probability of the gambler ruin if he or she has \$n. First of all, if the gambler wins the next game (with probability q) then his or her fortune will be $n + 1$ and the probability of being ruined is p_{n+1}. Second of all, if the gambler loses the next game (with probability $1 - q$) and the probability of being ruined is p_{n-1}. By applying the **Theorem of Total Probabilities**, we obtain the following recursive relation:

$$p_n = qp_{n+1} + (1 - q)p_{n-1}. \tag{4.90}$$

By replacing or transforming n with $n + 1$ in Eq. (4.90), we acquire the following second order linear Δ.E.:

$$p_{n+2} - \left(\frac{1}{q}\right) p_{n+1} + \left(\frac{1-q}{q}\right) p_n = 0, \quad n = 0, 1, \ldots, N, \tag{4.91}$$

with initial conditions $p_0 = 1$ and $p_N = 0$. The characteristic polynomial of Eq. (4.91) is:

$$\lambda^2 - \left(\frac{1}{q}\right) \lambda + \left(\frac{1-q}{q}\right) = 0,$$

with two distinct roots:

$$\lambda_1 = \frac{1-q}{q} \quad \text{and} \quad \lambda_2 = 1.$$

Provided that $q \ne \frac{1}{2}$, the general solution of Eq. (4.91) is:

$$p_n = C_1 + C_2 \left(\frac{1-q}{q}\right)^n, \quad n = 0, 1, \ldots, N. \tag{4.92}$$

Applying $p_0 = 1$ and $p_N = 0$ into Eq. (4.92), we procure:

$$C_1 + C_2 = 1 \quad \text{and} \quad C_1 + C_2 \left(\frac{1-q}{q}\right)^N = 0.$$

Hence:

$$C_1 = \frac{-\left(\frac{1-q}{q}\right)^N}{1-\left(\frac{1-q}{q}\right)^N}, \quad C_2 = \frac{1}{1-\left(\frac{1-q}{q}\right)^N}.$$

Therefore we get:

$$p_n = \frac{\left(\frac{1-q}{q}\right)^n - \left(\frac{1-q}{q}\right)^N}{1-\left(\frac{1-q}{q}\right)^N}, \quad n = 0, 1, \ldots, N.$$

Now note when $q = \frac{1}{2}$ then the characteristic polynomial Eq. (4.91) has a repeated root $\lambda_1 = \lambda_2 = 1$. In this case, the general solution of Eq. (4.91) is:

$$p_n = C_1 + nC_2,$$

with $p_0 = 1$ and $p_N = 0$ it gives us:

$$p_n = 1 - \frac{n}{N} = \frac{N-n}{N}, \quad n = 0, 1, \ldots, N.$$

4.2. Asymptotic Behavior of Second Order Linear Difference Equations

For example, show that every solution of the Δ.E. $4x_{n+2} - x_n = 0$ converges to 0. On the other hand, it can be shown that some solutions of the Δ.E. $2x_{n+2} - 5x_{n+1} - 2x_n$ converge to 0, some diverge to $+\infty$ and some diverge to $-\infty$. Our aim is to examine convergence (asymptotic behavior) of solutions of the second order linear homogeneous Δ.E. in the form:

$$x_{n+2} + px_{n+1} + qx_n = 0, \quad n = 0, 1, \ldots, \tag{4.93}$$

where $x_0, x_1, p \in \Re$ and $q \neq 0$. It is our goal to determine the **asymptotic behavior** of solutions of Eq. (4.93). The following theorem states the necessary and sufficient conditions for every solution of Eq. (4.93) to converge to 0.

Theorem 19. *Let $\{x_n\}_{n=0}^{\infty}$ be a solution of Eq. (4.93). Then*

$$\lim_{n \to \infty} x_n = 0$$

if and only if

$$|p| < 1 + q < 2.$$

Proof.   Recall that the **characteristic polynomial** of Eq. (4.93) is:

$$\lambda^2 + p\lambda + q = 0,$$

whose roots are

$$\lambda_1 = \frac{-p + \sqrt{p^2 - 4q}}{2} \quad \text{and} \quad \lambda_2 = \frac{-p - \sqrt{p^2 - 4q}}{2}.$$

To prove that

$$\lim_{n \to \infty} x_n = 0,$$

via (4.58), (4.59) and (4.60) it suffices to show that

$$|\lambda_1| < 1 \quad \text{and} \quad |\lambda_2| < 1.$$

Let $D = p^2 - 4q$. This will lead into three cases. We will consider the case where $D < 0$. In this case, we have two imaginary complex conjugate roots

$$\lambda_1 = -\frac{p}{2} + \frac{\sqrt{4q - p^2}}{2}i \quad \text{and} \quad \lambda_2 = -\frac{p}{2} - \frac{\sqrt{4q - p^2}}{2}i.$$

First of all,

$$|\lambda_1| = |\lambda_2| = \sqrt{\frac{p^2}{4} + \frac{4q - p^2}{4}} = \sqrt{q} < 1$$

if and only if $0 < q < 1$. Second of all, $p^2 - 4q < 0$ implies

$$p^2 < 4q.$$

Hence:

$$p < \sqrt{4q} = 2\sqrt{q}.$$

Now to show that

$$|p| < 1 + q,$$

it suffices to show that

$$2\sqrt{q} < 1 + q.$$

Observe that

$$4q < (1 + q)^2 = q^2 + 2q + 1$$

holds provided that

$$q^2 - 2q + 1 = (q - 1)^2 > 0.$$

Since $0 < q < 1$, the result follows.

Now suppose $D > 0$. Then we have two real distinct roots λ_1 and λ_2. Consider the quadratic function

$$f(\lambda) = \lambda^2 + p\lambda + q.$$

Notice that $-1 < \lambda_1 < 1$ and $-1 < \lambda_2 < 1$ if and only if:

$$f(1) = 1 + p + q > 0 \quad \text{and} \quad f(-1) = 1 - p + q > 0.$$

Hence the result follows with

$$|p| < 1 + q.$$

The case where $D = 0$ will be left as an exercise at the end of the chapter.

$\square$

The following theorem describes the necessary and sufficient conditions for the **characteristic polynomial**

$$\lambda^2 + p\lambda + q = 0$$

to have a root with modulus equal to 1.

Theorem 20. *Consider the **characteristic polynomial***

$$\lambda^2 + p\lambda + q = 0$$

whose roots are λ_1 and λ_2. Then either

$$|\lambda_1| = 1 \quad \text{or} \quad |\lambda_2| = 1$$

if and only if

$$|p| = 1 + q \quad \text{or} \quad q = 1.$$

Proof. We will consider three cases:

CASE 1. Suppose that $p^2 - 4q > 0$ and $p = 1 + q$. Then we have two distinct real roots:

$$\lambda_1 = \frac{-(1+q) + \sqrt{(1+q)^2 - 4q}}{2} \quad \text{and}$$

$$\lambda_2 = \frac{-(1+q) - \sqrt{(1+q)^2 - 4q}}{2},$$

and

$$|\lambda_1| = \left| \frac{-(1+q) + \sqrt{(1+q)^2 - 4q}}{2} \right| = \left| \frac{-(1+q) + (q-1)}{2} \right| = 1.$$

CASE 2. Suppose that $p^2 - 4q = 0$ and $q = 1$. Then we have a repeated root:

$$\lambda_1 = \lambda_2 = \frac{-p}{2},$$

and

$$|\lambda_1| = |\lambda_2| = \left| \frac{-p}{2} \right| = \left| \frac{-\sqrt{4q}}{2} \right| = 1.$$

CASE 3. Suppose that $p^2 - 4q < 0$ and $q = 1$. Then we have two imaginary complex conjugate roots:

$$\lambda_1 = -\frac{p}{2} + \frac{\sqrt{4q - p^2}}{2}i \quad \text{and} \quad \lambda_2 = -\frac{p}{2} - \frac{\sqrt{4q - p^2}}{2}i,$$

and

$$|\lambda_1| = |\lambda_2| = \sqrt{\frac{p^2}{4} + \frac{4q - p^2}{4}} = \sqrt{q} = 1.$$

Hence the result follows. □

The following theorem gives the necessary and sufficient conditions for the **characteristic polynomial**

$$\lambda^2 + p\lambda + q = 0$$

to have a root with modulus greater than 1.

Theorem 21. *Consider the characteristic polynomial*

$$\lambda^2 + p\lambda + q = 0$$

with roots λ_1 and λ_2. Then either

$$|\lambda_1| > 1 \quad or \quad |\lambda_2| > 1$$

if and only if either

$$|p| > 1 + q \quad or \quad q > 1.$$

Proof. The proof will be left as an exercise at the end of the chapter. □

We will proceed with studying Nonhomogeneous Second Order Linear Difference Equations in the form:

$$x_{n+2} + px_{n+1} + qx_n = r, \quad n = 0, 1, \ldots,$$

where $x_0, x_1, p \in \Re$ and $q, r \neq 0$.

4.3. Nonhomogeneous Second Order Linear Difference Equations with a Constant Coefficient

These are examples of second order linear nonhomogeneous difference equations:

(i) $x_{n+2} = 4x_{n+1} - 3x_n + 1, \quad n = 0, 1, \ldots$.
(ii) $9x_{n+2} = x_n + 2, \quad n = 0, 1, \ldots$.

Our aim is to obtain an explicit solution of the second order linear nonhomogeneous Δ.E.:

$$x_{n+2} + px_{n+1} + qx_n = r, \quad n = 0, 1, \ldots, \tag{4.94}$$

where $x_0, x_1, p \in \Re$ and $q, r \neq 0$. From (4.58), (4.59) and (4.60), let

$$x_n^h, \quad n = 0, 1, \ldots$$

be the **homogeneous solution** of Eq. (4.94). It is also our goal to determine the **particular solution**

$$x_n^P, \quad n = 0, 1, \ldots$$

of Eq. (4.94). Let $S = 1 + p + q$. If $S \neq 0$, then Eq. (4.94) has one equilibrium point $\bar{x} = \frac{r}{1+p+q}$. If $S = 0$, then Eq. (4.94) has no equilibrium points and this leads the investigation into two cases:

CASE 1. Suppose that $S \neq 0$. Then $\bar{x} = \frac{r}{1+p+q}$ is the only equilibrium point of Eq. (4.94) and:

$$x_n^P = \bar{x} = \frac{r}{1+p+q}, \qquad n = 0, 1, \ldots, \tag{4.95}$$

and the general solution of Eq. (4.94) is:

$$x_n = x_n^h + x_n^P = x_n^h + \bar{x}, \qquad n = 0, 1, \ldots. \tag{4.96}$$

CASE 2. Suppose that $S = 0$. Then Eq. (4.94) has no equilibrium points and we set

$$x_n^P = An, \qquad n = 0, 1, \ldots. \tag{4.97}$$

To solve for A, we substitute (4.97) into Eq. (4.94) and we obtain:

$$
\begin{aligned}
& x_{n+2} + px_{n+1} + qx_n \\
&= A(n+2) + pA(n+1) + qAn \\
&= An + 2A + pAn + pA + qAn \\
&= An(1+p+q) + 2A + pA = 2A + pA = r.
\end{aligned}
$$

Thus:

$$A = \frac{r}{p+2},$$

and the general solution of Eq. (4.94) is:

$$x_n = x_n^h + x_n^P = x_n^h + An, \qquad n = 0, 1, \ldots. \tag{4.98}$$

The following examples will illustrate the implementation of the two cases above.

Example 7. Solve the following Δ.E.:

$$x_{n+2} - 7x_{n+1} + 12x_n = 12, \qquad n = 0, 1, \ldots, \tag{4.99}$$

and verify that the solution is correct.

Solution: First of all, $\bar{x} = \frac{12}{1-7+12} = 2$. Second of all, via (4.58), the homogeneous solution is:

$$x_n^h = C_1 3^n + C_2 4^n, \quad n = 0, 1, \ldots \quad (4.100)$$

Also, via (4.95):

$$x_n^P = \bar{x} = 2, \quad n = 0, 1, \ldots \quad (4.101)$$

Hence

$$x_n = x_n^h + x_n^P = C_1 3^n + C_2 4^n + 2, \quad n = 0, 1, \ldots \quad (4.102)$$

Then

$$x_{n+1} = x_{n+1}^h + x_{n+1}^P = C_1 3^{n+1} + C_2 4^{n+1} + 2, \quad n = 0, 1, \ldots, \quad (4.103)$$

and

$$x_{n+2} = x_{n+2}^h + x_{n+2}^P = C_1 3^{n+2} + C_2 4^{n+2} + 2, \quad n = 0, 1, \ldots \quad (4.104)$$

Now we substitute (4.102), (4.103) and (4.104) into Eq. (4.99) and we acquire:

$$x_{n+2} - 7x_{n+1} + 12x_n$$
$$= [9C_1 3^n + 16C_2 4^n + 2] - 7[3C_1 3^n + 4C_2 4^n + 2]$$
$$+ 12[C_1 3^n + C_2 4^n + 2]$$
$$= 9C_1 3^n + 16C_2 4^n + 2 - 21C_1 3^n - 28C_2 4^n - 14 + 12C_1 3^n$$
$$+ 12C_2 4^n + 24 = 12.$$

Example 8. Solve the following Δ.E.:

$$x_{n+2} - 4x_{n+1} + 3x_n = 4, \quad n = 0, 1, \ldots, \quad (4.105)$$

and verify that the solution is correct.

Solution: Observe that Eq. (4.105) has no equilibrium points. In addition, via (4.58), the homogeneous solution is

$$x_n^h = C_1 1^n + C_2 3^n = C_1 + C_2 3^n, \quad n = 0, 1, \ldots. \tag{4.106}$$

To determine the Particular Solution, via (4.97), we set

$$x_n^P = An, \quad n = 0, 1, \ldots. \tag{4.107}$$

By substituting (4.107) into Eq. (4.105), we get

$$
\begin{aligned}
x_{n+2} &- 4x_{n+1} + 3x_n \\
&= A(n+2) - 4A(n+1) + 3An \\
&= An + 2A - 4An - 4A + 3An \\
&= -2A = 4.
\end{aligned}
$$

Thus

$$A = -2.$$

Hence

$$x_n^P = An = -2n, \quad n = 0, 1, \ldots. \tag{4.108}$$

Therefore, the general solution of Eq. (4.105) is:

$$x_n = x_n^h + x_n^P = C_1 + C_2 3^n - 2n, \quad n = 0, 1, \ldots. \tag{4.109}$$

To check the general solution, it suffices to check the homogeneous and the particular solutions separately. Substituting (4.108) into Eq. (4.105) gives us:

$$
\begin{aligned}
x_{n+2} &- 4x_{n+1} + 3x_n \\
&= [-2(n+2)] - 4[-2(n+1)] + 3[-2n] \\
&= -2n - 4 + 8n + 8 - 6n = 4.
\end{aligned}
$$

Now substitute (4.106) into Eq. (4.105) and we obtain:

$$
\begin{aligned}
x_{n+2} &- 4x_{n+1} + 3x_n \\
&= [C_1 + 9C_2 3^n] - 4[C_1 + 3C_2 3^n] + 3[C_1 + C_2 3^n] \\
&= C_1 + 16C_2 4^n - 5C_1 - 20C_2 4^n + 4C_1 + 4C_2 4^n = 0.
\end{aligned}
$$

Example 9. Solve the Initial Value Problem:

$$\begin{cases} x_{n+2} - 5x_{n+1} + 4x_n = 6, & n = 0, 1, \ldots, \\ x_0 = 1, \\ x_1 = 5. \end{cases}$$

Solution: Via (4.58), the homogeneous solution of the given Δ.E. is

$$x_n^h = C_1 1^n + C_2 4^n = C_1 + C_2 4^n, \quad n = 0, 1, \ldots. \tag{4.110}$$

To solve for the Particular Solution, via (4.97) we set

$$x_n^P = An, \quad n = 0, 1, \ldots. \tag{4.111}$$

By substituting (4.111) into the given Δ.E. we obtain:

$$x_{n+2} - 5x_{n+1} + 4x_n$$
$$= A(n+2) - 5A(n+1) + 4An = -3A = 6.$$

Therefore $A = -2$ and

$$x_n^P = An = -2n, \quad n = 0, 1, \ldots. \tag{4.112}$$

The general solution to the given Δ.E. is

$$x_n = x_n^h + x_n^P = C_1 + C_2 4^n - 2n, \quad n = 0, 1, \ldots. \tag{4.113}$$

Now we will solve for C_1 and C_2, and via (4.113):

$$x_0 = C_1 + C_2 = 1,$$
$$x_1 = C_1 + 4C_2 - 2 = 5.$$

Thus:

$$C_2 = 2 \quad \text{and} \quad C_1 = -1.$$

Therefore via (4.113) the specific solution is

$$x_n = C_1 + C_2 4^n - 2n = -1 + 2(4^n) - 2n, \quad n = 0, 1, \ldots.$$

Now we will study the applications of nonhomogeneous second order difference equations in the National Income.

4.3.1. *The National Income*

The U.S. national income Y_n in a given discrete time period n in years can be described as:

$$Y_n = C_n + I_n + G_n, \tag{4.114}$$

where

  (i) C_n is the consumer expenditure for purchase of consumer goods,
  (ii) I_n is the induced private investment for purchasing equipment,
  (iii) G_n is the government expenditure.

Now we will define the following recursive relations based on the assumptions by economists such as Paul Samuelson [78].

(a) C_n is α proportional to the national income:

$$C_n = \alpha Y_{n-1},$$

    where α is the *marginal tendency to consume.*
(b) I_n is β proportional to the increase in consumption:

$$I_n = \beta \left[C_n - C_{n-1} \right],$$

    where β is the *relation.*
(c) G_n is assumed to be constant over the years and we let

$$G_n = 1.$$

Now by substituting C_n, I_n, and G_n into Eq. (4.114) we obtain:

$$Y_n = \alpha Y_{n-1} + \beta \left[\alpha Y_{n-1} - \alpha Y_{n-2} \right] + 1,$$

from which we produce the following second order linear nonhomogeneous A.E.:

$$Y_{n+2} - \alpha(1 + \beta)Y_{n+1} + \alpha\beta Y_n = 1, \quad n = 0, 1, \ldots, \tag{4.115}$$

whose characteristic roots are:

$$\lambda_1 = \frac{\alpha(1 + \beta) + \sqrt{[\alpha(1 + \beta)]^2 - 4\alpha\beta}}{2},$$

$$\lambda_2 = \frac{\alpha(1 + \beta) - \sqrt{[\alpha(1 + \beta)]^2 - 4\alpha\beta}}{2}.$$

First of all, $\bar{Y} = \frac{1}{1-\alpha}$ is the equilibrium point of Eq. (4.115) and every solution of Eq. (4.115) converges to $\bar{Y}$ if and only if:

$$\alpha < 1, \quad 1 + \alpha + 2\alpha\beta > 0 \quad \text{and} \quad \alpha\beta < 1.$$

Second of all, when $\alpha < \frac{4\beta}{(1+\beta)^2}$ we have two imaginary roots. In this case every non-trivial solution of Eq. (4.115) is oscillatory.

We will advance our studies of second order nonhomogeneous and non-autonomous difference equation in the form:

$$x_{n+2} + px_{n+1} + qx_n = a_n, \quad n = 0, 1, \ldots,$$

where $x_0, x_1, p \in \mathfrak{R}$, $q \neq 0$, and $\{a_n\}_{n=0}^{\infty}$ is a sequence of real numbers. In the next two sections we will consider two cases when:

(i) $\{a_n\}_{n=0}^{\infty} = r^n$, where $r \neq 0$ and $r \neq 1$.
(ii) $\{a_n\}_{n=0}^{\infty} = n^k$, for $k \in \mathbb{N}$.

4.4. Nonhomogeneous Second Order Linear Difference Equations with a Variable Geometric Coefficient

These are examples of second order linear nonhomogeneous and non-autonomous difference equations with a variable geometric coefficient:

(i) $x_{n+2} = 5x_{n+1} - 6x_n + 2^n, \quad n = 0, 1, \ldots.$
(ii) $x_{n+2} = 4x_n + \left(\frac{-3}{4}\right)^n, \quad n = 0, 1, \ldots.$

Our plan is to determine an explicit solution of the second order nonhomogeneous and non-autonomous linear Δ.E. in the form:

$$x_{n+2} + px_{n+1} + qx_n = r^n, \quad n = 0, 1, \ldots, \tag{4.116}$$

where $x_0, x_1, p \in \mathfrak{R}$, $q, r \neq 0$ and $r \neq 1$. Similar to the previous section, via (4.58), (4.59) and (4.60), we let

$$x_n^h, n = 0, 1, \ldots$$

be the **homogeneous solution** of Eq. (4.116). Also, recall that Eq. (4.57) resembles the characteristic polynomial of the homogeneous solution with two roots λ_1 and λ_2. Now it is our goal to determine the **Particular Solution**

$$x_n^P, \quad n = 0, 1, \ldots$$

of Eq. (4.116). The **Particular Solution** will depend on the relationship between r, λ_1 and λ_2 and will guide us to the following three cases:

CASE 1. Suppose that $r \neq \lambda_1$ and $r \neq \lambda_2$. Then:

$$x_n^P = A(r^n), \quad n = 0, 1, \ldots. \tag{4.117}$$

To solve for A we substitute Eq. (4.117) into Eq. (4.116).

CASE 2. Suppose that $r = \lambda_1$ and $r \neq \lambda_2$. Then:

$$x_n^P = An(r^n), \quad n = 0, 1, \ldots. \tag{4.118}$$

To solve for A we substitute Eq. (4.118) into Eq. (4.116).

CASE 3. Suppose that $r = \lambda_1 = \lambda_2$. Then:

$$x_n^P = An^2(r^n), \quad n = 0, 1, \ldots. \tag{4.119}$$

To solve for A we substitute Eq. (4.119) into Eq. (4.116).

The following examples will illustrate the applications of the three cases.

Example 10. Solve the Δ.E.:

$$x_{n+2} - 4x_{n+1} + 3x_n = 2^n, \quad n = 0, 1, \ldots, \tag{4.120}$$

and verify that the solution is correct.

Solution: Via (4.58), the Homogeneous Solution is

$$x_n^h = C_1 1^n + C_2 3^n = C_1 + C_2 3^n, \quad n = 0, 1, \ldots. \tag{4.121}$$

To determine the Particular Solution set:

$$x_n^P = A(2^n), \quad n = 0, 1, \ldots. \tag{4.122}$$

By substituting (4.122) into Eq. (4.120), it gives us:

$$x_{n+2} - 4x_{n+1} + 3x_n$$
$$= 4A(2^n) - 4[2A(2^n)] + 3A2^n = 2^n,$$

and

$$A = -1.$$

Thus:

$$x_n^P = A(2^n) = -2^n, \quad n = 0, 1, \ldots. \tag{4.123}$$

Hence the general solution to Eq. (4.120) is:

$$x_n = x_n^h + x_n^P = C_1 + C_2 3^n - 2^n, \quad n = 0, 1, \ldots. \tag{4.124}$$

To check the general solution, it suffices to check the homogeneous and the particular solutions separately. First substitute (4.123) into Eq. (4.120):

$$x_{n+2} - 4x_{n+1} + 3x_n$$
$$= -4 \cdot 2^n - 4[-2 \cdot 2^n] + 3[-2^n] = 2^n.$$

Now substitute (4.121) into Eq. (4.120):

$$x_{n+2} - 4x_{n+1} + 3x_n$$
$$= [C_1 + 9C_2 3^n] - 4[C_1 + 3C_2 3^n] + 3[C_1 + C_2 3^n]$$
$$= C_1 + 9C_2 3^n - 4C_1 - 12C_2 3^n + 3C_1 + 3C_2 3^n = 0.$$

Example 11. Solve the Δ.E.:

$$x_{n+2} - 7x_{n+1} + 12x_n = 3^n, \quad n = 0, 1, \ldots, \tag{4.125}$$

and verify that the solution is correct.

Solution: Via (4.58), the homogeneous solution is

$$x_n^h = C_1 3^n + C_2 4^n, \quad n = 0, 1, \ldots. \tag{4.126}$$

To determine the Particular Solution, set:

$$x_n^P = An(3^n), \quad n = 0, 1, \ldots. \tag{4.127}$$

First substitute (4.127) into Eq. (4.125) and we get:

$$x_{n+2} - 7x_{n+1} + 12x_n$$
$$= 9A(n+2)(3^n) - 7[3A(n+1)(3^n)] + 12An3^n = 3^n.$$

Hence

$$9An + 18A - 21An - 21A + 12An = 1,$$

and

$$A = -\frac{1}{3}.$$

Therefore:

$$x_n^P = An(3^n) = -\frac{n3^n}{3}, \quad n = 0, 1, \ldots. \tag{4.128}$$

The general solution of Eq. (4.125) is:

$$x_n = x_n^h + x_n^P = C_1 3^n + C_2 4^n - \frac{n3^n}{3}, \quad n = 0, 1, \ldots. \tag{4.129}$$

To check the general solution, we will check the homogeneous and the particular solutions separately. First substitute (4.128) into Eq. (4.125) and we obtain:

$$x_{n+2} - 7x_{n+1} + 12x_n$$
$$= \frac{-9(n+2)(3^n)}{3} - 7\left[\frac{-3(n+1)(3^n)}{3}\right] + 12\left[\frac{-n3^n}{3}\right] = 3^n$$
$$= -3(n+2)(3^n) + 7(n+1)(3^n) - 4n3^n = 3^n.$$

Now substitute (4.126) into Eq. (4.125) and we procure:

$$x_{n+2} - 7x_{n+1} + 12x_n$$
$$= [9C_1 3^n + 16C_2 4^n] - 7[3C_1 3^n + 4C_2 4^n] + 12[C_1 3^n + C_2 4^n] = 0.$$

Example 12. Solve the Δ.E.:

$$x_{n+2} - 4x_{n+1} + 4x_n = 2^n, \quad n = 0, 1, \ldots, \tag{4.130}$$

and verify that the solution is correct.

Solution: Via (4.59), the homogeneous solution is

$$x_n^h = C_1 2^n + C_2 n 2^n, \quad n = 0, 1, \ldots. \tag{4.131}$$

To determine the Particular Solution of Eq. (4.130), set

$$x_n^P = An^2(2^n), \quad n = 0, 1, \ldots. \tag{4.132}$$

By substituting (4.132) into Eq. (4.130) we obtain:

$$x_{n+2} - 4x_{n+1} + 4x_n$$
$$= 4A(n+2)^2(2^n) - 4[2A(n+1)^2(2^n)] + 4An^2(2^n) = 2^n.$$

Then set:

$$4A(n+2)^2 - 8A(n+1)^2 + 4An^2$$
$$= 4A\left[(n+2)^2 - 2(n+1)^2 + n^2\right] = 1,$$

and we get $A = \frac{1}{8}$. Therefore:

$$x_n^P = An^2(2^n) = \frac{n^2 2^n}{8}, \quad n = 0, 1, \dots. \tag{4.133}$$

Thus the general solution of Eq. (4.130) is:

$$x_n = x_n^h + x_n^P = C_1 2^n + C_2 n 2^n + \frac{n^2 2^n}{8}, \quad n = 0, 1, \dots. \tag{4.134}$$

To check the general solution, we check the homogeneous and the particular solutions separately. First substitute (4.133) into Eq. (4.130):

$$x_{n+2} - 4x_{n+1} + 4x_n = \frac{4(n+2)^2 2^n}{8} - 4\left[\frac{2(n+1)^2 2^n}{8}\right] + 4\left[\frac{n^2 2^n}{8}\right]$$

$$= \frac{2^n}{2}\left[(n+2)^2 - 2(n+1)^2 + n^2\right] = 2^n.$$

Now by substituting (4.131) into Eq. (4.130) we obtain

$$x_{n+2} - 4x_{n+1} + 4x_n$$
$$= [4C_1 2^n + 4C_2(n+2)2^n] - 4[2C_1 2^n + 2C_2(n+1)2^n] + 4[C_1 2^n + C_2 n 2^n]$$
$$= 0.$$

4.5. Nonhomogeneous Second Order Linear Difference with a Variable Coefficient n^k

These are examples of nonhomogeneous second order linear difference equations with a variable coefficient n^k:

(i) $x_{n+2} = 6x_{n+1} - 8x_n + n^3, \quad n = 0, 1, \dots.$
(ii) $x_{n+2} = x_n + n^2, \quad n = 0, 1, \dots.$

We will examine the second order linear nonhomogeneous Δ.E. in the form:

$$x_{n+2} + px_{n+1} + qx_n = n^k, \quad n = 0, 1, \ldots, \tag{4.135}$$

where $x_0, x_1, p \in \Re$, $q \neq 0$ and $k \in \mathbb{N}$. We will assume that $1 + p + q = 0$ and set:

$$x_n^P = A_{k+1}n^{k+1} + A_k n^k + \ldots + A_1 n, \quad n = 0, 1, \ldots. \tag{4.136}$$

To solve for the coefficients $A_{k+1}, A_k, \ldots, A_1$ we substitute Eq. (4.136) into Eq. (4.135). The following examples will illustrate solving Eq. (4.136) using Eq. (4.135).

Example 13. Solve the Δ.E.:

$$x_{n+2} - 4x_{n+1} + 3x_n = n, \quad n = 0, 1, \ldots, \tag{4.137}$$

and verify that the solution is correct.

Solution: Via (4.58), the homogeneous solution is

$$x_n^h = C_1 1^n + C_2(3)^n = C_1 + C_2(3)^n, \quad n = 0, 1, \ldots. \tag{4.138}$$

To determine the Particular Solution of Eq. (4.137) set:

$$x_n^P = A_2 n^2 + A_1 n, \quad n = 0, 1, \ldots. \tag{4.139}$$

Now substitute (4.139) into Eq. (4.137):

$$x_{n+2} - 4x_{n+1} + 3x_n$$
$$= \left[A_2(n+2)^2 + A_1(n+2)\right] - 4\left[A_2(n+1)^2 + A_1(n+1)\right]$$
$$+ 3\left[A_2 n^2 + A_1 n\right]$$
$$= n.$$

To solve for A_1 and A_2, we set $n = 0$ and $n = 1$ into above equation and we obtain:

$$A_1 = 0 \quad (\text{when } n = 0),$$
$$-4A_2 - 2A_1 = 1 \quad (\text{when } n = 1),$$

with two solutions $A_2 = -\frac{1}{4}$ and $A_1 = 0$. Therefore:

$$x_n^P = A_2 n^2 + A_1 n = -\frac{n^2}{4}, \quad n = 0, 1, \ldots. \tag{4.140}$$

The general solution of Eq. (4.137) is:

$$x_n = x_n^h + x_n^P = C_1 + C_2(3)^n - \frac{n^2}{4}, \quad n = 0, 1, \ldots. \tag{4.141}$$

To check the general solution, we check the homogeneous and the particular solutions separately. First, by substituting (4.140) into Eq. (4.137) we obtain:

$$x_{n+2} - 4x_{n+1} + 3x_n$$

$$= \left[-\frac{(n+2)^2}{4} \right] - 3 \left[-\frac{(n+1)^2}{4} \right] + 4 \left[-\frac{n^2}{4} \right]$$

$$= \frac{1}{4} \left[-(n+2)^2 + 3(n+1)^2 - 4n^2 \right] = n.$$

Now substitute (4.138) into Eq. (4.137) and we procure:

$$x_{n+2} - 4x_{n+1} + 3x_n$$
$$= [C_1 + 9C_2(3)^n] - 4[C_1 + 3C_2(3)^n] + 3[C_1 + 3C_2(3)^n] = 0.$$

We will advance with applications of second order non-autonomous difference equations in Signal Processing.

4.5.1. *Applications of non-autonomous second order linear difference equations in signal processing*

Our goal is to pursue the study of the LTI (Linear and Time Invariance) of digital signal processing as we commenced with Eqs. (2.23) and (2.24) in Chapter 2. Now we introduce the following input and output signals:

(i) x_n is the input signal.
(ii) y_n, y_{n+1} and y_{n+2} are the output signals.

Then we acquire the following **LTI Δ.E.**:

$$bx_n - [y_{n+2} + py_{n+1} + qy_n] = 0, \tag{4.142}$$

where b is the **feed-forward coefficient** and p, q are the **feedback coefficients** that characterize the filter. Eq. (4.142) is applied for computing an output sample at time n based on the current and previous samples in the time domain. We can also rewrite Eq. (4.142) as:

$$y_{n+2} + py_{n+1} + qy_n = bx_n. \tag{4.143}$$

Example 14. Solve the following **LTI Δ.E.:**

$$y_{n+2} = ay_n + bx_n. \tag{4.144}$$

Solution: By iterations and induction we get:

$$y_0,$$

$$y_1,$$

$$y_2 = ay_0 + bx_0,$$

$$y_3 = ay_1 + bx_1,$$

$$y_4 = ay_2 + bx_2 = a^2 y_0 + abx_0 + bx_2,$$

$$y_5 = ay_3 + bx_3 = a^2 y_1 + abx_1 + bx_3,$$

$$y_6 = ay_4 + bx_4 = a^3 y_0 + a^2 bx_0 + abx_2 + bx_4,$$

$$y_7 = ay_5 + bx_5 = a^3 y_1 + a^2 bx_1 + abx_3 + bx_5,$$

$$\vdots$$

Thus for all $n \in \mathbb{N}$:

$$\begin{cases} y_{2n} = a^n y_0 + \left[\sum_{i=0}^{n-1} a^{n-(i+1)} bx_{2i} \right], \\ y_{2n+1} = a^n y_1 + \left[\sum_{i=0}^{n-1} a^{n-(i+1)} bx_{2i+1} \right]. \end{cases}$$

The solution of Eq. (4.144) consists of two components:

(i) $a^n y_0$ and $a^n y_1$ are the **natural responses** that depend on the initial condition x_0.

(ii) $\sum_{i=0}^{n-1} a^{n-(i+1)} bx_{2i}$ and $\sum_{i=0}^{n-1} a^{n-(i+1)} bx_{2i+1}$ are the **forced responses** that depend on the input signal x_n.

We can also extend Eq. (4.142) to the following LTI Δ.E.:

$$\left[\sum_{i=0}^{N-1} b_i x_{n+i} \right] - [y_{n+2} + py_{n+1} + qy_n] = 0, \tag{4.145}$$

where b_i are the **feed-forward coefficients** and p, q are the **feedback coefficients**. More details on the LTI Δ.E. will be discussed in Chapters 4 and 6.

4.6. Linear Independence of Solutions

For instance, we can verify that $x_n = 2^n - 3^n$ and $x_n = 2^n + 3^n$ are both solutions of $x_{n+2} - 5x_{n+1} + 6x_n = 0$. However, how do we determine if the two solutions are linearly independent? In this section, it is our objective to study the linear independence of solutions; in particular, consider two solutions

$$x_n^1 \quad \text{and} \quad x_n^2, \quad n = 0, 1, \dots$$

of Eq. (4.56) and then we will introduce the following definition.

Definition 22. Let $\{x_n^1\}_{n=0}^\infty$ and $\{x_n^2\}_{n=0}^\infty$ be solutions of Eq. (4.56). The **Casarotian** of x_n^1 and x_n^2 denoted by $\{C(x_n^1, x_n^2; n)\}_{n=0}^\infty$ is described as:

$$C(x_n^1, x_n^2; n) = \begin{vmatrix} x_n^1 & x_n^2 \\ x_{n+1}^1 & x_{n+1}^2 \end{vmatrix} = x_n^1 x_{n+1}^2 - x_{n+1}^1 x_n^2, \quad n = 0, 1, \dots.$$

Theorem 22. *Let $\{x_n^1\}_{n=0}^\infty$ and $\{x_n^2\}_{n=0}^\infty$ be two solutions of Eq. (4.56). Then the following statements are true:*

(i) *The **Casarotian** $\{C(x_n^1, x_n^2; n)\}_{n=0}^\infty$ of x_n^1 and x_n^2 is either never 0, or else identically equal to 0 for all $n = 0, 1, \dots$.*

(ii) *$\{x_n^1\}_{n=0}^\infty$ and $\{x_n^2\}_{n=0}^\infty$ are linearly independent solutions of Eq. (4.56) if and only if $C(x_n^1, x_n^2; n) \neq 0$ for all $n = 0, 1, \dots$.*

The following examples will show the use of Theorem 22.

Example 15. Consider the Δ.E.:

$$x_{n+2} - 4x_{n+1} + 4x_n = 0, \quad n = 0, 1, \dots. \tag{4.146}$$

Determine if the following two solutions of Eq. (4.146) are linearly independent:

(i) $x_n^1 = 2^n + n2^n, \quad n = 0, 1, \dots.$
(ii) $x_n^2 = 2^{n+1} + n2^n, \quad n = 0, 1, \dots.$

Solution: The **Casarotian** $\{C(x_n^1, x_n^2; n)\}_{n=0}^{\infty}$ of x_n^1 and x_n^2 is:

$$
C(x_n^1, x_n^2; n) = \begin{vmatrix} 2^n + n2^n & 2^{n+1} + n2^n \\ 2^{n+1} + (n+1)2^{n+1} & 2^{n+2} + (n+1)2^{n+1} \end{vmatrix}
$$

$$
= 2^n(1+n)2^n(4+2n+2) - 2^n(2+2n+2)2^n(2+n)
$$

$$
= 4^n\left[(1+n)(6+2n) - (4+2n)(2+n)\right]
$$

$$
= 4^n\left[6 + 8n + 2n^2 - (8 + 8n + 2n^2)\right]
$$

$$
= -2\,(4)^n \neq 0, \quad n = 0, 1, \dots.
$$

Hence x_n^1 and x_n^2 are linearly independent solutions of Eq. (4.146).

Now consider k solutions ($k \geq 2$) of Eq. (4.56). Then we extend Definition (22) as follows:

Definition 23. For $i = 1, \dots, k$ and $k \geq 2$, let $\{x_n^i\}_{n=0}^{\infty}$ be solutions of Eq. (4.56). The **Casarotian** of x_n^i denoted by $\{C(x_n^i; n)\}_{n=0}^{\infty}$ is described as:

$$
C(x_n^i; n) = \begin{vmatrix} x_n^1 & x_n^2 & \cdots & x_n^k \\ x_{n+1}^1 & x_{n+1}^2 & \cdots & x_{n+1}^k \\ \vdots & \vdots & \vdots & \\ x_{n+k}^1 & x_{n+k}^2 & \cdots & x_{n+k}^k \end{vmatrix}.
$$

Then $\{x_n^i\}_{n=0}^{\infty}$ are linearly independent if $\{C(x_n^i; n)\}_{n=0}^{\infty} \neq 0$ for all $n \geq 0$.

Now we will proceed with analyzing periodic traits of non-autonomous second order linear difference equations.

4.7. Periodic Solutions of Second Order Homogeneous Linear Difference Equations

Our plan is to show that Eq. (4.56) exhibits periodic solutions with any period-p, ($p \geq 2$). First of all, recall that every non-trivial solution of

$$
x_{n+2} = x_n, \quad n = 0, 1, \dots
$$

is periodic with period-2. Second of all, recall that Eq. (4.56) has periodic solutions with period-p ($p \geq 3$) when the characteristic polynomial of

Eq. (4.56) has two imaginary complex conjugate roots:

$$\lambda_1 = A + Bi, \quad \lambda_2 = A - Bi,$$

and

$$\Lambda = |A + Bi| = |A - Bi| = 1.$$

In this case, solution of Eq. (4.56) is:

$$x_n = C_1 sin(n\theta) + C_2 cos(n\theta), \quad n = 0, 1, \ldots. \tag{4.147}$$

Eq. (4.147) is periodic with period-p ($p \geq 3$), where $\theta = \frac{2\pi}{p}$, and either $\theta = arg(\lambda_1)$ or $\theta = arg(\lambda_2)$. Furthermore, Eq. (4.147) is a solution of:

$$x_{n+2} = 2cos\left(\frac{2\pi}{p}\right) x_{n+1} - x_n, \tag{4.148}$$

where every non-trivial solution is periodic with period-p ($p \geq 3$). The following examples describe various periodic patterns.

Example 16. Determine the period-2 pattern of:

$$x_{n+2} = x_n, \quad n = 0, 1, \ldots. \tag{4.149}$$

Solution: By iteration we obtain:

$$x_0,$$

$$x_1,$$

$$x_2 = x_0,$$

$$x_3 = x_1,$$

and the following period-2 pattern:

$$x_0, \ x_1, \ x_0, \ x_1, \ldots.$$

Hence every non-trivial solution is a period-2 solution.

Example 17. Determine the period-3 pattern of:

$$x_{n+2} = -x_{n+1} - x_n, \quad n = 0, 1, \ldots . \tag{4.150}$$

Solution: We acquire:

$$x_0,$$
$$x_1,$$
$$x_2 = -x_1 - x_0,$$
$$x_3 = -[x_2] - x_1 = x_0 + x_1 - x_1 = x_0,$$
$$x_4 = -[x_3] - [x_2] = -x_0 + x_1 + x_0 = x_1,$$

and the following period-3 pattern:

$$x_0, \ x_1, \ -x_1 - x_0, \ x_0, \ x_1, \ -x_1 - x_0, \ldots .$$

The graph below depicts a period-3 cycle with $x_0 = 2$ and $x_1 = 3$:

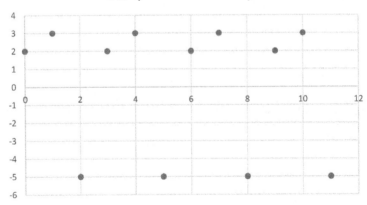

Example of a Period-3 Cycle

Observe that every non-trivial solution is a period-3 solution. The characteristic polynomial of Eq. (4.150) is:

$$\lambda^2 + \lambda + 1 = 0,$$

whose roots are $\lambda_1 = -\frac{1}{2} + \frac{\sqrt{3}}{2}i$ and $\lambda_2 = -\frac{1}{2} - \frac{\sqrt{3}}{2}i$. Notice that $\theta = arg(\lambda_1) = \frac{2\pi}{3}$ and the result follows.

Example 18. Determine the period-4 pattern of:

$$x_{n+2} = -x_n, \quad n = 0, 1, \ldots . \tag{4.151}$$

Solution: By iteration we procure the following period-4 pattern:

$$x_0, \ x_1, \ -x_0, \ -x_1, \ldots .$$

The graph below depicts a period-4 cycle with $x_0 = 4$ and $x_1 = 2$:

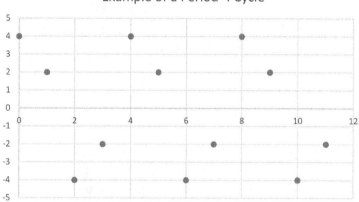

Example of a Period-4 Cycle

Every non-trivial solution portrays an alternating period-4 pattern. The characteristic polynomial of Eq. (4.151) is:

$$\lambda^2 + 1 = 0,$$

whose roots are $\lambda_1 = i$ and $\lambda_2 = -i$ and $\theta = arg(\lambda_1) = \frac{\pi}{2}$. The result follows.

Example 19. Determine the period-6 pattern of:

$$x_{n+2} = x_{n+1} - x_n, \quad n = 0, 1, \ldots . \tag{4.152}$$

Solution: We obtain the following period-6 pattern:

$$x_0, \ x_1, \ x_1 - x_0, \ -x_0, \ -x_1, \ x_0 - x_1, \ldots .$$

The graph below depicts a period-6 cycle with $x_0 = 1$ and $x_1 = 4$:

Example of a Period-6 Cycle

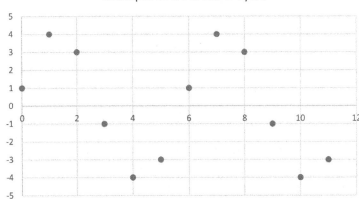

Every non-trivial solution evokes an alternating period-6 pattern. The characteristic polynomial of Eq. (4.152) is:

$$\lambda^2 - \lambda + 1 = 0,$$

whose roots are $\lambda_1 = \frac{1}{2} + \frac{\sqrt{3}}{2}i$ and $\lambda_2 = \frac{1}{2} - \frac{\sqrt{3}}{2}i$ and $\theta = arg(\lambda_1) = \frac{\pi}{3}$. The result follows.

From Examples 17–19, even ordered periodic cycles exhibit alternating patterns. By induction we can prove that every non-trivial solution of Eq. (4.148) is periodic with period-p $(p \geq 3)$. The characteristic polynomial of Eq. (4.148) is:

$$\lambda^2 - 2cos\left(\frac{2\pi}{p}\right)\lambda + 1 = 0,$$

with two imaginary roos λ_1 and λ_2 and either $\theta = \frac{2\pi}{p} = arg(\lambda_1)$ or $\theta = \frac{2\pi}{p} = arg(\lambda_2)$.

4.8. Periodic Traits of Non-autonomous Second Order Linear Difference Equations

Suppose $\{a_n\}_{n=0}^{\infty}$ is a period-k sequence $(k \geq 2)$. Our aim is to investigate the existence and patterns of the periodic cycles of non-autonomous second order linear Δ.E. in the form:

$$x_{n+2} = a_n x_n, \quad n = 0, 1, \ldots, \tag{4.153}$$

where $x_0 \neq 0$. The following theorem outlines the periodic traits of Eq. (4.153).

Theorem 23. *Suppose that* $\{a_n\}_{n=0}^{\infty}$ *is a period-k sequence* $(k \geq 2)$ *and* $x_0 \neq 0$. *Then the following statements are true:*

(i) *If* $\{a_n\}_{n=0}^{\infty}$ *is a period-2 sequence, then Eq.* (4.153) *has no period-2 cycles and for all* $n \in \mathbb{N}$:

$$\begin{cases} x_{2n} = a_0^n\, x_0, \\ x_{2n+1} = a_1^n\, x_1. \end{cases}$$

Every solution of Eq. (4.153) *is unbounded provided that* $a_0 > 1$ *or if* $a_1 > 1$. *Also, every solution of Eq.* (4.153) *converges to* 0 *provided that* $a_j < 1$ *for* $j = 0, 1$.

(ii) *If* $\{a_n\}_{n=0}^{\infty}$ *is a period-2 sequence, then every solution of Eq.* (4.153) *is periodic with period-4 if and only if* $a_0 = \pm 1$ *and* $a_1 = \pm 1$ *and* $a_0 \neq a_1$.

(iii) *If* $\{a_n\}_{n=0}^{\infty}$ *is a period-2k sequence* $(k \geq 2)$, *then every solution of Eq.* (4.153) *is periodic with period-2k if and only if:*

$$\prod_{i=0}^{k-1} a_{2i} = 1 \quad and \quad \prod_{i=0}^{k-1} a_{2i+1} = 1.$$

(iv) *If* $\{a_n\}_{n=0}^{\infty}$ *is a period-$(2k+1)$ sequence* $(k \in \mathbb{N})$ *then every solution of Eq.* (4.153) *is periodic with period-$2(2k+1)$ if and only if:*

$$\prod_{i=0}^{2k} a_i = 1.$$

Theorem 23 is proved by induction and will be left as an exercise at the end of the chapter. Our next objective is to determine the necessary and sufficient conditions for the existence and uniqueness of periodic cycles of:

$$x_{n+2} = \left[2\cos\left(\frac{2\pi}{p}\right) x_{n+1} - x_n \right] + a_n, \quad n = 0, 1, \ldots. \tag{4.154}$$

Recall that every non-trivial solution of Eq. (4.148) is periodic with period-p. The first three examples will focus on periodicity of:

$$x_{n+2} = x_n + a_n, \quad n = 0, 1, \ldots. \tag{4.155}$$

Recall that every non-trivial solution of Eq. (4.149) is periodic with period-2. The following three examples will assume that $\{a_n\}_{n=0}^{\infty}$ is a period-2k sequence $(k \in \mathbb{N})$ and will examine the periodic traits of Eq. (4.155).

Example 20. Suppose that $\{a_n\}_{n=0}^{\infty}$ is a period-2 sequence. Show that:

$$x_{n+2} = x_n + a_n, \quad n = 0, 1, \ldots$$

has no period-2 cycles and explain why.

Solution: Notice:

$$x_0,$$
$$x_1,$$
$$x_2 = x_0 + a_0,$$
$$x_3 = x_1 + a_1,$$
$$x_4 = [x_2] + a_0 = x_0 + a_0 + a_0 = x_0 + 2a_0,$$
$$x_5 = [x_3] + a_1 = x_1 + a_1 + a_1 = x_1 + 2a_1.$$

Hence the existence of a period-2 cycle is possible only when $a_0 = 0$ and $a_1 = 0$, which is clearly a contradiction as we assumed that $\{a_n\}_{n=0}^{\infty}$ is a period-2 sequence. Every solution of Eq. (4.149) is periodic with period-2. However, it is impossible to obtain a period-2 cycle as a_0 and a_1 do not cancel. Furthermore, for all $n \in \mathbb{N}$:

$$\begin{cases} x_{2n} = x_0 + na_0, \\ x_{2n+1} = x_1 + na_1. \end{cases}$$

Then every solution of Eq. (4.155) is unbounded.

Example 21. Suppose that $\{a_n\}_{n=0}^{\infty}$ is a period-4 sequence. Determine the necessary and sufficient conditions for existence of period-4 cycles of:

$$x_{n+2} = x_n + a_n, \quad n = 0, 1, \ldots.$$

Solution: Observe:

$$x_0,$$
$$x_1,$$
$$x_2 = x_0 + a_0,$$
$$x_3 = x_1 + a_1,$$
$$x_4 = [x_2] + a_2 = x_0 + a_0 + a_2 = x_0,$$
$$x_5 = [x_3] + a_3 = x_1 + a_1 + a_3 = x_1.$$

Hence every solution is periodic with period-4 if and only if:

$$a_0 + a_2 = 0 \quad \text{and} \quad a_1 + a_3 = 0.$$

Every solution of Eq. (4.149) is periodic with period-2. Since $\{a_n\}_{n=0}^{\infty}$ is a period-4 sequence, we cannot acquire period-2 cycles.

Example 22. Suppose that $\{a_n\}_{n=0}^{\infty}$ is a period-6 sequence. Determine the necessary and sufficient conditions for the existence of period-6 solutions of:

$$x_{n+2} = x_n + a_n, \quad n = 0, 1, \ldots.$$

Solution: Similar to the previous example, we show that every solution is periodic with period-6 if and only if:

$$a_0 + a_2 + a_4 = 0 \quad \text{and} \quad a_1 + a_3 + a_5 = 0.$$

Since every solution of Eq. (4.149) is periodic with period-2 and as $\{a_n\}_{n=0}^{\infty}$ is a period-6 sequence, we cannot exhibit period-2 cycles but exhibit period-6 cycles instead.

From Examples 20–22 we conclude that Eq. (4.155) has period-2k cycles $(k \geq 2)$ and the following theorem outlines the result.

Theorem 24. *Suppose that $\{a_n\}_{n=0}^{\infty}$ is a period-2k sequence $(k \geq 2)$. Then every solution of*

$$x_{n+2} = x_n + a_n, \quad n = 0, 1, \ldots$$

is periodic with period-2k $(k \geq 2)$ if and only if:

$$\sum_{i=0}^{k-1} a_{2i} = 0 \quad \text{and} \quad \sum_{i=0}^{k-1} a_{2i+1} = 0.$$

Proof. Similar to Examples 20–22, we get:

$$x_0,$$
$$x_1,$$
$$x_2 = x_0 + a_0,$$
$$x_3 = x_1 + a_1,$$
$$x_4 = x_2 + a_2 = x_0 + [a_0 + a_2],$$
$$x_5 = x_3 + a_3 = x_1 + [a_1 + a_3],$$
$$x_6 = x_4 + a_4 = x_0 + [a_0 + a_2 + a_4],$$
$$x_7 = x_5 + a_5 = x_1 + [a_1 + a_3 + a_5],$$

$$x_8 = x_6 + a_6 = x_0 + [a_0 + a_2 + a_4 + a_6],$$

$$x_9 = x_7 + a_7 = x_1 + [a_1 + a_3 + a_5 + a_7],$$

$$\vdots$$

Then:

$$
\begin{cases}
x_{2k} = x_0 + \displaystyle\sum_{i=0}^{k-1} a_{2i}, \\[2mm]
x_{2k+1} = x_1 + \displaystyle\sum_{i=0}^{k-1} a_{2i+1}.
\end{cases}
$$

Thus the result follows. $\qquad\qquad\qquad\qquad\qquad\qquad\qquad\qquad$ $\square$

The case when $\{a_n\}_{n=0}^{\infty}$ is periodic with an odd period-$(2k+1)$ $(k \in \mathbb{N})$ will be left as an exercise at the end of the chapter to investigate by addressing the following two questions: Do periodic cycles exist? What is the period (even order or odd order)? Now we will shift our focus on the periodic traits of:

$$x_{n+2} = -[x_{n+1} - x_n] + a_n, \quad n = 0, 1, \ldots . \tag{4.156}$$

Recall that every non-trivial solution of Eq. (4.150) is periodic with period-3. The next two examples will assume that $\{a_n\}_{n=0}^{\infty}$ is a period-3k sequence $(k \in \mathbb{N})$ and will examine the periodic properties of Eq. (4.156).

Example 23. Suppose that $\{a_n\}_{n=0}^{\infty}$ is a period-3 sequence. Show that:

$$x_{n+2} = -[x_{n+1} + x_n] + a_n, \quad n = 0, 1, \ldots$$

has no period-3 solutions and explain why.

Solution: Observe:

$$x_0,$$

$$x_1,$$

$$x_2 = -x_1 - x_0 + a_0,$$

$$x_3 = -[x_2] - x_1 + a_1 = x_0 - a_0 + a_1 = x_0,$$

$$x_4 = -[x_3] - [x_2] + a_2 = x_1 - a_1 + a_2 = x_1.$$

A period-3 cycle is possible only when

$$a_0 = a_1 = a_2,$$

which is clearly a contradiction as we assumed that $\{a_n\}_{n=0}^{\infty}$ is a period-3 sequence. On one hand, every solution of Eq. (4.150) is period with period-3. On the other hand, it is impossible to obtain a period-3 cycle as it contradicts that $\{a_n\}_{n=0}^{\infty}$ is a period-3 sequence. This similar phenomenon occurred in Example 20. Furthermore, for all $n \in \mathbb{N}$ and for all $j = 0, 1, 2$:

$$x_{3n+j} = x_j + na_j.$$

Thus every solution of Eq. (4.156) is unbounded.

Example 24. Suppose that $\{a_n\}_{n=0}^{\infty}$ is a period-6 sequence. Determine the necessary and sufficient conditions for the existence of period-6 solutions of:

$$x_{n+2} = -[x_{n+1} + x_n] + a_n, \quad n = 0, 1, \ldots.$$

Solution: By iteration we get:

$$x_0,$$
$$x_1,$$
$$x_2 = -x_1 - x_0 + a_0,$$
$$x_3 = -[x_2] - x_1 + a_1 = x_0 - a_0 + a_1,$$
$$x_4 = -[x_3] - [x_2] + a_2 = x_1 - a_1 + a_2,$$
$$x_5 = -[x_4] - [x_3] + a_3 = -x_0 - x_1 + a_0 - a_2 + a_3,$$
$$x_6 = -[x_5] - [x_4] + a_4 = x_0 - a_0 - a_3 + a_1 + a_4 = x_0,$$
$$x_7 = -[x_6] - [x_5] + a_5 = x_1 - a_0 - a_2 - a_3 + a_5 = x_1.$$

Period-6 cycle is possible only when:

$$a_0 + a_3 = a_1 + a_4 = a_2 + a_5.$$

Every non-trivial solution of Eq. (4.150) is periodic with period-3. As $\{a_n\}_{n=0}^{\infty}$ is a period-6 sequence, we cannot acquire a period-3 cycle.

From Example 24, the following theorem outlines the result when $\{a_n\}_{n=0}^{\infty}$ is a period-3k sequence $(k \geq 2)$.

Theorem 25. *Suppose that* $\{a_n\}_{n=0}^{\infty}$ *is a period-3k sequence* $(k \geq 2)$. *Then every solution of*

$$x_{n+2} = -[x_{n+1} + x_n] + a_n, \quad n = 0, 1, \ldots$$

is periodic with period-3k $(k \geq 2)$ *if and only if:*

$$\sum_{i=1}^{k} a_{3i-3} = \sum_{i=1}^{k} a_{3i-2} = \sum_{i=1}^{k} a_{3i-1}.$$

Theorem 25 is proved by induction and will be left as an exercise at the end of the chapter. The next pertinent question to address: will periodic solutions exist if $\{a_n\}_{n=0}^{\infty}$ is a period-p sequence where p is not a multiple of 3? Several computer observations will be required to answer this question. The next sequential examples will focus on the periodic nature of solutions of:

$$x_{n+2} = -[x_n] + a_n, \quad n = 0, 1, \ldots. \tag{4.157}$$

Recall that every non-trivial solution of Eq. (4.151) is periodic with period-4.

Example 25. Suppose that $\{a_n\}_{n=0}^{\infty}$ is a period-2 sequence. Show that every solution of

$$x_{n+2} = -[x_n] + a_n, \quad n = 0, 1, \ldots$$

is periodic with period-4.

Solution: Observe that

$$x_0,$$
$$x_1,$$
$$x_2 = -x_0 + a_0,$$
$$x_3 = -x_1 + a_1,$$
$$x_4 = -[x_2] + a_0 = x_0 - a_0 + a_0 = x_0,$$
$$x_5 = -[x_3] + a_1 = x_1 - a_1 + a_1 = x_1$$

describe the following period-4 pattern:

$$x_0, \ x_1, \ -x_0 + a_0, \ -x_1 + a_1, \ldots.$$

Every non-trivial solution of Eq. (4.151) is periodic with period-4. In addition, we see that every solution of Eq. (4.157) is also periodic with period-4. On the other hand we see that the period of the sequence $\{a_n\}_{n=0}^{\infty}$

is shorter than the period of Eq. (4.151). The immediate question to address: is it possible to obtain a period-2 solution? The next example will give the answer to this question.

Example 26. Suppose that $\{a_n\}_{n=0}^{\infty}$ is a period-2 sequence. Determine the unique period-2 solution of:

$$x_{n+2} = -[x_n] + a_n, \quad n = 0, 1, \ldots.$$

Solution: Set $x_2 = x_0$ and $x_3 = x_1$, and:

$$x_0,$$
$$x_1,$$
$$x_2 = -x_0 + a_0 = x_0,$$
$$x_3 = -x_1 + a_1 = x_1.$$

Solving for x_0 and x_1 gives us the unique period-2 pattern:

$$\frac{a_0}{2}, \frac{a_1}{2}, \ldots.$$

Example 27. Suppose that $\{a_n\}_{n=0}^{\infty}$ is a period-4 sequence. Show that

$$x_{n+2} = -[x_n] + a_n, \quad n = 0, 1, \ldots$$

has no period-4 solutions and explain why.

Solution: Notice:

$$x_0,$$
$$x_1,$$
$$x_2 = -x_0 + a_0,$$
$$x_3 = -x_1 + a_1,$$
$$x_4 = -x_2 + a_2 = x_0 - a_0 + a_2 = x_0,$$
$$x_5 = -x_3 + a_3 = x_0 - a_1 + a_3 = x_1.$$

Period-4 cycles are possible only when $a_0 = a_2$ and $a_1 = a_3$, which is clearly a contradiction as we assumed that $\{a_n\}_{n=0}^{\infty}$ is a period-4 sequence. Every solution of Eq. (4.151) is periodic with period-4. On the other hand, period-4 cycles are impossible as $a_0 = a_2$ and $a_1 = a_3$ contradict that $\{a_n\}_{n=0}^{\infty}$ is a period-4 sequence. Similar phenomenon happened in Examples 20 and 23. Furthermore, for all $n \in \mathbb{N}$ and for all $j = 0, 1, 2, 3$:

$$x_{4n+j} = x_j + n a_j.$$

Hence every solution of Eq. (4.157) is unbounded.

Example 28. Suppose that $\{a_n\}_{n=0}^{\infty}$ is a period-8 sequence. Determine the necessary and sufficient conditions for the existence of period-8 solutions of:

$$x_{n+2} = -[x_n] + a_n, \quad n = 0, 1, \ldots.$$

Solution: Similar to the previous examples, every solution is periodic with period-8 if and only if:

$$a_0 + a_4 = a_2 + a_6 \quad \text{and} \quad a_1 + a_5 = a_1 + a_7.$$

Every solution of Eq. (4.151) is periodic with period-4 and as $\{a_n\}_{n=0}^{\infty}$ is a period-8 sequence, then period-4 cycles are not possible.

From Example 28, the following theorem describes the result when $\{a_n\}_{n=0}^{\infty}$ is a period-4k sequence $(k \geq 2)$.

Theorem 26. *Suppose that $\{a_n\}_{n=0}^{\infty}$ is a period-4k sequence $(k \geq 2)$. Then every solution of*

$$x_{n+2} = -[x_n] + a_n, \quad n = 0, 1, \ldots$$

is periodic with period-4k $(k \geq 2)$ if and only if:

$$\sum_{i=1}^{k} a_{4i-4} = \sum_{i=1}^{k} a_{4i-2} \quad \text{and} \quad \sum_{i=1}^{k} a_{4i-3} = \sum_{i=1}^{k} a_{4i-1}.$$

The proof of Theorem 26 will be left as an exercise. Can periodic solutions exist when $\{a_n\}_{n=0}^{\infty}$ is a period-k sequence where k is not a multiple of 4? The next four examples will focus on the periodic nature of:

$$x_{n+2} = [x_{n+1} - x_n] + a_n, \quad n = 0, 1, \ldots. \tag{4.158}$$

Recall that every non-trivial solution of Eq. (4.152) is periodic with period-6.

Example 29. Suppose that $\{a_n\}_{n=0}^{\infty}$ is a period-3 sequence. Show that every solution of

$$x_{n+2} = [x_{n+1} - x_n] + a_n, \quad n = 0, 1, \ldots$$

is periodic with period-6.

Solution: Similar to Example 25, we acquire:

$$x_0,$$
$$x_1,$$
$$x_2 = x_1 - x_0 + a_0,$$
$$x_3 = x_2 - x_1 + a_1 = -x_0 + a_0 + a_1,$$
$$x_4 = x_3 - x_2 + a_2 = -x_1 + a_1 + a_2,$$
$$x_5 = x_4 - x_3 + a_0 = x_0 - x_1 + a_2,$$
$$x_6 = x_5 - x_4 + a_1 = x_0,$$
$$x_7 = x_6 - x_5 + a_2 = x_1.$$

The result follows.

Can Eq. (4.158) have period-3 cycles when $\{a_n\}_{n=0}^{\infty}$ is a period-3 sequence? The next example will remit the answer.

Example 30. Suppose that $\{a_n\}_{n=0}^{\infty}$ is a period-3 sequence. Determine the unique period-3 solution of:

$$x_{n+2} = -[x_n] + a_n, \quad n = 0, 1, \ldots.$$

Solution: Setting $x_3 = x_0$ and $x_4 = x_1$ gives us:

$$x_0,$$
$$x_1,$$
$$x_2 = x_1 - x_0 + a_0,$$
$$x_3 = x_2 - x_1 + a_1 = -x_0 + a_0 + a_1 = x_0,$$
$$x_4 = x_3 - x_2 + a_2 = -x_1 + a_1 + a_2 = x_1.$$

By solving for x_0 and x_1, we procure the following unique period-3 pattern:

$$\frac{a_0 + a_1}{2}, \frac{a_1 + a_2}{2}, \frac{a_2 + a_0}{2} \ldots.$$

Example 31. Suppose that $\{a_n\}_{n=0}^{\infty}$ is a period-6 sequence. Show that

$$x_{n+2} = [x_{n+1} - x_n] + a_n, \quad n = 0, 1, \ldots$$

has no period-6 solutions and explain why.

Solution: Similar to Examples 20, 23 and 27, period-6 cycles are possible only when $a_0 = a_3$, $a_1 = a_4$ and $a_2 = a_5$, which is clearly a contradiction as we assumed that $\{a_n\}_{n=0}^{\infty}$ is a period-6 sequence. Furthermore, for all $n \in \mathbb{N}$ and for all $j = 0, 1, 2, 3, 4, 5$:

$$x_{6n+j} = x_j + na_j.$$

Hence every solution of Eq. (4.158) is unbounded.

Example 32. Suppose that $\{a_n\}_{n=0}^{\infty}$ is a period-12 sequence. Determine the necessary and sufficient conditions for the existence of period-12 solutions of:

$$x_{n+2} = [x_{n+1} - x_n] + a_n, \quad n = 0, 1, \ldots.$$

Solution: Similar to previous examples, we show that every solution is periodic with period-12 if and only if:

$$a_0 + a_6 = a_2 + a_8 = a_4 + a_{10} \quad \text{and} \quad a_1 + a_7 = a_3 + a_9 = a_5 + a_{11}.$$

From Example 32, the following theorem extends the result when $\{a_n\}_{n=0}^{\infty}$ is a period-6k sequence $(k \geq 2)$.

Theorem 27. *Suppose that $\{a_n\}_{n=0}^{\infty}$ is a period-6k sequence $(k \geq 2)$. Then every solution of*

$$x_{n+2} = [x_{n+1} - x_n] + a_n, \quad n = 0, 1, \ldots$$

is periodic with period-6k $(k \geq 2)$ if and only if

$$\sum_{i=1}^{k} a_{6i-6} = \sum_{i=1}^{k} a_{6i-4} = \sum_{i=1}^{k} a_{6i-2} \quad \text{and}$$

$$\sum_{i=1}^{k} a_{6i-5} = \sum_{i=1}^{k} a_{6i-3} = \sum_{i=1}^{k} a_{6i-1}.$$

The proof of Theorem 27 will be left as an exercise to prove at the end of the chapter. From Example 23, 27 and 31, the following theorem generalizes the result when $\{a_n\}_{n=0}^{\infty}$ is a period-k sequence $(k \geq 3)$.

Theorem 28. *Suppose that $\{a_n\}_{n=0}^{\infty}$ is a period-k sequence ($k \geq 3$). Then*

$$x_{n+2} = \left[2\cos\left(\frac{2\pi}{k}\right)x_{n+1} - x_n\right] + a_n, \quad n = 0, 1, \ldots$$

has no periodic solutions with period-k.

Proving Theorem 28 will require two cases: when k is even and when k is odd. Furthermore, from Examples 25 and 31, we will pose the following conjecture that can be verified by computer observations and analysis.

Conjecture 2. *Suppose that $\{a_n\}_{n=0}^{\infty}$ is a period-k sequence ($k \geq 3$). Then every solution of*

$$x_{n+2} = \left[2\cos\left(\frac{2\pi}{k}\right)x_{n+1} - x_n\right] + a_n, \quad n = 0, 1, \ldots$$

is periodic with period-k if $p < k$, and $k = Np$ for some $N \geq 2$.

Furthermore, from Examples 26 and 30, we will pose the following conjecture:

Conjecture 3. *Suppose that $\{a_n\}_{n=0}^{\infty}$ is a period-k sequence ($k \geq 4$). Then*

$$x_{n+2} = \left[2\cos\left(\frac{2\pi}{p}\right)x_{n+1} - x_n\right] + a_n, \quad n = 0, 1, \ldots$$

either

(1) *has a unique periodic cycle with period-k, or*
(2) *every solution is periodic with period-p,*

where $k < p$, and $p = Nk$ for some $N \geq 2$.

Now we will suggest the following **Open Problem** that addresses the existence of specific periodic cycles.

Open Problem 4. Suppose that $\{a_n\}_{n=0}^{\infty}$ is a period-k sequence ($k \geq 3$). Does Eq. (4.154) exhibit period-p solutions when p is not a multiple of k? For example, will periodic solutions exist when $p = 3$ and $k = 4$?

Further studies on periodicity can be found in [29, 30, 31 and 35]. Moreover, applications of these periodic structures can be found in **Resonance** and in **Signal Processing in Sigma–Delta Domain** in [25] and [67].

4.9. Third and Higher Order Linear Difference Equations

Here are two examples of third and higher order homogeneous linear difference equations:

(i) (Third Order) $x_{n+3} - x_{n+2} - 4x_{n+1} + 4x_n = 0, \quad n = 0, 1, \ldots$.
(ii) (Fourth Order) $x_{n+4} - 5x_{n+2} + 4x_n = 0, \quad n = 0, 1, \ldots$.

From the two examples above, we can inquire a homogeneous linear Δ.E. of order $m \geq 3$ in the form:

$$x_{n+m} + \sum_{i=1}^{m} a_i x_{n+i-1} = 0, \quad n = 0, 1, \ldots, \tag{4.159}$$

where $a_1, a_2, a_3, \ldots, a_m \in \Re$. The periodic character of solutions of Eq. (4.159) has been studied by [29, 30, 31 and 35]. The asymptotic stability has been addressed of higher order linear difference equations and has been studied in [27, 53].

More details on the periodic traits of solutions, asymptotic stability of solutions of Eq. (4.159) and new conjectures will be discussed in Chapter 6 to answer these questions. Moreover, we will study applications of higher order linear difference equations and systems of linear difference equations in Signal Processing and in Vibrations in Chapter 6.

4.10. Chapter 4 Exercises

In problems 1–10, show that the given solution **satisfies** the given Δ.E.

1. $x_n = (3)^n + (-3)^n$ is a solution of $x_{n+2} - 9x_n = 0$.

2. $x_n = 2^{n+1} - 5^{n+2}$ is a solution of $x_{n+2} - 7x_{n+1} + 10x_n = 0$.

3. $x_n = 7^n - (-3)^n$ is a solution of $x_{n+2} - 4x_{n+1} - 21x_n = 0$.

4. $x_n = n3^{n+1}$ is a solution of $x_{n+2} - 6x_{n+1} + 9x_n = 0$.

5. $x_n = 2^n + 3^n + 2$ is a solution of $x_{n+2} - 5x_{n+1} + 6x_n = 4$.

6. $x_n = 2^n + 4^n + 3$ is a solution of $x_{n+2} - 6x_{n+1} + 8x_n = 9$.

7. $x_n = 5(4)^n - 2 - 3n$ is a solution of $x_{n+2} - 5x_{n+1} + 4x_n = 9$.

8. $x_n = 2 + 2^{n+1} - n2^{n-1}$ is a solution of $x_{n+2} - 3x_{n+1} + 2x_n = -2^n$.

9. $x_n = 3^{n+1} + n3^n + \frac{n^2 3^{n-1}}{2}$ is a solution of $x_{n+2} - 6x_{n+1} + 9x_n = 3^n$.

10. $x_n = 1 + 2^{n+1} + (-2)^n$ is a solution of $x_{n+3} - x_{n+2} - 4x_{n+1} + 4x_n = 0$.

In problems 11–22, determine the **general solution** to each Δ.E.

11. $x_{n+2} + x_{n+1} - 20x_n = 0$, $\quad n = 0, 1, \ldots$.

12. $x_{n+2} - 5x_{n+1} - 6x_n = 0$, $\quad n = 0, 1, \ldots$.

13. $x_{n+2} - 10x_{n+1} + 21x_n = 0$, $\quad n = 0, 1, \ldots$.

14. $x_{n+2} - 8x_{n+1} - 48x_n = 0$, $\quad n = 0, 1, \ldots$.

15. $x_{n+2} - 12x_{n+1} + 36x_n = 0$, $\quad n = 0, 1, \ldots$.

16. $x_{n+2} - 14x_{n+1} + 49x_n = 0$, $\quad n = 0, 1, \ldots$.

17. $4x_{n+2} + x_n = 0$, $\quad n = 0, 1, \ldots$.

18. $x_{n+2} - x_{n+1} + x_n = 0$, $\quad n = 0, 1, \ldots$.

19. $x_{n+2} - \sqrt{2}x_{n+1} + x_n = 0$, $\quad n = 0, 1, \ldots$.

20. $x_{n+2} - \sqrt{3}x_{n+1} + x_n = 0$, $\quad n = 0, 1, \ldots$.

21. $x_{n+2} - 2x_{n+1} + 4x_n = 0$, $\quad n = 0, 1, \ldots$.

22. $x_{n+2} + 2x_{n+1} + 2x_n = 0$, $\quad n = 0, 1, \ldots$.

In problems 23–34, determine the **homogeneous solution** and the **particular solution** to each Δ.E.

23. $x_{n+2} - 7x_{n+1} + 10x_n = 16$, $\quad n = 0, 1, \ldots$.

24. $x_{n+2} - 3x_{n+1} - 4x_n = 18$, $\quad n = 0, 1, \ldots$.

25. $x_{n+2} - 9x_{n+1} + 18x_n = 15$, $\quad n = 0, 1, \ldots$.

26. $x_{n+2} - 3x_{n+1} - 4x_n = 9$, $\quad n = 0, 1, \ldots$.

27. $x_{n+2} - 6x_{n+1} + 5x_n = 2$, $\quad n = 0, 1, \ldots$.

28. $x_{n+2} + 5x_{n+1} - 6x_n = 4$, $\quad n = 0, 1, \ldots$.

29. $x_{n+2} - 5x_{n+1} + 6x_n = 4^n$, $\quad n = 0, 1, \ldots$.

30. $x_{n+2} - 7x_{n+1} + 12x_n = 2^n$, $\quad n = 0, 1, \ldots$.

31. $x_{n+2} - 3x_{n+1} + 2x_n = 2^n$, $\quad n = 0, 1, \ldots$.

32. $x_{n+2} - 7x_{n+1} + 12x_n = 4^n, \quad n = 0, 1, \ldots.$

33. $x_{n+2} - 8x_{n+1} + 16x_n = 4^n, \quad n = 0, 1, \ldots.$

34. $x_{n+2} - 6x_{n+1} + 8x_n = 2^n + 4^n, \quad n = 0, 1, \ldots.$

In problems 35–40, solve the following **Initial Value Problem**.

35. $\begin{cases} x_{n+2} - 3x_{n+1} + 2x_n = 0, \quad n = 0, 1, \ldots. \\ \qquad\qquad x_0 = 3, \\ \qquad\qquad x_1 = 4. \end{cases}$

36. $\begin{cases} x_{n+2} - 5x_{n+1} + 6x_n = 0, \quad n = 0, 1, \ldots. \\ \qquad\qquad x_0 = 0, \\ \qquad\qquad x_1 = 1. \end{cases}$

37. $\begin{cases} x_{n+2} - x_{n+1} - 12x_n = 0, \quad n = 0, 1, \ldots. \\ \qquad\qquad x_0 = 1, \\ \qquad\qquad x_1 = -10. \end{cases}$

38. $\begin{cases} x_{n+2} - 6x_{n+1} + 8x_n = 6, \quad n = 0, 1, \ldots. \\ \qquad\qquad x_0 = 4, \\ \qquad\qquad x_1 = 8. \end{cases}$

39. $\begin{cases} x_{n+2} - 6x_{n+1} + 5x_n = 4, \quad n = 0, 1, \ldots. \\ \qquad\qquad x_0 = 0, \\ \qquad\qquad x_1 = 7. \end{cases}$

40. $\begin{cases} x_{n+2} - 4x_{n+1} + 3x_n = 3^{n+1}, \quad n = 0, 1, \ldots. \\ \qquad\qquad x_0 = \dfrac{1}{2}, \\ \qquad\qquad x_1 = 3. \end{cases}$

In problems 41–44, show that every non-trivial solution is periodic and determine the period.

41. $x_{n+2} = x_{n+1} - x_n, \quad n = 0, 1, \ldots.$

42. $x_{n+2} = \sqrt{2}x_{n+1} - x_n, \quad n = 0, 1, \ldots.$

43. $x_{n+2} = \sqrt{3}x_{n+1} - x_n, \quad n = 0, 1, \ldots.$

44. From Exercises 41–43, generalize by induction that every non-trivial solution of the Δ.E. is periodic with period-k $(k \geq 3)$:

$$x_{n+2} = 2\cos\left(\frac{2\pi}{k}\right) x_{n+1} - x_n, \quad n = 0, 1, \ldots.$$

In problems 45–49, determine if the following given solutions are **linearly independent**.

45. (i) $x_n^1 = 2^n + 4^n$, $n = 0, 1, \ldots$.
    (ii) $x_n^2 = 2^{n+1} + 4^{n+1}$, $n = 0, 1, \ldots$.

46. (i) $x_n^1 = 3^n + 6^n$, $n = 0, 1, \ldots$.
    (ii) $x_n^2 = 2(3)^{n+1} + 6^{n+1}$, $n = 0, 1, \ldots$.

47. (i) $x_n^1 = 1 + 2^n$, $n = 0, 1, \ldots$.
    (ii) $x_n^2 = 2^{n+1}$, $n = 0, 1, \ldots$.
    (iii) $x_n^3 = 2^n + (-2)^n$, $n = 0, 1, \ldots$.

48. (i) $x_n^1 = 2^{n+1} - n(2)^n$, $n = 0, 1, \ldots$.
    (ii) $x_n^2 = (3)^{n+1} - n(2)^n$, $n = 0, 1, \ldots$.

49. (i) $x_n^1 = 3^n + 4^n + 2^{n+1}$, $n = 0, 1, \ldots$.
    (ii) $x_n^2 = (4)^{n+1} + (2)^{n+3}$, $n = 0, 1, \ldots$.

In problems 50–55, using the Linear Transformation, **solve** the following *Riccati Difference Equations* and determine $\lim_{n \to \infty} x_n$.

50. $x_{n+1} = \dfrac{2 + x_n}{3 + x_n}$, $n = 0, 1, \ldots$.

51. $x_{n+1} = \dfrac{1 + x_n}{x_n}$, $n = 0, 1, \ldots$.

52. $x_{n+1} = \dfrac{x_n - 1}{1 + x_n}$, $n = 0, 1, \ldots$.

53. $x_{n+1} = \dfrac{1 + x_n}{4 + x_n}$, $n = 0, 1, \ldots$.

54. $x_{n+1} = \dfrac{x_n}{x_n - 1}$, $n = 0, 1, \ldots$.

55. $x_{n+1} = \dfrac{4x_n}{1 + x_n}$, $n = 0, 1, \ldots$.

In problems 56–59, using Theorem 19, determine if $\lim_{n \to \infty} x_n = 0$.

56. $9x_{n+2} - 4x_n = 0$, $n = 0, 1, \ldots$.

57. $5x_{n+2} - 2x_{n+1} - x_n = 0$, $n = 0, 1, \ldots$.

58. $9x_{n+2} + 4x_{n+1} - 4x_n = 0$, $n = 0, 1, \ldots$.

59. $7x_{n+2} + 5x_{n+1} - 2x_n = 0, \quad n = 0, 1, \ldots$.

60. Prove the case of Theorem 19 when $p^2 - 4q = 0$.

In problems 61–64, determine the general solution to each **LTI** Δ.**E.**

61. $y_{n+2} = ay_n + x_n + x_{n+1}$.

62. $y_{n+2} = ay_n + b_1 x_n + b_2 x_{n+1}$.

63. $y_{n+2} = ay_n + x_n + x_{n+1} + x_{n+2}$.

64. $y_{n+2} = ay_n + \left[\sum_{i=0}^{N-1} x_{n+i} \right]$.

Consider the Δ.E.:

$$x_{n+2} = a_n x_n, \quad n = 0, 1, \ldots,$$

where $x_0 \neq 0$ and $\{a_n\}_{n=0}^{\infty}$ is a period-k sequence ($k \geq 2$). In problems 65–68:

65. Prove statement (i) of Theorem 23.

66. Prove statement (ii) of Theorem 23.

67. Prove statement (iii) of Theorem 23.

68. Prove statement (iv) of Theorem 23.

In problems 69–89, determine the necessary and sufficient conditions for the existence of periodic solutions:

69. Existence of Periodic Solutions of:

$$x_{n+2} = -(x_{n+1} - x_n) + a_n, \quad n = 0, 1, \ldots,$$

where $\{a_n\}_{n=0}^{\infty}$ is a period-3k sequence ($k \geq 2$).

70. Existence of Periodic Solutions of:

$$x_{n+2} = -x_n + a_n, \quad n = 0, 1, \ldots,$$

where $\{a_n\}_{n=0}^{\infty}$ is a period-8 sequence.

71. Existence of Periodic Solutions of:

$$x_{n+2} = -x_n + a_n, \quad n = 0, 1, \ldots,$$

where $\{a_n\}_{n=0}^{\infty}$ is a period-12 sequence.

72. Existence of Periodic Solutions of:

$$x_{n+2} = -x_n + a_n, \quad n = 0, 1, \ldots,$$

where $\{a_n\}_{n=0}^{\infty}$ is a period-4k sequence $(k \geq 2)$.

73. Existence of Periodic Solutions of:

$$x_{n+2} = -(x_{n+1} + x_n) + a_n, \quad n = 0, 1, \ldots,$$

where $\{a_n\}_{n=0}^{\infty}$ is a period-12 sequence $(k \geq 2)$.

74. Existence of Periodic Solutions of:

$$x_{n+2} = -(x_{n+1} + x_n) + a_n, \quad n = 0, 1, \ldots,$$

where $\{a_n\}_{n=0}^{\infty}$ is a period-3k sequence $(k \geq 2)$.

75. Existence of Periodic Solutions of:

$$x_{n+2} = -(x_{n+1} + x_n) + a_n, \quad n = 0, 1, \ldots,$$

where $\{a_n\}_{n=0}^{\infty}$ is a period-9 sequence $(k \geq 2)$.

76. Existence of Periodic Solutions of:

$$x_{n+2} = (-1)^n x_n + a_n, \quad n = 0, 1, \ldots,$$

where $\{a_n\}_{n=0}^{\infty}$ is a period-2 sequence.

77. Existence of Periodic Solutions of:

$$x_{n+2} = (-1)^n x_n + a_n, \quad n = 0, 1, \ldots,$$

where $\{a_n\}_{n=0}^{\infty}$ is a period-4 sequence.

78. Existence of Periodic Solutions of:

$$x_{n+2} = (-1)^n x_n + a_n, \quad n = 0, 1, \ldots,$$

where $\{a_n\}_{n=0}^{\infty}$ is a period-8 sequence.

79. Existence of Periodic Solutions of:

$$x_{n+2} = (-1)^n x_n + a_n, \quad n = 0, 1, \ldots,$$

where $\{a_n\}_{n=0}^{\infty}$ is a period-12 sequence.

80. Existence of Periodic Solutions of:

$$x_{n+2} = (-1)^n x_n + a_n, \quad n = 0, 1, \ldots,$$

where $\{a_n\}_{n=0}^{\infty}$ is a period-4k sequence $(k \in \mathbb{N})$.

81. Existence of Periodic Solutions of:

$$x_{n+2} = \sqrt{2}x_{n+1} - x_n + a_n, \quad n = 0, 1, \ldots,$$

where $\{a_n\}_{n=0}^{\infty}$ is a period-2 sequence.

82. Existence of Periodic Solutions of:

$$x_{n+2} = \sqrt{2}x_{n+1} - x_n + a_n, \quad n = 0, 1, \ldots,$$

where $\{a_n\}_{n=0}^{\infty}$ is a period-4 sequence.

83. Existence of Periodic Solutions of:

$$x_{n+2} = \sqrt{3}x_{n+1} - x_n + a_n, \quad n = 0, 1, \ldots,$$

where $\{a_n\}_{n=0}^{\infty}$ is a period-2 sequence.

84. Existence of Periodic Solutions of:

$$x_{n+2} = \sqrt{3}x_{n+1} - x_n + a_n, \quad n = 0, 1, \ldots,$$

where $\{a_n\}_{n=0}^{\infty}$ is a period-3 sequence.

85. Existence of Periodic Solutions of:

$$x_{n+2} = \sqrt{3}x_{n+1} - x_n + a_n, \quad n = 0, 1, \ldots,$$

where $\{a_n\}_{n=0}^{\infty}$ is a period-4 sequence.

86. Existence of Periodic Solutions of:

$$x_{n+2} = \sqrt{3}x_{n+1} - x_n + a_n, \quad n = 0, 1, \ldots,$$

where $\{a_n\}_{n=0}^{\infty}$ is a period-6 sequence.

87. Existence of Periodic Solutions of:

$$x_{n+2} = \sqrt{2}x_{n+1} - x_n + a_n, \quad n = 0, 1, \ldots,$$

where $\{a_n\}_{n=0}^{\infty}$ is a period-4 sequence.

88. Existence of Periodic Solutions of:

$$x_{n+2} = x_{n+1} - x_n + a_n, \quad n = 0, 1, \ldots,$$

where $\{a_n\}_{n=0}^{\infty}$ is a period-12 sequence.

89. Existence of Periodic Solutions of:

$$x_{n+2} = x_{n+1} - x_n + a_n, \quad n = 0, 1, \ldots,$$

where $\{a_n\}_{n=0}^{\infty}$ is a period-6k sequence ($k \geq 2$).

In problems 90–93, determine the reasons for no existence of periodic solutions:

90. Periodicity of:

$$x_{n+2} = -x_n + a_n, \quad n = 0, 1, \ldots,$$

where $\{a_n\}_{n=0}^{\infty}$ is a period-4 sequence.

91. Periodicity of:

$$x_{n+2} = x_{n+1} - x_n + a_n, \quad n = 0, 1, \ldots,$$

where $\{a_n\}_{n=0}^{\infty}$ is a period-6 sequence.

92. Periodicity of:

$$x_{n+2} = \sqrt{2}x_{n+1} - x_n + a_n, \quad n = 0, 1, \ldots,$$

where $\{a_n\}_{n=0}^{\infty}$ is a period-8 sequence.

93. From Exercise 69 and Exercise 70, the Periodicity of:

$$x_{n+2} = 2\cos\left(\frac{2\pi}{k}\right) x_{n+1} - x_n + a_n, \quad n = 0, 1, \ldots,$$

where $\{a_n\}_{n=0}^{\infty}$ is a period-k sequence and $\theta = \frac{2\pi}{k}$ $(k \geq 2)$.

CHAPTER 5

SECOND ORDER NONLINEAR
DIFFERENCE EQUATIONS

The intents of this chapter are to study the local stability character of equilibrium points, periodicity properties, and the boundedness nature of second order nonlinear difference equations. We will study the linearized stability analysis of equilibrium points of rational difference equations and of difference equations in exponential form. Furthermore, we will investigate the periodic traits of rational difference equations and Max-Type difference equations. Moreover, we will study applications of second order nonlinear difference equations in population dynamics (Pielou's Model, Ricker Model, Perennial Grass Model, etc.). We will emerge with examples of second order nonlinear difference equations that will be analyzed throughout this chapter:

(i) (Special Case of **Rational Δ.E.** (Pielou's Δ.E.); [68, 69])

$$x_{n+2} = \frac{Ax_{n+1}}{x_n + B}, \quad n = 0, 1, \ldots.$$

(ii) (Special Case of **Rational Δ.E.**)

$$x_{n+2} = \frac{A + x_n}{\alpha + x_{n+1}}, \quad n = 0, 1, \ldots.$$

(iii) (**Δ.E. in Exponential Form**; Perennial Grass Model from Harvard School of Public Health [28])

$$x_{n+2} = ax_{n+1} + (b + cx_n)e^{-x_{n+1}}, \quad n = 0, 1, \ldots.$$

(iv) (**Max-Type Δ.E.**)

$$x_{n+2} = \max\left\{ \frac{A}{x_{n+1}}, \frac{B}{x_n} \right\}, \quad n = 0, 1, \ldots.$$

We will advance our studies with graphical examples that convey the convergence nature of solutions.

Example 1. The solution of the special case of **Rational Δ.E.**

$$x_{n+2} = \frac{0.9x_n}{1 + x_{n+1}},$$

where $x_0 = 0.6$ and $x_1 = 0.3$, is graphically described as:

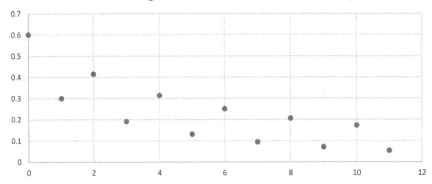

Monotonic Convergence to 0 From Above in Two Sub-sequences

Now note:

(i) $x_{2n+2} < x_{2n}$ and $x_{2n+3} < x_{2n+1}$ for all $n \geq 0$,
(ii) $\lim_{n \to \infty} x_{2n} = 0$ and $\lim_{n \to \infty} x_{2n+1} = 0$.

The solution converges **monotonically** to zero in two sub-sequences.

Example 2. The solution of the special case of **Rational Δ.E.**

$$x_{n+2} = \frac{3x_n}{1 + x_{n+1} + x_n},$$

where $x_0 = 0.8$ and $x_1 = 0.3$, is graphically depicted as:

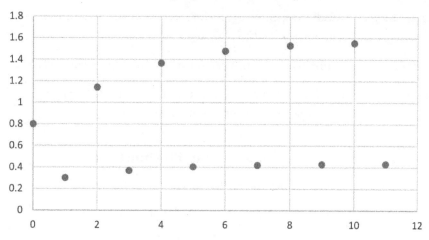

Converging to Period-2 Cycle

Now note:

(i) $x_{2n} < x_{2n+2}$ and $x_{2n+1} < x_{2n+3}$ for all $n \geq 0$,

(ii) $\lim_{n\to\infty} x_{2n} = L_1$ and $\lim_{n\to\infty} x_{2n+1} = L_2$.

(iii) $L_1 \neq L_2$.

There are two different converging sub-sequences whose limits are not equal and hence converge to a period-2 solution.

Example 3. The solution of the special case of **Rational Δ.E.**

$$x_{n+2} = 0.6 + \frac{x_n}{x_{n+1}},$$

where $x_0 = 2$ and $x_1 = 0.8$, is described by the following graph:

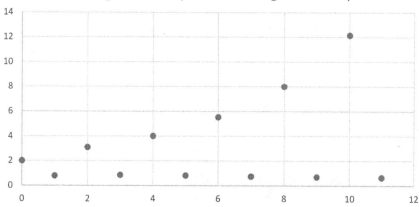

Convergent Sub-sequence & Divergent Sub-sequence

Now note:

(i) $x_{2n} < x_{2n+2}$ and $x_{2n+1} < x_{2n+3}$ for all $n \geq 0$,
(ii) $\lim_{n\to\infty} x_{2n} = +\infty$ and $\lim_{n\to\infty} x_{2n+1} = 0.6$.

Observe that one limit diverges to $+\infty$ and the other limit converges to 0.6.

In the next section we advance our studies with the local stability character of equilibrium points of second order nonlinear difference equations.

5.1. Local Stability Character of Equilibrium Points

From Chapter 1 recall the second order Δ.E. in the form:

$$x_{n+2} = f(x_{n+1}, x_n), \quad n = 0, 1, \ldots, \tag{5.160}$$

with two initial conditions x_0, x_1. The function $f(x, y)$ describes Eq. (5.160) on an interval (domain) $I \times I$. Also, the initial conditions $x_0, x_1 \in I$, and (range) $f : I \times I \to I$. Furthermore, recall that $\bar{x}$ is an **equilibrium point** of Eq. (5.160) provided that

$$\bar{x} = f(\bar{x}, \bar{x}).$$

Now suppose that $f(x, y)$ is continuously differentiable. Then the Linearized Equation of Eq. (5.160) about $\bar{x}$ is

$$y_{n+2} - \frac{\partial f}{\partial x}(\bar{x}, \bar{x})y_{n+1} - \frac{\partial f}{\partial y}(\bar{x}, \bar{x})y_n = 0, \quad n = 0, 1, 2, \ldots.$$

Now let

$$p = -\frac{\partial f}{\partial x}(\bar{x}, \bar{x}) \quad \text{and} \quad q = -\frac{\partial f}{\partial y}(\bar{x}, \bar{x}).$$

The following theorem which is a consequence of Theorems 19, 20 and 21 will describe the local stability character of the equilibrium points of Eq. (5.160).

Theorem 29. *Suppose that $f(x, y)$ is continuously differentiable on $I \times I$ and let $\bar{x}$ be an equilibrium point of Eq. (5.160). Then the following statements are true:*

(i) *$\bar{x}$ is locally asymptotically stable if $|p| < 1 + q < 2$.*
(ii) *$\bar{x}$ is unstable if either $|p| > 1 + q$ or $1 + q > 2$.*
(iii) *If $|p| = 1 + q$ then test fails.*

Next sequence of examples will analyze the local stability character of equilibrium points of Eq. (5.160).

Example 4. Determine all the equilibrium point(s) and their local stability character of:

$$x_{n+2} = \frac{Ax_{n+1}}{1 + x_n}, \quad n = 0, 1, \ldots,$$ (5.161)

where $x_0, x_1, A > 0$.

Solution: Eq. (5.161) has two equilibrium points $\bar{x}_1 = 0$ and $\bar{x}_2 = A - 1$ (when $A > 1$). Furthemore:

$$f(x, y) = \frac{Ax}{1 + y}, \quad f_x(x, y) = \frac{A}{1 + y} \quad \text{and} \quad f_y(x, y) = \frac{-Ax}{(1 + y)^2}.$$

Then

(i) $f_x(0, 0) = A$ and $f_y(0, 0) = 0$.
(ii) $f_x(A - 1, A - 1) = 1$ and $f_y(A - 1, A - 1) = \frac{1-A}{A}$.

The characteristic polynomial about $\bar{x}_1 = 0$ is:

$$\lambda^2 - A\lambda = 0.$$

The characteristic polynomial about $\bar{x}_2 = A - 1$ (when $A > 1$) is:

$$\lambda^2 - \lambda + \frac{A - 1}{A} = 0.$$

Therefore from Theorem 29 we conclude:

(i) $\bar{x}_1 = 0$ is locally asymptotically stable if $A < 1$.
(ii) $\bar{x}_1 = 0$ is unstable if $A > 1$.
(iii) $\bar{x}_2 = A - 1$ is locally asymptotically stable if $A > 1$.

The first graph below depicts convergence to $\bar{x} = 0$ from above when $A = 0.7$, $x_0 = 0.6$ and $x_1 = 0.4$:

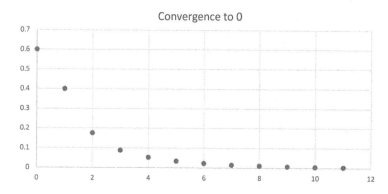

Convergence to 0

The next graph below depicts convergence to $\bar{x} = 2$ from below when $A = 3$, $x_0 = 2.8$ and $x_1 = 2.7$:

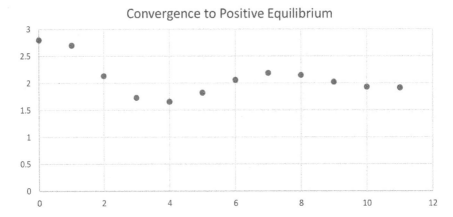

Convergence to Positive Equilibrium

Pielou's Δ.E. has various applications in Biology [68, 69].

Example 5. Determine all the equilibrium point(s) and their local stability character of:

$$x_{n+2} = \frac{A x_n}{1 + x_{n+1}}, \quad n = 0, 1, \ldots, \tag{5.162}$$

where $x_0, x_1, A > 0$.

Solution: Eq. (5.162) has two equilibrium points $\bar{x}_1 = 0$ and $\bar{x}_2 = A - 1$ (when $A > 1$). In addition:

$$f(x, y) = \frac{Ay}{1 + x}, \quad f_x(x, y) = \frac{-Ay}{(1 + x)^2} \quad \text{and} \quad f_y(x, y) = \frac{A}{1 + x}.$$

Then

(i) $f_x(0, 0) = 0$ and $f_y(0, 0) = A$.
(ii) $f_x(A - 1, A - 1) = \frac{1-A}{A}$ and $f_y(A - 1, A - 1) = 1$.

The characteristic polynomial about $\bar{x}_1 = 0$ is:

$$\lambda^2 - A = 0.$$

The characteristic polynomial about $\bar{x}_2 = A - 1$ (when $A > 1$) is:

$$\lambda^2 + \left(\frac{A - 1}{A}\right)\lambda - 1 = 0.$$

Thus from Theorem 29 we conclude:

(i) $\bar{x}_1 = 0$ is locally asymptotically stable if $A < 1$.
(ii) $\bar{x}_1 = 0$ is unstable if $A > 1$.
(iii) $\bar{x}_2 = A - 1$ is unstable if $A > 1$.

The first graph below depicts convergence to $\bar{x} = 0$ from above in two sub-sequences when $A = 0.8$, $x_0 = 0.3$ and $x_1 = 0.15$:

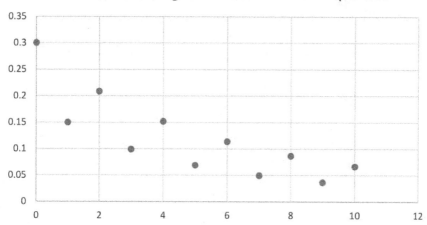

Monotonic Convergence to 0 in Two Sub-sequences

The next graph below depicts divergence when $A = 1.5$, $x_0 = 0.5$ and $x_1 = 0.2$:

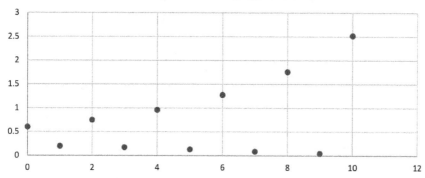

One Sub-sequence Converging to 0 and One Sub-sequence Diverging to Infinity

Note that one sub-sequence diverges to $+\infty$ while the other sub-sequence converges to 0. In the next section we will see the existence of period-2 cycles of Eq. (5.162) when $A = 1$.

Example 6. Determine all the equilibrium point(s) and their local stability character of:

$$x_{n+2} = \frac{Ax_n}{1 + x_{n+1} + x_n}, \quad n = 0, 1, \ldots, \tag{5.163}$$

where $x_0, x_1, A > 0$.

Solution: Eq. (5.163) has two equilibrium points $\bar{x}_1 = 0$ and $\bar{x}_2 = \frac{A-1}{2}$ (when $A > 1$). Also:

$$f(x, y) = \frac{Ay}{1 + x + y}, \quad f_x(x, y) = \frac{-Ay}{(1 + x + y)^2} \quad \text{and}$$

$$f_y(x, y) = \frac{A + Ax}{(1 + x + y)^2}.$$

Then

(i) $f_x(0, 0) = 0$ and $f_y(0, 0) = A$.

(ii) $f_x \left(\frac{A-1}{2}, \frac{A-1}{2} \right) = \frac{1-A}{2A}$ and $f_y \left(\frac{A-1}{2}, \frac{A-1}{2} \right) = \frac{A+1}{2A}$.

The characteristic polynomial about $\bar{x}_1 = 0$ is:

$$\lambda^2 - A = 0.$$

The characteristic polynomial about $\bar{x}_2 = \frac{A-1}{2}$ (when $A > 1$) is:

$$\lambda^2 + \left(\frac{A-1}{2A} \right) \lambda - \left(\frac{A+1}{2A} \right) = 0.$$

Therefore, from Theorem 29 we conclude that:

(i) $\bar{x}_1 = 0$ is locally asymptotically stable if $A < 1$.

(ii) $\bar{x}_1 = 0$ is unstable if $A > 1$.

(iii) $\bar{x}_2 = \frac{A-1}{2}$ is unstable if $A > 1$.

The first graph below depicts convergence to $\bar{x} = 0$ from above in two subsequences when $A = 0.8$, $x_0 = 0.6$ and $x_1 = 0.1$:

Convergence to 0 in Two Sub-sequences

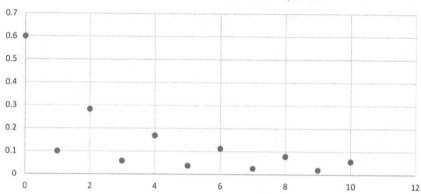

The next graph below depicts convergence to a period-2 cycle when $A = 5$, $x_0 = 2.2$ and $x_1 = 0.5$:

Converging to Period-2 Cycle

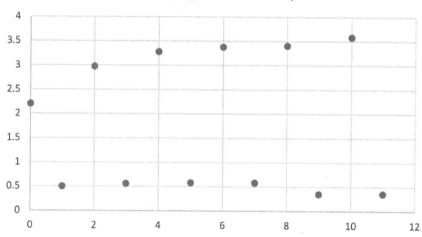

Notice that one sub-sequence converges to an upper limit while the other sub-sequence to a lower limit. In the next section we will discover the existence of period-2 cycles of Eq. (5.163) when $A > 1$.

Example 7. Determine all the equilibrium point(s) and their local stability character of:

$$x_{n+2} = Ax_{n+1} + Bx_n e^{-x_{n+1}}, \quad n = 0, 1, \ldots, \qquad (5.164)$$

where $x_0, x_1, A, B > 0$.

Solution: Eq. (5.164) has two equilibrium points $\bar{x}_1 = 0$ and $\bar{x}_2 = Ln\left[\frac{B}{1-A}\right]$ (when $A < 1$). In addition:

$$f(x,y) = Ax + Bye^{-x}, \quad f_x(x,y) = A - Bye^{-x} \quad \text{and} \quad f_y(x,y) = Be^{-x}.$$

Then:

(i) $f_x(0,0) = A$ and $f_y(0,0) = B$.

(ii) $f_x\left(Ln\left[\frac{B}{1-A}\right], Ln\left[\frac{B}{1-A}\right]\right) = A - (1-A)Ln\left[\frac{B}{1-A}\right]$.

(iii) $f_y\left(Ln\left[\frac{B}{1-A}\right], Ln\left[\frac{B}{1-A}\right]\right) = 1 - A$.

The characteristic polynomial about $\bar{x}_1 = 0$ is:

$$\lambda^2 - A\lambda - B = 0.$$

The characteristic polynomial about $\bar{x}_2 = Ln\left[\frac{B}{1-A}\right]$ (when $A < 1$) is:

$$\lambda^2 \left(A - (1-A)Ln\left[\frac{B}{1-A}\right]\right)\lambda - (1-A) = 0.$$

Hence from Theorem 29 we conclude that:

(i) $\bar{x}_1 = 0$ is locally asymptotically stable if $A + B < 1$.

(ii) $\bar{x}_1 = 0$ is unstable if $A + B > 1$.

(iii) $\bar{x}_2 = Ln\left[\frac{B}{1-A}\right]$ is stable if $A + B > 1$ and $A < 1$.

This is a special case of a Δ.E. in Exponential Form which has been studied by several authors in [28, 34, 48, 65, 66].

Example 8. Determine all the equilibrium point(s) and their local stability character of:

$$x_{n+2} = A + \frac{x_n}{x_{n+1}}, \quad n = 0, 1, \dots, \tag{5.165}$$

where $x_0, x_1, A > 0$.

Solution: Eq. (5.165) has one positive equilibrium point $\bar{x} = A + 1$. In addition:

$$f(x,y) = A + \frac{y}{x}, \quad f_x(x,y) = \frac{-y}{x^2} \quad \text{and} \quad f_y(x,y) = \frac{1}{x}.$$

Now we see that

$$f_x(A+1, A+1) = \frac{-1}{A+1} \quad \text{and} \quad f_y(A+1, A+1) = \frac{1}{A+1}.$$

The characteristic polynomial about $\bar{x} = A + 1$ is:

$$\lambda^2 + \left(\frac{1}{A+1}\right)\lambda - \left(\frac{1}{A+1}\right) = 0.$$

Therefore, from Theorem 29 we conclude that:

(i) $\bar{x} = A + 1$ is locally asymptotically stable if $A > 1$.
(ii) $\bar{x} = A + 1$ is unstable if $A < 1$.

The first graph below depicts **oscillatory** convergence to $\bar{x} = 3$ in two sub-sequences when $A = 2$, $x_0 = 1.5$ and $x_1 = 6$:

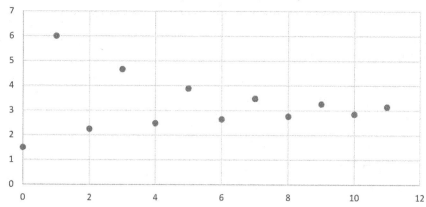

Oscillatory Convergence to Positive Equilibrium

In Example 3 one sub-sequence diverged to positive infinity while the other sub-sequence converged to 0.6 when $A = 0.6$, $x_0 = 0.2$ and $x_1 = 0.8$. In the next section period-2 cycles will exist when $A = 1$.

From Examples 5, 6 and 8 the following theorem generalizes the result about the **oscillatory character** of non-trivial solutions about the positive equilibrium.

Theorem 30. *Let $\{x_n\}_{n=0}^{\infty}$ be a solution of Eq. (5.160). Suppose that:*

(i) *$f(x,y)$ is a continuously differentiable function.*
(ii) *$f_x(x,y) < 0$ and $f_y(x,y) > 0$.*
(iii) *Eq. (5.160) has exactly one positive equilibrium $\bar{x}$.*

Then every non-trivial solution of Eq. (5.160) is oscillatory.

Proof.   First of all, suppose that $x_0 > \bar{x}$ and $x_1 < \bar{x}$. By the monotonic properties of $f(x,y)$, iterations and induction we acquire the following properties:

$$
\begin{aligned}
x_0 &> \bar{x}, \\
x_1 &< \bar{x}, \\
x_2 = f(x_1, x_0) &> f(\bar{x}, \bar{x}) = \bar{x}, \\
x_3 = f(x_2, x_1) &< f(\bar{x}, \bar{x}) = \bar{x}, \\
x_4 = f(x_3, x_2) &> f(\bar{x}, \bar{x}) = \bar{x}, \\
x_5 = f(x_4, x_3) &< f(\bar{x}, \bar{x}) = \bar{x}, \\
&\vdots
\end{aligned}
$$

Hence for all $n \geq 0$:

$$x_{2n} > \bar{x} \quad \text{and} \quad x_{2n+1} < \bar{x}.$$

Thus the result follows. The case when $x_0 < \bar{x}$ and $x_1 > \bar{x}$ is similar and will be omitted. $\qquad \square$

Now we will examine some of the discrete biological models rendered by second order nonlinear difference equations.

5.1.1. *Pielou's Δ.E. (Model)*

Pielou's Δ.E. (Model) is a discrete population model resembled by the following second order nonlinear Δ.E.:

$$x_{n+2} = \frac{A x_{n+1}}{x_n + B},$$

where $A, B, x_0, x_1 > 0$ and:

(i) *A is the birth rate of the beetles.*
(ii) *B is the death rate of the beetles.*
(iii) *x_n is the number of flour beetles at year n.*

(iv) x_{n+1} is the number of flour beetles at year $n+1$.

(v) x_{n+2} is the number of flour beetles at year $n+2$.

The model was introduced by Evelyn Chrystalla Pielou in 1969 and in 1974 [68, 69] who was a researcher for the Canadian Department of Forestry (1963–1964) and the Canadian Department of Agriculture (1964–1967). First of all, notice that the **Pielou's Δ.E. (Model)** is in the similar pattern as the Riccati Δ.E. with two equilibrium points $\bar{x} = 0$ and $\bar{x} = A - B$ (when $A > B$). Second of all we get:

(i) $\lim_{n \to \infty} x_n = 0$ if $A \le B$. This implies extinction.

(ii) $\lim_{n \to \infty} x_n = A - B$ if $A > B$. This implies survival.

5.1.2. *Delayed Ricker Model*

Delayed Ricker Model is a discrete population model resembled by the following second order nonlinear Δ.E. in Exponential Form:

$$x_{n+2} = x_{n+1} e^{R - \frac{x_{n+1} + x_n}{K}},$$

where $R, K, x_0, x_1 > 0$ and:

(i) R is the growth rate.

(ii) K is the carrying capacity.

(iii) x_n is the population at year n.

(iv) x_{n+1} is the population at year $n+1$.

(v) x_{n+2} is the population at year $n+2$.

To determine the equilibrium points and their local stability character will be left as an exercise at the end of the chapter. More details on the Ricker Δ.E. can be found in [77].

5.1.3. *Harvard School of Public Health population model*

The population model posed by Richard Levins from Harvard School of Public Health is a discrete population model resembled by the following second order nonlinear Δ.E. in Exponential Form:

$$x_{n+2} = \alpha + \beta x_n e^{-x_{n+1}},$$

where $\alpha, \beta, x_0, x_1 > 0$ and:

(i) α is the immigration rate.

(ii) β is the population growth rate.

(iii) x_n is the population at year n.

(iv) x_{n+1} is the population at year $n+1$.

(v) x_{n+2} is the population at year $n+2$.

The model was introduced in 2000 by Richard Levins from the Harvard School of Public Health [34]. First of all, notice that the model has exactly one equilibrium point $\bar{x}$ and $\bar{x} > \alpha$. Second of all we get:

(i) $\bar{x}$ is locally asymptotically stable if $\beta < \frac{-\alpha+\sqrt{a^2+4\alpha}}{\alpha+\sqrt{a^2+4\alpha}} e^{\frac{-\alpha+\sqrt{a^2+4\alpha}}{2}}$.

(ii) $\bar{x}$ is globally asymptotically stable if $\beta < e^\alpha$.

(iii) $\bar{x}$ is unstable if $\beta > \frac{-\alpha+\sqrt{a^2+4\alpha}}{\alpha+\sqrt{a^2+4\alpha}} e^{\frac{-\alpha+\sqrt{a^2+4\alpha}}{2}}$.

(iv) Every positive solution is bounded if $\beta < e^\alpha$.

(v) Unbounded solutions exist if $\beta > e^\alpha$.

Observe that the model is valid only when $\beta < e^\alpha$.

5.1.4. *Perennial Grass Model*

The **Perennial Grass Model** was introduced by Richard Levins from the Harvard School of Public Health in 1995 in [28]. This is a discrete model resembled by the following second order nonlinear Δ.E. in Exponential Form:

$$x_{n+2} = ax_{n+1} + (b + cx_n)e^{-x_{n+1}},$$

where $a, b, c, x_0, x_1 > 0$ and:

(i) x_n is the litter per square meter on the ground at year n.

(ii) x_{n+1} is the litter per square meter on the ground at year $n+1$.

(iii) x_{n+2} is the litter per square meter on the ground at year $n+2$.

(iv) ax_{n+1} is the fraction of the previous litter that has not decayed.

(v) $(b+cx_n)e^{-x_{n+1}}$ is from new growth which depends on the nutrients and space.

The model was introduced in 2000 by Richard Levins from the Harvard School of Public Health [34]. First of all, notice that the model has exactly one equilibrium point $\bar{x}$ and $\bar{x} \leq \frac{a}{1-a}$; and $\bar{x}$ is locally asymptotically stable and globally asymptotically stable if

$$b \leq a \left[e^{\frac{a}{1-a}} - \frac{a}{1-a} \right].$$

The next section will discuss some of the global stability results of equilibrium points of Eq. (5.160).

5.2. Global Asymptotic Stability (Convergence)

Our aims of this section is to apply the monotonic properties of functions to show global stability of either the zero equilibrium point or the positive equilibrium point. Recall from Chapter 1, the function $f(x,y)$ describes Eq. (5.160). We will assume that $f(x,y)$ is continuously differentiable on an interval (domain) I; the initial conditions $x_0, x_1 \in I$. In addition, we will assume that $f_x(x,y) < 0$ and $f_y(x,y) > 0$. We will illustrate analytical and graphical examples of global asymptotic stability.

Example 9. Consider the following Δ.E.:

$$x_{n+2} = \frac{Ax_n}{1 + x_{n+1}}, \quad n = 0, 1, \ldots, \tag{5.166}$$

with $x_0, x_1 > 0$ and $A \in (0,1)$. Show that

$$\lim_{n \to \infty} x_n = 0.$$

Solution: First of all, when $A < 1$, Eq. (5.166) has only one equilibrium point $\bar{x} = 0$. Second of all, in Example 5 we showed that $\bar{x} = 0$ is locally asymptotically stable. The graph below depicts convergence to zero in two monotonic decreasing sub-sequences when $A = 0.7$, $x_0 = 0.6$ and $x_1 = 0.2$:

Convergence to 0 in Two Sub-sequences

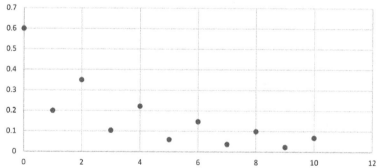

Now observe:

$$x_0,$$

$$x_1,$$

$$x_2 = \frac{Ax_0}{1 + x_1} < Ax_0,$$

$$x_3 = \frac{Ax_1}{1 + x_2} < Ax_1,$$

$$x_4 = \frac{Ax_2}{1 + x_3} < Ax_2 < A^2 x_0,$$

$$x_5 = \frac{Ax_3}{1 + x_2} < Ax_3 < A^2 x_1,$$

$$\vdots$$

Hence for all $n \in \mathbb{N}$:

$$x_{2n} < A^n x_0 \quad \text{and} \quad x_{2n+1} < A^n x_1.$$

Thus

$$\lim_{n \to \infty} x_{2n} = 0 \quad \text{and} \quad \lim_{n \to \infty} x_{2n+1} = 0.$$

Now observe that when $A = 1$, Eq. (5.166) has only one equilibrium point $\bar{x} = 0$. However, the solutions of Eq. (5.166) will not converge to $\bar{x} = 0$. The graph below depicts convergence to a period-2 cycle in two monotonic sub-sequences when $A = 1$, $x_0 = 0.4$ and $x_1 = 0.2$:

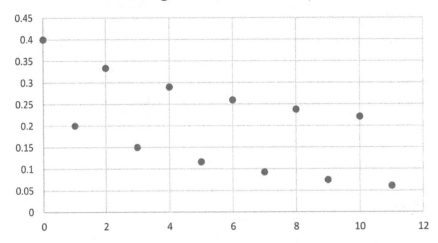

Convergence to a Period-2 Cycle

Furthermore, when $A > 1$, Eq. (5.166) has two equilibrium points $\bar{x}_1 = 0$ and $\bar{x}_2 = A - 1$ which are both unstable as shown in Example 5. The graph below depicts one sub-sequence diverging to $+\infty$ and one sub-sequence converging to 0 when $A = 1.5$, $x_0 = 0.6$ and $x_1 = 0.2$:

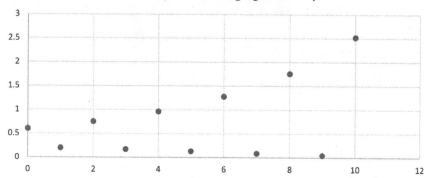

Finally we see that this particular rational Δ.E. exhibits trichotomy behavior of solutions depending on the value of the parameter A.

The next two examples will focus on the **boundedness nature** of solutions. Show that every positive solution of Eq. (5.160) is bounded.

Example 10. Show that every positive solution $\{x_n\}_{n=0}^{\infty}$ of

$$x_{n+2} = \frac{A x_n}{1 + x_{n+1} + x_n}, \quad n = 0, 1, \ldots$$

is bounded, where $x_0, x_1, A > 0$.

Solution: By iterations and induction we acquire:

$$x_0,$$

$$x_1,$$

$$x_2 = \frac{A x_0}{1 + x_1 + x_0} < \frac{A x_0}{x_0} = A,$$

$$x_3 = \frac{A x_1}{1 + x_2 + x_1} < \frac{A x_1}{x_1} = A,$$

$$x_4 = \frac{A x_2}{1 + x_3 + x_2} < \frac{A x_2}{x_2} = A,$$

$$\vdots$$

We see that for all $n \geq 2$:

$$0 < x_n < A.$$

The result follows.

Example 11. Show that every positive solution $\{x_n\}_{n=0}^{\infty}$ of

$$x_{n+2} = A + \frac{x_n}{x_{n+1}}, \quad n = 0, 1, \ldots$$

is bounded, where $x_0, x_1 > 0$ and $A > 1$.

Solution: First of all, note that $x_n > A$ for all $n \geq 2$. Hence for all $n \geq 2$:

$$x_{n+2} = A + \frac{x_n}{x_{n+1}} < A + \frac{x_n}{A}.$$

Observe that, when $A > 1$, every positive solution of the second order linear Δ.E.

$$y_{n+2} - \frac{y_n}{A} = A, \quad n = 0, 1, \ldots$$

converges to the positive equilibrium $\bar{y} = \frac{A^2}{A-1}$. Hence given $\varepsilon > 0$, there exists $n \geq N$ such that:

$$y_n < \frac{A^2 + \varepsilon}{A - 1}.$$

Therefore the result follows that for all $n \geq N$:

$$A < x_n < \frac{A^2 + \varepsilon}{A - 1}.$$

From Example 11 the following theorem (Theorem 5.2 in [51]) outlines the results for global asymptotic stability of the positive equilibrium point of Eq. (5.160).

Theorem 31. *Let* $f : (0, \infty) \times (0, \infty) \to (0, \infty)$ *be a continuous function and suppose that* $f(x, y)$ *satisfies the following conditions:*

(i) *There exist positive values* a *and* b $(a < b)$ *such that*

$$a \leq f(x, y) \leq b \quad \text{for all} \quad x, y \in [a, b].$$

(ii) $f_x(x, y) < 0$ *for all* $x \in [a, b]$ *and* $f_y(x, y) > 0$ *for all* $y \in [a, b]$.
(iii) *Eq.* (5.160) *has no solutions with prime period-2 in* $[a, b]$.

Then Eq. (5.160) *has a unique positive equilibrium* $\bar{x}$ *and every solution of Eq.* (5.160) *converges to* $\bar{x}$.

Proof. First set

$$m_0 = a \quad \text{and} \quad M_0 = b,$$

and for $i \in \mathbb{N}$ set

$$M_i = f(m_{i-1}, M_{i-1}) \quad \text{and} \quad m_i = f(M_{i-1}, m_{i-1}).$$

Now notice that:

$$m_0 \le m_1 \le \ldots \le m_i \le \ldots \le \ldots \le M_i \le \ldots \le \ldots \le M_1 \le M_0,$$

and for $k \ge 2i + 1$:

$$m_i \le x_k \le M_i.$$

Set

$$m = \lim_{i \to \infty} m_i \quad \text{and} \quad M = \lim_{i \to \infty} M_i.$$

Then

$$M \ge \limsup_{i \to \infty} x_i \ge \liminf_{i \to \infty} x_i \ge m,$$

and as $f(x, y)$ is continuous, then

$$m = f(M, m) \quad \text{and} \quad M = f(m, M).$$

Hence

$$m = M.$$

Otherwise Eq. (5.160) would have a period-2 cycle which would be a contradiction. □

Example 12. Show that every positive solution $\{x_n\}_{n=0}^\infty$ of

$$x_{n+2} = A + \frac{x_n}{x_{n+1}}, \quad n = 0, 1, \ldots \tag{5.167}$$

converges to the positive equilibrium $\bar{x} = A + 1$, where $x_0, x_1 > 0$ and $A > 1$.

Solution: First of all:

(i) $f(x, y) = A + \frac{y}{x}$,

(ii) $f_x(x, y) = \frac{-y}{x^2} < 0$ and $f_x(x, y) = \frac{y}{x} > 0$.

Second of all, in Example 11 we showed that when $A > 1$, every positive solution of Eq. (5.167) is bounded. In fact, for all $n \geq N$:

$$A < x_n < \frac{A^2 + \varepsilon}{A - 1}.$$

In Example 16 we will show that Eq. (5.167) has period-2 solutions if and only if $A = 1$. Hence the result follows via Theorem 31.

5.3. Patterns of Periodic Solutions of Second Order Rational Difference Equations

Our aim is to examine the existence and patterns of periodic solutions of the Second Order Rational Δ.E. in the form:

$$x_{n+2} = \frac{A + Bx_{n+1} + Cx_n}{D + Ex_{n+1} + Fx_n}, \quad n = 0, 1, \ldots, \tag{5.168}$$

where $A, B, C, D, E, F \geq 0$ and the initial conditions $x_0, x_1 \geq 0$. Eq. (5.168) has 49 special cases and we will investigate the periodic traits of some of these 49 special cases. Rational Difference Equations have been studied by several authors [2, 18, 20, 38, 40, 41, 44, 50, 51, 80]. Eq. (5.160) is periodic with period-2:

$$\alpha, \; \beta, \; \alpha, \; \beta, \; \ldots,$$

where $\alpha \neq \beta$ if:

$$f(\alpha, \beta) = \alpha \quad \text{and} \quad f(\beta, \alpha) = \beta.$$

The next two examples will show the existence and patterns of periodic solutions of the Second Order Riccati Δ.E.

Example 13. Show that every non-trivial solution of

$$x_{n+2} = \frac{1}{x_n}, \quad n = 0, 1, \ldots$$

is periodic with period-4 and determine the pattern of the period-4 cycle.

Solution: Notice:

$$x_0,$$

$$x_1,$$

$$x_2 = \frac{1}{x_0},$$

$$x_3 = \frac{1}{x_1},$$

$$x_4 = \frac{1}{x_2} = \frac{1}{\left[\frac{1}{x_0}\right]} = x_0,$$

$$x_5 = \frac{1}{x_3} = \frac{1}{\left[\frac{1}{x_1}\right]} = x_1.$$

We then obtain the following period-4 pattern:

$$x_0, \ x_1, \ \frac{1}{x_0}, \ \frac{1}{x_1}, \ \ldots\ldots$$

Note that $x_0, x_1 \neq 0$ and the product of the neighboring terms is constant:

$$x_0 \cdot x_1 \cdot \frac{1}{x_0} \cdot \frac{1}{x_1} = 1.$$

Example 14. Show that every non-trivial solution of

$$x_{n+2} = \frac{x_n}{x_n - 1}, \quad n = 0, 1, \ldots$$

is periodic with period-4 and determine the pattern of the period-4 cycle.

Solution: Observe:

$$x_0,$$

$$x_1,$$

$$x_2 = \frac{x_0}{x_0 - 1},$$

$$x_3 = \frac{x_1}{x_1 - 1},$$

$$x_4 = \frac{x_2}{x_2 - 1} = \frac{\left[\frac{x_0}{x_0-1}\right]}{\left[\frac{x_0}{x_0-1}\right] - 1} = \frac{x_0}{x_0 - (x_0 - 1)} = x_0,$$

$$x_5 = \frac{x_3}{x_3 - 1} = \frac{\left[\frac{x_1}{x_1-1}\right]}{\left[\frac{x_1}{x_1-1}\right] - 1} = \frac{x_1}{x_1 - (x_1 - 1)} = x_1.$$

Hence we acquire the following period-4 pattern:

$$x_0, \ x_1, \ \frac{x_0}{x_0 - 1}, \ \frac{x_1}{x_1 - 1}, \ \ldots.$$

Notice that $x_0, x_1 \neq 1$ and the product and the sum of all the neighboring terms are always equal:

$$\frac{x_0^2}{x_0 - 1} + \frac{x_1^2}{x_1 - 1} = x_0 + x_1 + \frac{x_0}{x_0 - 1} + \frac{x_1}{x_1 - 1}.$$

The next example will illustrate the existence of period-6 cycles and their patterns.

Example 15. Determine the pattern of periodic cycles of:

$$x_{n+2} = \frac{x_{n+1}}{x_n}, \quad n = 0, 1, \ldots.$$

Solution: By iteration we obtain the following period-6 pattern:

$$x_0, \ x_1, \ \frac{x_1}{x_0}, \ \frac{1}{x_0}, \ \frac{1}{x_1}, \ \frac{x_0}{x_1}, \ \ldots,$$

where $x_0, x_1 \neq 0$.

The next three examples will be directed on the existence and patterns of period-2 cycles of specific rational difference equations.

Example 16. Determine the necessary and sufficient conditions for the existence of period-2 cycles of:

$$x_{n+2} = A + \frac{x_n}{x_{n+1}}, \quad n = 0, 1, \ldots, \tag{5.169}$$

where $A, x_0, x_1 > 0$.

Solution: Set $x_2 = x_0$ and $x_3 = x_1$ and we produce the following system of equations:

$$x_0,$$

$$x_1,$$

$$x_2 = A + \frac{x_0}{x_1} = x_0,$$

$$x_3 = A + \frac{x_1}{x_2} = A + \frac{x_1}{x_0} = x_1,$$

and we procure the following equality:

$$Ax_1 + x_0 = x_0 x_1 = Ax_0 + x_1$$

that reduces to

$$A(x_0 - x_1) = x_0 - x_1.$$

Thus we see that $A = 1$ as we assumed that $x_0 \neq x_1$. Then Eq. (5.169) reduces to:

$$x_{n+2} = 1 + \frac{x_n}{x_{n+1}}, \quad n = 0, 1, \ldots.$$

By repeating the process above, we get:

$$x_0,$$

$$x_1,$$

$$x_2 = 1 + \frac{x_0}{x_1} = x_0,$$

$$x_3 = 1 + \frac{x_1}{x_2} = 1 + \frac{x_1}{x_0} = x_1.$$

We solve for x_1 and get $x_1 = \frac{x_0}{x_0 - 1}$ ($x_0 \neq 1$), and obtain the following period-2 pattern:

$$x_0, \frac{x_0}{x_0 - 1}, x_0, \frac{x_0}{x_0 - 1}, \ldots.$$

Recall that this identical periodic pattern appeared in the Riccati Δ.E. $x_{n+1} = \frac{x_n}{x_n-1}$, whose periodic solutions are on the hyperbolic curve $y = \frac{x}{x-1}$:

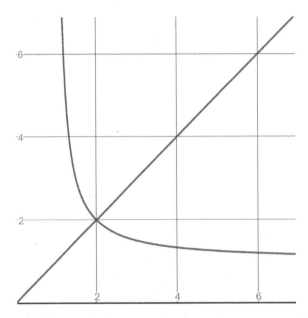

Observe that the hyperbola intersects the bisector at the point $(2,2)$ and every period-2 cycle is oscillatory with semi-cycles of length 1.

Example 17. Determine the necessary and sufficient conditions for the existence of period-2 cycles of:

$$x_{n+2} = \frac{Ax_n}{1 + x_{n+1}}, \quad n = 0, 1, \ldots, \tag{5.170}$$

where $A > 0$ and $x_0, x_1 \geq 0$.

Solution: Set $x_2 = x_0$ and $x_3 = x_1$ and we assemble the following system of equations:

$$x_0,$$
$$x_1,$$
$$x_2 = \frac{Ax_0}{1 + x_1} = x_0,$$
$$x_3 = \frac{Ax_1}{1 + x_2} = \frac{Ax_1}{1 + x_0} = x_1,$$

and we procure the following equality:

$$Ax_0 - x_0 = x_0 x_1 = Ax_1 - x_1$$

that reduces to

$$x_0 \left(A - 1 \right) = x_1 \left(A - 1 \right).$$

Hence we see that $A = 1$ as we assumed that $x_0 \neq x_1$. Then Eq. (5.170) reduces to:

$$x_{n+2} = \frac{x_n}{1 + x_{n+1}}, \quad n = 0, 1, \ldots.$$

By repeating the above process, we procure the following system of equations:

$$x_0,$$
$$x_1,$$
$$x_2 = \frac{x_0}{1 + x_1} = x_0,$$
$$x_3 = \frac{x_1}{1 + x_2} = \frac{x_1}{1 + x_0} = x_1.$$

Therefore $x_0 x_1 = 0$. Then either $x_0 = 0$ or $x_1 = 0$ and we acquire one of the following period-2 patterns:

$$0, \ x_1, \ 0, \ x_1, \ldots, \quad \text{or}$$
$$x_0, \ 0, \ x_0, \ 0, \ldots.$$

This is the first time that we see a period-2 pattern where one of the initial conditions must be 0. In this case it is impossible to obtain a positive period-2 cycle.

Example 18. Determine the necessary and sufficient conditions for the existence of period-2 cycles of:

$$x_{n+2} = \frac{A x_n}{1 + x_{n+1} + x_n}, \quad n = 0, 1, \ldots, \quad (5.171)$$

where $A > 0$ and $x_0 + x_1 > 0$.

Solution: We set $x_2 = x_0$ and $x_3 = x_1$ and procure the following system of equations:

$$x_0,$$

$$x_1,$$

$$x_2 = \frac{Ax_0}{1 + x_1 + x_0} = x_0,$$

$$x_3 = \frac{Ax_1}{1 + x_2 + x_1} = \frac{Ax_1}{1 + x_0 + x_1} = x_1,$$

and we acquire the following equality:

$$1 + x_0 + x_1 = A.$$

Hence $A > 1$ as $x_0 + x_1 > 0$. We then obtain one of the following period-2 patterns:

$$x_0, \; A - (1 + x_0), \; x_0, \; A - (1 + x_0), \; \ldots, \; \text{or}$$
$$A - (1 + x_1), \; x_1, \; A - (1 + x_1), \; x_1, \; \ldots.$$

In this situation, the periodic solutions are on the line segment $y = A - (1 + x)$ on the restricted interval $[0, A - 1]$ as we can see in the diagram below:

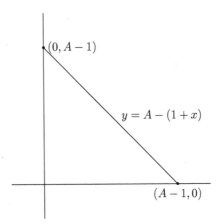

Graph of $y = A - (1 + x)$ on the restricted interval $[0, A - 1]$.

The next section will pursue with determining periodic traits of non-autonomous rational difference equations.

5.4. Periodic Patterns of Second Order Non-autonomous Rational Difference Equations

We will broaden our analysis of periodic essence of solutions (necessary and sufficient conditions for existence and uniqueness of periodic solutions) of Non-autonomous Rational Difference Equations by introducing a period-k sequence $\{A_n\}_{n=0}^{\infty}$ ($k \geq 2$). Our goal is to compare the similarities and differences with the autonomous rational difference equations studied in the previous section. We will commence our studies with periodic traits of the following Second Order Non-autonomous Riccati Δ.E.:

$$x_{n+2} = \frac{A_n}{x_n}, \quad n = 0, 1, \ldots, \tag{5.172}$$

where $x_0, x_1 \neq 0$. We will examine several examples and compare the differences between when $\{A_n\}_{n=0}^{\infty}$ is an even ordered sequence and when $\{A_n\}_{n=0}^{\infty}$ is an odd ordered sequence. In the previous chapters we encountered major differences that addressed the uniqueness of periodic patterns.

Example 19. Suppose that $\{A_n\}_{n=0}^{\infty}$ is a period-2 sequence. Determine the period-4 pattern of:

$$x_{n+2} = \frac{A_n}{x_n}, \quad n = 0, 1, \ldots.$$

Solution: By iteration we procure the following period-4 pattern:

$$x_0, \; x_1, \; \frac{A_0}{x_0}, \; \frac{A_1}{x_1}, \ldots.$$

The upcoming question to ask: can the Eq. (5.172) exhibit period-2 cycles when $\{A_n\}_{n=0}^{\infty}$ is a period-2 sequence? The next example will remit the answer.

Example 20. Suppose that $\{A_n\}_{n=0}^{\infty}$ is a period-2 sequence. Determine the period-2 pattern of:

$$x_{n+2} = \frac{A_n}{x_n}, \quad n = 0, 1, \ldots.$$

Solution: Notice:

$$x_0,$$

$$x_1,$$

$$x_2 = \frac{A_0}{x_0} = x_0,$$

$$x_3 = \frac{A_1}{x_1} = x_1,$$

and we acquire:

$$x_0 = \pm\sqrt{A_0} \quad \text{and} \quad x_1 = \pm\sqrt{A_1},$$

and hence obtain four distinct period-2 cycles:

- $\sqrt{A_0}, \sqrt{A_1}, \ldots$
- $-\sqrt{A_0}, \sqrt{A_1}, \ldots$
- $\sqrt{A_0}, -\sqrt{A_1}, \ldots$
- $-\sqrt{A_0}, -\sqrt{A_1}, \ldots$

The next question to address: what will happen when $\{A_n\}_{n=0}^{\infty}$ is either an even ordered periodic sequence or an odd ordered periodic sequence? The following examples will convey the answer.

Example 21. Suppose that $\{A_n\}_{n=0}^{\infty}$ is a period-3 sequence. Determine the existence, uniqueness and the pattern of period-3 cycles of:

$$x_{n+2} = \frac{A_n}{x_n}, \quad n = 0, 1, \ldots.$$

Solution: Set $x_6 = x_0$ and $x_7 = x_1$ and we get:

$$x_0,$$

$$x_1,$$

$$x_2 = \frac{A_0}{x_0},$$

$$x_3 = \frac{A_1}{x_1},$$

$$x_4 = \frac{A_2}{[x_2]} = \frac{A_2}{\left[\frac{A_0}{x_0}\right]} = \frac{A_2 x_0}{A_0},$$

$$x_5 = \frac{A_0}{[x_3]} = \frac{A_0}{\left[\frac{A_1}{x_1}\right]} = \frac{A_0 x_1}{A_1},$$

$$x_6 = \frac{A_1}{[x_4]} = \frac{A_1}{\left[\frac{A_2 x_0}{A_0}\right]} = \frac{A_1 A_0}{A_2 x_0} = x_0,$$

$$x_7 = \frac{A_2}{[x_5]} = \frac{A_2}{\left[\frac{A_0 x_1}{A_1}\right]} = \frac{A_1 A_2}{A_0 x_1} = x_1,$$

and we acquire:

$$x_0 = \pm\sqrt{\frac{A_0 A_1}{A_2}} \quad \text{and} \quad x_1 = \pm\sqrt{\frac{A_1 A_2}{A_0}}.$$

Therefore we generate four distinct period-3 cycles:

- $\sqrt{\frac{A_0 A_1}{A_2}}, \ \sqrt{\frac{A_1 A_2}{A_0}}, \ \sqrt{\frac{A_2 A_0}{A_1}}, \dots$
- $\sqrt{\frac{A_0 A_1}{A_2}}, \ -\sqrt{\frac{A_1 A_2}{A_0}}, \ \sqrt{\frac{A_2 A_0}{A_1}}, \dots$
- $-\sqrt{\frac{A_0 A_1}{A_2}}, \ \sqrt{\frac{A_1 A_2}{A_0}}, \ -\sqrt{\frac{A_2 A_0}{A_1}}, \dots$
- $-\sqrt{\frac{A_0 A_1}{A_2}}, \ -\sqrt{\frac{A_1 A_2}{A_0}}, \ -\sqrt{\frac{A_2 A_0}{A_1}}, \dots$

Observe that from neighbor to neighbor the indices of the sequence $\{A_n\}_{n=0}^{\infty}$ shift by 1.

Example 22. Suppose that $\{A_n\}_{n=0}^{\infty}$ is a period-4 sequence. Determine the existence, uniqueness and the pattern of period-4 cycles of:

$$x_{n+2} = \frac{A_n}{x_n}, \quad n = 0, 1, \dots.$$

Solution: Similar to the previous two examples, set $x_4 = x_0$ and $x_5 = x_1$ and we obtain:

$$x_0,$$

$$x_1,$$

$$x_2 = \frac{A_0}{x_0},$$

$$x_3 = \frac{A_1}{x_1},$$

$$x_4 = \frac{A_2}{[x_2]} = \frac{A_2}{\left[\frac{A_0}{x_0}\right]} = \frac{A_2 x_0}{A_0} = x_0,$$

$$x_5 = \frac{A_3}{[x_3]} = \frac{A_3}{\left[\frac{A_1}{x_1}\right]} = \frac{A_3 x_1}{A_1} = x_1.$$

Now observe that $x_4 = x_0$ and $x_5 = x_1$ if and only if

$$A_2 = A_0 \quad \text{and} \quad A_1 = A_3.$$

Every solution is then periodic with the following period-4 pattern:

$$x_0, \ x_1, \ \frac{A_0}{x_0}, \ \frac{A_1}{x_1}, \dots.$$

Example 23. Suppose that $\{A_n\}_{n=0}^{\infty}$ is a period-6 sequence. Determine the existence, uniqueness and the pattern of period-6 cycles of:

$$x_{n+2} = \frac{A_n}{x_n}, \quad n = 0, 1, \dots.$$

Solution: Set $x_6 = x_0$ and $x_7 = x_1$ and we produce:

$$x_0,$$

$$x_1,$$

$$x_2 = \frac{A_0}{x_0},$$

$$x_3 = \frac{A_1}{x_1},$$

$$x_4 = \frac{A_2}{[x_2]} = \frac{A_2 x_0}{A_0},$$

$$x_5 = \frac{A_3}{[x_3]} = \frac{A_3 x_1}{A_1},$$

$$x_6 = \frac{A_4}{[x_4]} = \frac{A_4 A_0}{A_2 x_0} = x_0,$$

$$x_7 = \frac{A_5}{[x_5]} = \frac{A_5 A_1}{A_3 x_1} = x_1,$$

and we obtain:

$$x_0 = \pm\sqrt{\frac{A_4 A_0}{A_2}} \quad \text{and} \quad x_1 = \pm\sqrt{\frac{A_5 A_1}{A_3}}.$$

Thus we acquire four distinct period-6 cycles:

- $\sqrt{\frac{A_4 A_0}{A_2}}, \ \sqrt{\frac{A_5 A_1}{A_3}}, \ \sqrt{\frac{A_0 A_2}{A_4}}, \ \sqrt{\frac{A_1 A_3}{A_5}}, \ \sqrt{\frac{A_2 A_4}{A_0}}, \ \sqrt{\frac{A_3 A_5}{A_1}}, \dots$

- $-\sqrt{\frac{A_4 A_0}{A_2}}, \ \sqrt{\frac{A_5 A_1}{A_3}}, \ -\sqrt{\frac{A_0 A_2}{A_4}}, \ \sqrt{\frac{A_1 A_3}{A_5}}, \ -\sqrt{\frac{A_2 A_4}{A_0}}, \ \sqrt{\frac{A_3 A_5}{A_1}}, \dots$

- $\sqrt{\frac{A_4 A_0}{A_2}}, \ -\sqrt{\frac{A_5 A_1}{A_3}}, \ \sqrt{\frac{A_0 A_2}{A_4}}, \ -\sqrt{\frac{A_1 A_3}{A_5}}, \ \sqrt{\frac{A_2 A_4}{A_0}}, \ -\sqrt{\frac{A_3 A_5}{A_1}}, \dots$

- $-\sqrt{\frac{A_4 A_0}{A_2}}, \ -\sqrt{\frac{A_5 A_1}{A_3}}, \ -\sqrt{\frac{A_0 A_2}{A_4}}, \ -\sqrt{\frac{A_1 A_3}{A_5}}, \ -\sqrt{\frac{A_2 A_4}{A_0}}, \ -\sqrt{\frac{A_3 A_5}{A_1}}, \dots$

Observe from $x_0 - x_2$ and from $x_2 - x_4$, the indices of the sequence $\{A_n\}_{n=0}^{\infty}$ shift by 2. Similar phenomena occurs from $x_1 - x_3$ and from $x_3 - x_5$.

From Examples 21–23, we can see contrasts of periodic traits of Eq. (5.172) when $\{A_n\}_{n=0}^{\infty}$ is periodic with various periods. The following three theorems outline the conclusions.

Theorem 32. *Suppose that $\{A_n\}_{n=0}^{\infty}$ is a period-4k sequence ($k \geq 2$). Then every solution of*

$$x_{n+2} = \frac{A_n}{x_n}, \quad n = 0, 1, \dots$$

is periodic with period-4k if and only if:

$$\prod_{i=1}^{k} A_{4i-4} = \prod_{i=1}^{k} A_{4i-2} \quad \text{and} \quad \prod_{i=1}^{k} A_{4i-3} = \prod_{i=1}^{k} A_{4i-1}.$$

Theorem 33. *Suppose that $\{A_n\}_{n=0}^{\infty}$ is a period-$(4k + 2)$ sequence ($k \in \mathbb{N}$). Then*

$$x_{n+2} = \frac{A_n}{x_n}, \quad n = 0, 1, \dots$$

has four distinct period-$(4k + 2)$ cycles with

$$x_0 = \pm\sqrt{\frac{\prod_{i=1}^{k+1} A_{4i-4}}{\prod_{i=1}^{k} A_{4i-2}}} \quad \text{and} \quad x_1 = \pm\sqrt{\frac{\prod_{i=1}^{k+1} A_{4i-3}}{\prod_{i=1}^{k} A_{4i-1}}}.$$

Theorem 34. *Suppose that $\{A_n\}_{n=0}^{\infty}$ is a period-$(2k+1)$ sequence $(k \in \mathbb{N})$. Then*

$$x_{n+2} = \frac{A_n}{x_n}, \quad n = 0, 1, \ldots$$

has four distinct period-$(2k+1)$ cycles.

To prove Theorem 34, we require two cases: when $\{A_n\}_{n=0}^{\infty}$ is a period-$(4k-1)$ sequence $(k \in \mathbb{N})$ and when $\{A_n\}_{n=0}^{\infty}$ is a period-$(4k+1)$ sequence $(k \in \mathbb{N})$.

Now we will proceed with studying periodic nature of additional types of non-autonomous rational difference equations. The next series of examples will analyze the periodic make up of solutions of the following Rational Non-autonomous Δ.E.:

$$x_{n+2} = \frac{A_n x_n}{1 + x_{n+1}}, \quad n = 0, 1, \ldots, \tag{5.173}$$

where $x_0 + x_1 > 0$ and $\{A_n\}_{n=0}^{\infty}$ is a period-k sequence $(k \geq 2)$. Our aim is to compare the periodic traits of Eq. (5.173) with the periodicity character of Eq. (5.170); the differences in the length of the periods depending on whether $\{A_n\}_{n=0}^{\infty}$ is an even period or an odd period and the existence of multiple periodic solutions. We observed similar phenomenon with Piecewise Difference Equations in Chapter 3.

Example 24. Suppose that $\{A_n\}_{n=0}^{\infty}$ is a period-2 sequence. Determine the necessary and sufficient conditions for the existence of period-2 cycles of:

$$x_{n+2} = \frac{A_n x_n}{1 + x_{n+1}}, \quad n = 0, 1, \ldots.$$

Solution: We set $x_2 = x_0$ and $x_3 = x_1$ and we get:

$$x_0,$$
$$x_1,$$
$$x_2 = \frac{A_0 x_0}{1 + x_1} = x_0,$$
$$x_3 = \frac{A_1 x_1}{1 + x_2} = \frac{A_1 x_1}{1 + x_0} = x_1,$$

and obtain one of the following equalities:

$$x_0 (A_0 - 1) = x_0 x_1 \quad \text{or} \quad x_1 (A_1 - 1) = x_0 x_1.$$

Notice that they cannot hold true simultaneously as we assumed that $A_0 \neq A_1$. Compared to Eq. (5.170) in Example 17, period-2 solutions will exist if either $A_0 = 1$ or $A_1 = 1$. This leads the analysis to two cases:

CASE 1: Suppose that $A_0 = 1$, then similar to Example 17, $x_1 = 0$ with the following period-2 pattern:

$$x_0, \ 0, \ x_0, \ 0, \ldots.$$

CASE 2: Suppose that $A_1 = 1$, then similar to Example 17, $x_0 = 0$ with the following period-2 pattern:

$$0, \ x_1, 0, \ x_1, \ldots.$$

In Case 1 and Case 2, the match of parity between A_0 and x_1 and between A_1 and x_0 becomes a vital factor for the existence of period-2 cycles. We did not encounter such a parity dependence in Eq. (5.170).

The next example will assume that $\{A_n\}_{n=0}^{\infty}$ is a period-3 sequence and determine the periodic nature of solutions of Eq. (5.173).

Example 25. Suppose that $\{A_n\}_{n=0}^{\infty}$ is a period-3 sequence. Determine the necessary and sufficient conditions for the existence of period-6 cycles of:

$$x_{n+2} = \frac{A_n x_n}{1 + x_{n+1}}, \quad n = 0, 1, \ldots.$$

Solution: Analogous to Examples 17 and 24, either $x_0 = 0$ or $x_1 = 0$. In this case let $x_1 = 0$ and set $x_6 = x_0$ and $x_7 = x_1$. The case when $x_0 = 0$ is similar and will be omitted. Notice:

$$x_0,$$

$$x_1 = 0,$$

$$x_2 = \frac{A_0 x_0}{1 + x_1} = A_0 x_0,$$

$$x_3 = \frac{A_1 x_1}{1 + x_2} = \frac{A_1 x_1}{1 + x_0} = 0,$$

$$x_4 = \frac{A_2 [x_2]}{1 + x_3} = A_2 A_0 x_0,$$

$$x_5 = \frac{A_0 x_3}{1 + x_4} = 0,$$

$$x_6 = \frac{A_1 [x_4]}{1 + x_5} = A_1 A_2 A_0 x_0 = x_0,$$

$$x_7 = \frac{A_2 x_5}{1 + x_6} = 0 = x_1.$$

Hence $x_6 = x_0$ if and only if $A_1 A_2 A_0 = 1$ with the following period-6 pattern:

$$x_0, \ 0, \ A_0 x_0, \ 0, \ A_2 A_0 x_0, \ 0, \ A_1 A_2 A_0 x_0, \ \ldots .$$

Observe that the even ordered indices A_0 and A_2 are multiplied in the beginning of the pattern and the odd ordered index A_1 is multiplied at the very end of the pattern. First of all, it is impossible to obtain a period-2 cycle or a period-3 cycle. Second of all, period-6 is the shortest periodic cycle. In fact, period-6 cycles come from period-2 of Eq. (5.170) and the period-3 sequence $\{A_n\}_{n=0}^{\infty}$. On one hand, we can see that $x_1 = x_3 = x_5 = 0$ (all the odd ordered terms are 0). On the other hand, when $x_0 = 0$, we then produce the following period-6 pattern:

$$0, \ x_1, \ 0, \ A_1 x_1, \ 0, \ A_0 A_1 x_1, \ 0, \ A_2 A_0 A_1 x_1, \ldots,$$

where $x_0 = x_2 = x_4 = 0$ (all the even ordered terms are 0) and the pattern emerges with an odd ordered index A_1 instead.

From Example 25, when $\{A_n\}_{n=0}^{\infty}$ is an odd ordered period-$(2k+1)$ sequence $(k \in \mathbb{N})$, then we can expect the existence of only period-$2(2k+1)$ cycles of Eq. (5.173). The following theorem summarizes the result.

Theorem 35. *Suppose that $\{A_n\}_{n=0}^{\infty}$ is a period-$(2k+1)$ sequence $(k \in \mathbb{N})$. Then every solution of*

$$x_{n+2} = \frac{A_n x_n}{1 + x_{n+1}}, \quad n = 0, 1, \ldots$$

is periodic with period-$2(2k+1)$ if and only if either

$$x_1 = 0 \quad and \quad \prod_{i=1}^{2k+1} A_{i-1} = 1, \quad or$$

$$x_0 = 0 \quad and \quad \prod_{i=1}^{2k+1} A_{i-1} = 1.$$

Proof. Suppose that $x_1 = 0$. The case when $x_0 = 0$ is similar and will be omitted. Let

$$P_0 = \prod_{i=1}^{k+1} A_{2i-2} \quad \text{and} \quad P_1 = \prod_{i=1}^{k} A_{2i-1}.$$

As mentioned in Example 25, the even ordered indices will be multiplied first and then the odd ordered indices. First we will see P_0 and then P_1.

$$x_0,$$
$$x_1 = 0,$$
$$x_2 = \frac{A_0 x_0}{1 + x_1} = A_0 x_0,$$
$$x_3 = 0,$$
$$x_4 = \frac{A_2 [x_2]}{1 + x_3} = A_2 A_0 x_0,$$
$$x_5 = 0,$$
$$x_6 = \frac{A_4 [x_4]}{1 + x_5} = A_4 A_2 A_0 x_0,$$
$$\vdots$$
$$x_{2k+1} = 0,$$
$$x_{2k+2} = P_0 x_0,$$
$$x_{2k+3} = 0,$$
$$x_{2k+4} = A_1 P_0 x_0,$$
$$x_{2k+5} = 0,$$
$$x_{2k+6} = A_3 A_1 P_0 x_0,$$
$$\vdots$$
$$x_{4k+1} = 0,$$
$$x_{4k+2} = P_1 P_0 x_0.$$

The result follows. $\square$

Now suppose that $\{A_n\}_{n=0}^{\infty}$ is an even ordered period-2k sequence ($k \geq 2$). For the first time we will discern the existence of multiple periodic cycles of Eq. (5.173). For instance, in the next example when $\{A_n\}_{n=0}^{\infty}$ is a period-4 sequence, we will discover the existence of period-2 cycles and period-4 cycles.

Example 26. Suppose that $\{A_n\}_{n=0}^{\infty}$ is a period-4 sequence. Determine the necessary and sufficient conditions for the existence of period-2 cycles and period-4 cycles of:

$$x_{n+2} = \frac{A_n x_n}{1 + x_{n+1}}, \quad n = 0, 1, \ldots.$$

Solution: From Example 24, period-2 solutions will exist if either $A_0 = 1$ or $A_1 = 1$. This time there are four periodic coefficients A_0, A_1, A_2, A_3. This will guide us to four cases:

CASE 1: Suppose that $A_0 = A_2 = 1$, then similar to Example 24, $x_1 = 0$ with the following period-2 pattern:

$$x_0, \ 0, \ x_0, \ 0, \ldots.$$

CASE 2: Suppose that $A_1 = A_3 = 1$, then similar to Example 24, $x_0 = 0$ with the following period-2 pattern:

$$0, \ x_1, \ 0, \ x_1, \ldots.$$

CASE 3: Suppose that $A_0 A_2 = 1$, then similar to Example 24, $x_1 = 0$ with the following period-4 pattern:

$$x_0, \ 0, \ A_0 x_0, \ 0, \ldots.$$

CASE 4: Suppose that $A_1 A_3 = 1$, then similar to Example 24, $x_0 = 0$ with the following period-4 pattern:

$$0, \ x_1, \ 0, \ A_1 x_1, \ldots.$$

From Example 26 we can expect the existence of multiple periodic solutions when $\{A_n\}_{n=0}^{\infty}$ is an even ordered sequence. This leads to the following conjecture:

Conjecture 4. Suppose that $\{A_n\}_{n=0}^{\infty}$ is a period-2k sequence $(k \geq 2)$. Then

$$x_{n+2} = \frac{A_n x_n}{1 + x_{n+1}}, \quad n = 0, 1, \ldots$$

has even ordered period-p solutions such that $2k = Np$ for some $N \in \mathbb{N}$.

Furthermore, the following theorems describe the asymptotic properties of Eq. (5.173).

Theorem 36. *Let* $\{A_n\}_{n=0}^{\infty}$ *be a solution of Eq.* (5.173) *and suppose that* $\{A_n\}_{n=0}^{\infty}$ *is a period-$(2k+1)$ sequence* $(k \in \mathbb{N})$. *Then*

$$\lim_{n \to \infty} x_n = 0,$$

if and only if

$$\prod_{i=0}^{2k} a_i < 1.$$

Theorem 37. *Let* $\{A_n\}_{n=0}^{\infty}$ *be a solution of Eq.* (5.173) *and suppose that* $\{A_n\}_{n=0}^{\infty}$ *is a period-$2k$ sequence* $(k \in \mathbb{N})$. *Then*

$$\lim_{n \to \infty} x_n = 0,$$

if and only if for all $i = 0, 1, \ldots, k - 1$

$$a_{2i} < 1 \quad and \quad a_{2i+1} < 1.$$

The next series of examples will analyze the periodicity of:

$$x_{n+2} = \frac{A_n x_n}{1 + x_{n+1} + x_n}, \quad n = 0, 1, \ldots, \tag{5.174}$$

where $x_0 + x_1 > 0$ and $\{A_n\}_{n=0}^{\infty}$ is a period-k sequence $(k \geq 2)$. Similar phenomenon will occur with the existence of multiple periodic cycles and the differences in periodicity properties depending on whether $\{A_n\}_{n=0}^{\infty}$ is an even ordered period or an odd ordered period. However, the primary contrast with Eq. (5.171) will be the uniqueness of periodic cycles.

Example 27. Suppose that $\{A_n\}_{n=0}^{\infty}$ is a period-2 sequence. Determine the necessary and sufficient conditions for the existence of period-2 cycles of:

$$x_{n+2} = \frac{A_n x_n}{1 + x_{n+1} + x_n}, \quad n = 0, 1, \ldots.$$

Solution: Set $x_2 = x_0$ and $x_3 = x_1$ and we get:

$$x_0,$$
$$x_1,$$
$$x_2 = \frac{A_0 x_0}{1 + x_1 + x_0} = x_0,$$
$$x_3 = \frac{A_1 x_1}{1 + x_2 + x_1} = \frac{A_1 x_1}{1 + x_0 + x_1} = x_1,$$

and we obtain two equalities:

$$A_0 = 1 + x_0 + x_1, \quad \text{or}$$
$$A_1 = 1 + x_0 + x_1.$$

Notice that they cannot hold true simultaneously as we assumed that $A_0 \neq A_1$. This steers us into two cases:

CASE 1: Suppose that $A_0 = 1 + x_0 + x_1$. Then similar to Example 18, let $x_0 = A_0 - (x_1 + 1)$ and we get:

$$x_0 = A_0 - (x_1 + 1),$$
$$x_1,$$
$$x_2 = \frac{A_0 x_0}{1 + x_1 + [x_0]} = \frac{A_0 x_0}{1 + x_1 + [A_0 - (x_1 + 1)]} = x_0,$$
$$x_3 = \frac{A_1 x_1}{1 + x_2 + x_1} = \frac{A_1 x_1}{1 + [x_0] + x_1}$$
$$= \frac{A_1 x_1}{1 + [A_0 - (x_1 + 1)] + x_1} = \frac{A_1 x_1}{A_0}.$$

Note that $x_3 = x_1$ if and only if $x_1 = 0$ as we assumed that $A_0 \neq A_1$ and we acquire the following unique period-2 pattern:

$$A_0 - 1, \ 0, \ A_0 - 1, \ 0, \ \dots.$$

CASE 2: Suppose that $A_0 = 1 + x_0 + x_1$, then similar to Case 1, we obtain the following unique period-2 pattern:

$$0, \ A_1 - 1, \ 0, \ A_1 - 1, \ \dots.$$

In Example 24, the parity match becomes an essential factor for the existence of the period-2 cycle in Case 1 and in Case 2. Furthermore, it is of paramount importance to note that period-2 cycles of Eq. (5.171) in Example 18 were on a line segment $y = A - (x + 1)$. Contrarily, Eq. (5.174) has two unique period-2 cycles instead.

The next example will assume that $\{A_n\}_{n=0}^{\infty}$ is a period-3 sequence and determine the periodic nature of solutions of Eq. (5.174).

Example 28. Suppose that $\{A_n\}_{n=0}^{\infty}$ is a period-3 sequence. Determine the necessary and sufficient conditions for the existence of period-6 cycles of:

$$x_{n+2} = \frac{A_n x_n}{1 + x_{n+1} + x_n}, \quad n = 0, 1, \ldots.$$

Solution: Similar to the previous example, we will analyze two cases when $x_0 = 0$ and when $x_1 = 0$. Suppose that $x_1 = 0$. Then we acquire

$x_0,$

$x_1 = 0,$

$$x_2 = \frac{A_0 x_0}{1 + x_1 + x_0} = \frac{A_0 x_0}{1 + x_0},$$

$x_3 = 0,$

$$x_4 = \frac{A_2 x_2}{1 + x_3 + x_2} = \frac{A_2 x_2}{1 + x_2} = \frac{A_0 A_2 x_0}{1 + x_0 + A_0 x_0},$$

$x_5 = 0,$

$$x_6 = \frac{A_1 x_4}{1 + x_5 + x_4} = \frac{A_1 x_4}{1 + x_4} = \frac{A_1 A_0 A_2 x_0}{1 + x_0 + A_0 x_0 + A_0 A_2 x_0} = x_0.$$

Therefore

$$x_0 = \frac{A_0 A_1 A_2 - 1}{1 + A_0 + A_0 A_2}.$$

Similarly, set $x_0 = 0$ and we obtain:

$$x_1 = \frac{A_0 A_1 A_2 - 1}{1 + A_1 + A_1 A_0}.$$

The two unique period-6 cycles exist if and only if $A_0 A_1 A_2 \neq 1$.

From Example 28 we can conclude that when $\{A_n\}_{n=0}^{\infty}$ is an odd ordered period-$(2k+1)$ sequence, then we can expect the existence of only period-$2(2k+1)$ cycles $(k \in \mathbb{N})$. The following theorem summarizes the results and the proof will be left as an exercise at the end of the chapter.

Theorem 38. *Suppose that* $\{A_n\}_{n=0}^{\infty}$ *is a period-*$(2k+1)$ *sequence* $(k \in \mathbb{N})$. *Then every solution of*

$$x_{n+2} = \frac{A_n x_n}{1 + x_{n+1} + x_n}, \quad n = 0, 1, \dots$$

is periodic with period-$2(2k+1)$ *if and only if* $\left[\prod_{i=1}^{2k+1} A_{i-1}\right] \neq 1$ *and either*

$$x_1 = 0 \quad and \quad x_0 = \frac{\left[\prod_{i=1}^{2k+1} A_{i-1}\right] - 1}{1 + A_0 + A_0 A_2 + \cdots + \prod_{i=1}^{k+1} A_{2i-2}}, \quad or$$

$$x_0 = 0 \quad and \quad x_1 = \frac{\left[\prod_{i=1}^{2k+1} A_{i-1}\right] - 1}{1 + A_1 + A_1 A_3 + \cdots + A_0 \left[\prod_{i=1}^{k} A_{2i-1}\right]}.$$

Further investigation of periodic properties when $\{A_n\}_{n=0}^{\infty}$ is an even ordered period will be left as exercises at the end of the chapter. Similar periodic phenomena will occur with the existence of multiple periodic cycles as we saw in Example 26. We can then conclude that when $\{A_n\}_{n=0}^{\infty}$ is an even ordered period, we can expect the existence of multiple periodic solutions only of even ordered periods and that will pose the following conjecture:

Conjecture 5. Suppose that $\{A_n\}_{n=0}^{\infty}$ is a period-2k sequence $(k \geq 2)$. Then

$$x_{n+2} = \frac{A_n x_n}{1 + x_{n+1} + x_n}, \quad n = 0, 1, \dots$$

has even ordered period-p solutions provided that $2k = Np$ for some $N \in \mathbb{N}$.

5.5. Periodic and Eventually Periodic Solutions of Max-Type Difference Equations

In this section we will examine the existence and patterns of periodic and eventually periodic solutions of the following Max-Type Δ.E.:

$$x_{n+2} = \max\left\{\frac{A}{x_{n+1}}, \frac{B}{x_n}\right\}, \quad n = 0, 1, \dots,$$

where $A, B, x_0, x_1 > 0$. By a change of variables, the above A.E. can be rewritten as:

$$x_{n+2} = \max\left\{\frac{1}{x_{n+1}}, \frac{C}{x_n}\right\}, \quad n = 0, 1, \ldots,$$ (5.175)

where $C, x_0, x_1 > 0$. Eq. (5.175) has a unique equilibrium point $\bar{x} = \max\{1, \sqrt{C}\}$. If $C \leq 1$ then $\bar{x} = 1$ and if $C > 1$ then $\bar{x} = \sqrt{C}$. In [3], it was shown that every positive solution of Eq. (5.175) is eventually periodic with the following periods:

$$\begin{cases} 2 & \text{if } C < 1, \\ 3 & \text{if } C = 1, \\ 4 & \text{if } C > 1. \end{cases}$$

For instance, the following graph:

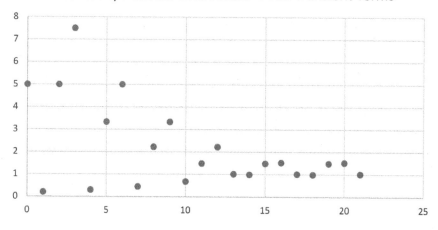

Eventually Periodic with Period-4 : 13 Transient Terms

depicts an eventually periodic solution with period-4 with thirteen transient terms when $C = 1.5$, $x_0 = 5$ and $x_1 = 0.2$. This time the transient terms portray quite a different set of patterns compared to eventually periodic solutions in the Logistic A.E. and in the Piecewise Difference Equations that we analyzed in Chapter 3.

First of all, the left-hand side of Eq. (5.175) is the $\Delta.E.$:

$$x_{n+2} = \frac{1}{x_{n+1}},$$

which is the Riccati $\Delta.E.$ with period-2 cycles. Second of all, the right-hand side of Eq. (5.175) is the $\Delta.E.$:

$$x_{n+2} = \frac{C}{x_n},$$

which is the **Delayed Riccati $\Delta.E.$** with period-4 cycles. We will study the case when $C < 1$ and show that every positive solution of Eq. (5.175) is either periodic with period-2 or eventually periodic with period-2 and describe the pattern of the transient terms. Other cases are similar and will left as exercises at the end of the chapter. Eq. (5.175) will not exhibit unique periodic solutions in comparison with the Piecewise Difference Equations. The periodic essence of Max-Type Difference Equations was investigated by several authors in [3, 11, 12, 15, 45, 46, 50, 51, 55, 80]. The following theorem and the next two examples will assume that $C < 1$ and we will derive various periodic traits.

Theorem 39. *Consider the Max-Type $\Delta.E.$:*

$$x_{n+2} = max\left\{\frac{1}{x_{n+1}}, \frac{C}{x_n}\right\}, \quad n = 0, 1, \ldots,$$

where $C < 1$. Then there exists $N \geq 0$ such that

$$x_{N+1} = \frac{1}{x_N}.$$

Proof. For the sake of contradiction, suppose that $x_{n+2} = \frac{C}{x_n}$ for all $n \geq 0$. Then:

$$x_0,$$

$$x_1,$$

$$x_2 = max\left\{\frac{1}{x_1}, \frac{C}{x_0}\right\} = \frac{C}{x_0} \quad \left(\text{if } \frac{x_0}{x_1} < C < 1\right),$$

$$x_3 = \max\left\{\frac{1}{[x_2]}, \frac{C}{x_1}\right\} = \max\left\{\frac{1}{\left[\frac{C}{x_0}\right]}, \frac{C}{x_1}\right\} = \max\left\{\frac{x_0}{C}, \frac{C}{x_1}\right\}$$

$$= \frac{C}{x_1} \quad \left(\text{if } x_0 x_1 < C^2 < 1\right),$$

$$x_4 = \max\left\{\frac{1}{[x_3]}, \frac{C}{[x_2]}\right\} = \max\left\{\frac{1}{\left[\frac{C}{x_1}\right]}, \frac{C}{\left[\frac{C}{x_0}\right]}\right\} = \max\left\{\frac{x_1}{C}, x_0\right\}$$

$$= x_0 \quad \left(\text{if } \frac{x_1}{x_0} < C < 1\right).$$

It is interesting to see that from the above iterations we produce the following two inequalities:

$$\frac{x_0}{x_1} < C \quad \text{and} \quad \frac{x_1}{x_0} < C,$$

which is clearly a contradiction. Thus Eq. (5.175) cannot exhibit period-4 solutions when $C < 1$. Therefore, when $C < 1$, it suffices to consider the following initial conditions:

$$x_0 \quad \text{and} \quad x_1 = \frac{1}{x_0}.$$

$\square$

The following example will outline the necessary and sufficient conditions for every solution of Eq. (5.175) to be periodic with period-2.

Example 29. Suppose that $C < 1$. Determine the necessary and sufficient conditions for the existence of period-2 cycles of:

$$x_{n+2} = \max\left\{\frac{1}{x_{n+1}}, \frac{C}{x_n}\right\}, \quad n = 0, 1, \ldots.$$

Solution: From Theorem 39 we assume that $x_1 = \frac{1}{x_0}$. Then:

$$x_0,$$

$$x_1 = \frac{1}{x_0},$$

$$x_2 = \max\left\{\frac{1}{[x_1]}, \frac{C}{x_0}\right\} = \max\left\{\frac{1}{\left[\frac{1}{x_0}\right]}, \frac{C}{x_0}\right\} = \max\left\{x_0, \frac{C}{x_0}\right\}$$

$$= x_0 \quad (\text{if } x_0^2 > C),$$

$$x_3 = \max\left\{\frac{1}{[x_2]}, \frac{C}{[x_1]}\right\} = \max\left\{\frac{1}{x_0}, \frac{C}{\left[\frac{1}{x_0}\right]}\right\} = \max\left\{\frac{1}{x_0}, Cx_0\right\}$$

$$= \frac{1}{x_0} \quad \left(\text{if } x_0^2 < \frac{1}{C}\right).$$

We obtain a period-2 cycle if and only if:

$$C < x_0^2 < \frac{1}{C}.$$

Hence if either $x_0^2 < C$ or $x_0^2 > \frac{1}{C}$, Eq. (5.175) will evince eventually periodic solutions with transient terms. Now the fundamental question to ask: exactly how many transient terms will Eq. (5.175) have and under what criteria? The next two examples will address the answers to these two questions. In fact, Eq. (5.175) will portray 3N transient terms ($N \in \mathbb{N}$).

Example 30. Suppose that $C < 1$ and $x_0^2 < C$. Determine the necessary and sufficient conditions for the existence of eventually period-2 solutions with three transient terms of:

$$x_{n+2} = \max\left\{\frac{1}{x_{n+1}}, \frac{C}{x_n}\right\}, \quad n = 0, 1, \ldots.$$

Solution: As in Example 29, let $x_1 = \frac{1}{x_0}$. Then:

$$x_0,$$

$$x_1 = \frac{1}{x_0},$$

$$x_2 = \max\left\{\frac{1}{[x_1]}, \frac{C}{x_0}\right\} = \max\left\{\frac{1}{\left[\frac{1}{x_0}\right]}, \frac{C}{x_0}\right\} = \max\left\{x_0, \frac{C}{x_0}\right\}$$

$$= \frac{C}{x_0} \quad (\text{as } x_0^2 < C),$$

$$x_3 = \max\left\{\frac{1}{[x_2]}, \frac{C}{[x_1]}\right\} = \max\left\{\frac{1}{\left[\frac{C}{x_0}\right]}, \frac{C}{\left[\frac{1}{x_0}\right]}\right\} = \max\left\{\frac{x_0}{C}, Cx_0\right\}$$

$$= \frac{x_0}{C} \quad (\text{as } C < 1),$$

$$x_4 = \max\left\{\frac{1}{[x_3]}, \frac{C}{[x_2]}\right\} = \max\left\{\frac{1}{\left[\frac{x_0}{C}\right]}, \frac{C}{\left[\frac{C}{x_0}\right]}\right\} = \max\left\{\frac{C}{x_0}, x_0\right\}$$

$$= \frac{C}{x_0} \quad (\text{as } x_0^2 < C),$$

$$x_5 = \max\left\{\frac{1}{[x_4]}, \frac{C}{[x_3]}\right\} = \max\left\{\frac{1}{\left[\frac{C}{x_0}\right]}, \frac{C}{\left[\frac{x_0}{C}\right]}\right\} = \max\left\{\frac{x_0}{C}, \frac{C^2}{x_0}\right\}$$

$$= \frac{x_0}{C} = x_3 \quad (\text{if } C^3 < x_0^2 < C),$$

$$x_6 = \max\left\{\frac{1}{[x_5]}, \frac{C}{[x_4]}\right\} = \max\left\{\frac{1}{\left[\frac{x_0}{C}\right]}, \frac{C}{\left[\frac{C}{x_0}\right]}\right\} = \max\left\{\frac{C}{x_0}, x_0\right\}$$

$$= \frac{C}{x_0} = x_4 \quad (\text{as } x_0^2 < C).$$

Thus when

$$C^3 < x_0^2 < C,$$

we obtain three transient terms in square brackets prior to the period-2 pattern:

$$\left[x_0, \frac{1}{x_0}, \frac{C}{x_0}\right], \frac{x_0}{C}, \frac{C}{x_0}, \ldots$$

Example 31. Suppose that $C < 1$ and $x_0^2 < C^3$. Determine the necessary and sufficient conditions for the existence of eventually period-2 solutions with six transient terms of:

$$x_{n+2} = \max\left\{\frac{1}{x_{n+1}}, \frac{C}{x_n}\right\}, \quad n = 0, 1, \ldots.$$

Solution: Let $x_1 = \frac{1}{x_0}$. Then:

$$x_0,$$

$$x_1 = \frac{1}{x_0},$$

$$x_2 = \max\left\{\frac{1}{[x_1]}, \frac{C}{x_0}\right\} = \max\left\{x_0, \frac{C}{x_0}\right\} = \frac{C}{x_0}$$
$$\left(\text{as } x_0^2 < C\right),$$

$$x_3 = \max\left\{\frac{1}{[x_2]}, \frac{C}{[x_1]}\right\} = \max\left\{\frac{x_0}{C}, Cx_0\right\} = \frac{x_0}{C}$$
$$(\text{as } C < 1),$$

$$x_4 = \max\left\{\frac{1}{[x_3]}, \frac{C}{[x_2]}\right\} = \max\left\{\frac{C}{x_0}, x_0\right\} = \frac{C}{x_0}$$
$$\left(\text{as } x_0^2 < C\right),$$

$$x_5 = \max\left\{\frac{1}{[x_4]}, \frac{C}{[x_3]}\right\} = \max\left\{\frac{x_0}{C}, \frac{C^2}{x_0}\right\} = \frac{C^2}{x_0}$$
$$\left(\text{as } x_0^2 < C^3\right),$$

$$x_6 = \max\left\{\frac{1}{[x_5]}, \frac{C}{[x_4]}\right\} = \max\left\{\frac{x_0}{C^2}, x_0\right\} = \frac{x_0}{C^2}$$
$$(\text{as } C < 1),$$

$$x_7 = \max\left\{\frac{1}{[x_6]}, \frac{C}{[x_5]}\right\} = \max\left\{\frac{C^2}{x_0}, \frac{x_0}{C}\right\} = \frac{C^2}{x_0}$$
$$\left(\text{as } x_0^2 < C^3\right),$$

$$x_8 = \max\left\{\frac{1}{[x_7]}, \frac{C}{[x_6]}\right\} = \max\left\{\frac{x_0}{C^2}, \frac{C^3}{x_0}\right\} = \frac{x_0}{C^2} = x_6$$
$$\left(\text{if } C^5 < x_0^2 < C^3\right).$$

Note when

$$C^5 < x_0^2 < C^3,$$

we acquire six transient terms in square brackets prior to the period-2 pattern:

$$\left[x_0, \frac{1}{x_0}, \frac{C}{x_0}, \frac{x_0}{C}, \frac{C}{x_0}, \frac{C^2}{x_0}\right], \frac{x_0}{C^2}, \frac{C^2}{x_0}, \ldots$$

It is interesting to observe that the six transient terms can be decomposed into three groups of geometric sequences. In the diagram below:

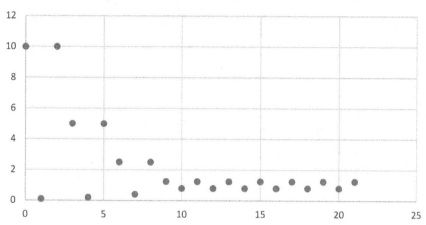

we see an eventually periodic solution with period-2 with nine transient terms when $C = 0.5$, $x_0 = 10$ and $x_1 = 0.1$. Also note that the periodic cycle oscillates about $\bar{x} = 1$.

From Examples 30 and 31, there exists $k \in \mathbb{N}$ such that:

$$C^{2k+1} < x_0^2 < C^{2k-1}.$$

Furthermore, from Examples 30 and 31, the following theorem describes the results.

Theorem 40. *Every solution of Eq. (5.175) is eventually periodic with period-2 with $3k$ transient terms if:*

(1) $C < 1$;
(2) *There exists $k \in \mathbb{N}$ such that:*

$$C^{2k+1} < x_0^2 < C^{2k-1}.$$

Furthermore, when $x_0^2 > C$, we can similarly conclude that there exists $k \in \mathbb{N}$ such that:

$$\frac{1}{C^{2k-1}} < x_0^2 < \frac{1}{C^{2k+1}}.$$

It is of paramount interest to note when $x_0^2 = \frac{1}{C^{2k+1}}$ for some $k \in \mathbb{N}$, we acquire an **eventually constant solution**. In fact, the diagram below

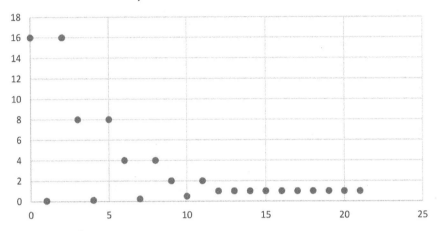

evokes an eventually periodic solution $\bar{x} = 1$ with 12 transient terms when $C = 0.5$, $x_0 = 16$ and $x_1 = \frac{1}{16}$.

In addition, using similar techniques with subintervals and decomposing the transient terms into three groups of geometric sub-sequences, we can show that every solution is periodic or eventually periodic with:

- Period-4 if $C > 1$;
- Period-3 if $C = 1$.

Max-Type Difference Equations can be applied in statistics, computer science, electrical engineering, biological sciences and in economics. It is of paramount importance to remit the following questions that address the periodicity nature of solutions of Max-Type Difference Equations:

- When $\{C_n\}_{n=0}^{\infty}$ is a period-k sequence $(k \geq 2)$.
- Delayed Max-Type Difference Equations.
- Max-Type Difference Equations with three or more components in the form:

$$x_{n+m} = \max \left\{ \frac{C_{n+m-1}}{x_{n+m-1}}, \ \ldots, \ \frac{C_1}{x_{n+1}}, \frac{C_0}{x_n} \right\}, \ n = 0, 1, \ldots.$$

Further properties on the boundedness and periodic nature of solutions of Max-Type Difference Equations have been studied in [46, 47 and 55].

5.6. Chapter 5 Exercises

In problems 1–20, determine the **local stability character** of all the equilibrium point(s) of each Δ.E.; assume that $A, B, C, \alpha, \beta, \gamma > 0$ and $x_0, x_1 \geq 0$.

1. $x_{n+2} = \dfrac{A x_{n+1} + B x_n}{\alpha + \beta x_n}$, $n = 0, 1, \ldots$.

2. $x_{n+2} = \dfrac{A x_{n+1} + B x_n}{\alpha x_{n+1} + \beta}$, $n = 0, 1, \ldots$.

3. $x_{n+2} = \dfrac{B x_n}{\alpha x_{n+1} + \beta x_n}$, $n = 0, 1, \ldots$.

4. $x_{n+2} = \dfrac{A x_{n+1} + B x_n}{\alpha x_{n+1} + \beta x_n + \gamma}$, $n = 0, 1, \ldots$.

5. $x_{n+2} = \dfrac{A x_{n+1}}{\alpha x_{n+1} + \beta x_n}$, $n = 0, 1, \ldots$.

6. $x_{n+2} = \dfrac{B x_n}{\alpha x_{n+1} + \beta x_n + \gamma}$, $n = 0, 1, \ldots$.

7. $x_{n+2} = \dfrac{A x_{n+1}}{\alpha x_{n+1} + \beta x_n + \gamma}$, $n = 0, 1, \ldots$.

8. $x_{n+2} = \dfrac{B x_n + C}{\alpha x_{n+1} + \gamma}$, $n = 0, 1, \ldots$.

9. $x_{n+2} = \dfrac{A}{x_{n+1} + x_n}$, $n = 0, 1, \ldots$.

10. $x_{n+2} = \dfrac{A x_{n+1} + B x_n}{\alpha x_{n+1} + \beta x_n}$, $n = 0, 1, \ldots$.

11. $x_{n+2} = \dfrac{A}{x_{n+1}} + \dfrac{B}{x_n}$, $n = 0, 1, \ldots$.

12. $x_{n+2} = \dfrac{x_{n+1} x_n}{x_{n+1} + x_n}$, $n = 0, 1, \ldots$.

13. $x_{n+2} = \dfrac{x_{n+1} x_n}{1 + x_{n+1} + x_n}$, $n = 0, 1, \ldots$.

14. $x_{n+2} = \dfrac{x_{n+1} + x_n}{1 + x_{n+1} x_n}$, $n = 0, 1, \ldots$.

15. $x_{n+2} = B x_{n+1} e^{-x_n}$, $n = 0, 1, \ldots$.

16. $x_{n+2} = Ax_{n+1}e^{-x_n}$, $\quad n = 0, 1, \ldots$.

17. $x_{n+2} = Ax_{n+1}e^{-(x_{n+1}+x_n)}$, $\quad n = 0, 1, \ldots$.

18. $x_{n+2} = Bx_n e^{-(x_{n+1}+x_n)}$, $\quad n = 0, 1, \ldots$.

19. $x_{n+2} = x_n e^{A-x_{n+1}-x_n}$, $\quad n = 0, 1, \ldots$.

20. $x_{n+2} = [Ax_{n+1} + Bx_n]e^{-(x_{n+1}+x_n)}$, $\quad n = 0, 1, \ldots$.

In problems 21–32, suppose that $A, B, C, D > 0$ and $x_0, x_1 \geq 0$. Determine the necessary and sufficient conditions for the existence of periodic cycles and their patterns:

21. $x_{n+2} = \dfrac{A + Bx_n}{C + Dx_{n+1}}$, $\quad n = 0, 1, \ldots$.

22. $x_{n+2} = \dfrac{Bx_n}{Cx_{n+1} + Dx_n}$, $\quad n = 0, 1, \ldots$.

23. $x_{n+2} = \dfrac{Ax_{n+1} + Bx_n}{1 + Cx_{n+1}}$, $\quad n = 0, 1, \ldots$.

24. $x_{n+2} = \dfrac{Ax_{n+1} + Bx_n}{1 + Cx_n}$, $\quad n = 0, 1, \ldots$.

25. $x_{n+2} = \dfrac{Ax_{n+1} + Bx_n}{1 + Cx_{n+1} + Dx_n}$, $\quad n = 0, 1, \ldots$.

26. $x_{n+2} = \dfrac{1 + Ax_{n+1} + Bx_n}{Cx_{n+1} + Dx_n}$, $\quad n = 0, 1, \ldots$.

27. $x_{n+2} = \dfrac{1}{x_n} - \dfrac{1}{x_{n+1}}$, $\quad n = 0, 1, \ldots$.

28. $x_{n+2} = \dfrac{x_n}{x_{n+1}}$, $\quad n = 0, 1, \ldots$.

29. $x_{n+2} = \dfrac{1}{x_n x_{n+1}}$, $\quad n = 0, 1, \ldots$.

30. $x_{n+2} = \dfrac{(-1)^n}{x_n}$, $\quad n = 0, 1, \ldots$.

31. $x_{n+2} = \dfrac{(-1)^n}{x_n x_{n+1}}$, $\quad n = 0, 1, \ldots$.

32. $x_{n+2} = \dfrac{(-1)^n x_{n+1}}{x_n}$, $\quad n = 0, 1, \ldots$.

Consider the **Non-autonomous Rational Δ.E.**:

$$x_{n+2} = \frac{A_n x_n}{1 + x_{n+1}}, \quad n = 0, 1, \ldots,$$

where $\{A_n\}_{n=0}^{\infty}$ is a periodic sequence. In problems 33–41:

33. Determine the necessary and sufficient conditions for the existence and pattern of period-2 solutions when $\{A_n\}_{n=0}^{\infty}$ is a period-12 sequence.
34. Determine the necessary and sufficient conditions for the existence and pattern of period-4 solutions when $\{A_n\}_{n=0}^{\infty}$ is a period-12 sequence.
35. Determine the necessary and sufficient conditions for the existence and pattern of period-6 solutions when $\{A_n\}_{n=0}^{\infty}$ is a period-12 sequence.
36. Determine the necessary and sufficient conditions for the existence and pattern of period-12 solutions when $\{A_n\}_{n=0}^{\infty}$ is a period-12 sequence.
37. Using Exercises 33–36, determine the necessary and sufficient conditions for the existence and pattern of period-2 solutions when $\{A_n\}_{n=0}^{\infty}$ is a period-8k sequence $(k \in \mathbb{N})$.
38. Using Exercises 33–36, determine the necessary and sufficient conditions for the existence and pattern of period-4 solutions when $\{A_n\}_{n=0}^{\infty}$ is a period-8k sequence $(k \in \mathbb{N})$.
39. Using Exercises 33–36, determine the necessary and sufficient conditions for the existence and pattern of period-8 solutions when $\{A_n\}_{n=0}^{\infty}$ is a period-8k sequence $(k \in \mathbb{N})$.
40. Using Exercises 33–36, determine the necessary and sufficient conditions for the existence and pattern of period-2k solutions when $\{A_n\}_{n=0}^{\infty}$ is a period-8k sequence $(k \in \mathbb{N})$.
41. Using Exercises 33–36, determine the necessary and sufficient conditions for the existence and pattern of period-4k solutions when $\{A_n\}_{n=0}^{\infty}$ is a period-8k sequence $(k \in \mathbb{N})$.

Consider the **Non-autonomous Rational Δ.E.**:

$$x_{n+2} = \frac{A_n x_n}{1 + x_{n+1} + x_n}, \quad n = 0, 1, \ldots,$$

where $\{A_n\}_{n=0}^{\infty}$ is a periodic sequence. In problems 42–50:

42. Determine the necessary and sufficient conditions for the existence and pattern of a period-2 solution when $\{A_n\}_{n=0}^{\infty}$ is a period-4 sequence.
43. Determine the necessary and sufficient conditions for the existence and pattern of a period-4 solution when $\{A_n\}_{n=0}^{\infty}$ is a period-4 sequence.

44. Determine the necessary and sufficient conditions for the existence and pattern of a period-2 solution when $\{A_n\}_{n=0}^{\infty}$ is a period-8 sequence.
45. Determine the necessary and sufficient conditions for the existence and pattern of a period-4 solution when $\{A_n\}_{n=0}^{\infty}$ is a period-8 sequence.
46. Determine the necessary and sufficient conditions for the existence and pattern of a period-8 solution when $\{A_n\}_{n=0}^{\infty}$ is a period-8 sequence.
47. Determine the necessary and sufficient conditions for the existence and pattern of a period-2 solution when $\{A_n\}_{n=0}^{\infty}$ is a period-4k sequence (for $k \geq 2$).
48. Determine the necessary and sufficient conditions for the existence and pattern of a period-2k solution when $\{A_n\}_{n=0}^{\infty}$ is a period-4k sequence (for $k \geq 2$).
49. Determine the necessary and sufficient conditions for the existence and pattern of a period-4k solution when $\{A_n\}_{n=0}^{\infty}$ is a period-4k sequence (for $k \geq 2$).
50. Determine the necessary and sufficient conditions for the existence and pattern of a period-$2(2k+1)$ when $\{A_n\}_{n=0}^{\infty}$ is a period-$(2k+1)$ sequence (for $k \geq 1$).

Consider the **Non-autonomous Riccati Δ.E.:**

$$x_{n+2} = \frac{A_n}{x_n}, \quad n = 0, 1, \ldots,$$

where $\{A_n\}_{n=0}^{\infty}$ is a periodic sequence. In problems 51–59:

51. Determine the necessary and sufficient conditions for the existence and pattern of period-8 solutions when $\{A_n\}_{n=0}^{\infty}$ is a period-8 sequence.
52. Determine the necessary and sufficient conditions for the existence and pattern of period-8 solutions when $\{A_n\}_{n=0}^{\infty}$ is a period-12 sequence.
53. Using Exercise 51 and 52, determine the necessary and sufficient conditions for the existence and pattern of period-4k solutions when $\{A_n\}_{n=0}^{\infty}$ is a period-4k sequence (for $k \geq 2$).
54. Determine the necessary and sufficient conditions for the existence and pattern of period-8 solutions when $\{A_n\}_{n=0}^{\infty}$ is a period-6 sequence.
55. Determine the necessary and sufficient conditions for the existence and pattern of period-10 solutions when $\{A_n\}_{n=0}^{\infty}$ is a period-10 sequence.
56. Using Exercise 54 and 55, determine the necessary and sufficient conditions for the existence and pattern of period-$(4k + 2)$ solutions when $\{A_n\}_{n=0}^{\infty}$ is a period-$(4k + 2)$ sequence (for $k \geq 2$).

57. Determine the necessary and sufficient conditions for the existence and pattern of period-5 solutions when $\{A_n\}_{n=0}^{\infty}$ is a period-5 sequence. **Hint:** set $x_{10} = x_0$ and $x_{11} = x_1$.

58. Determine the necessary and sufficient conditions for the existence and pattern of period-7 solutions when $\{A_n\}_{n=0}^{\infty}$ is a period-7 sequence. **Hint:** set $x_{14} = x_0$ and $x_{15} = x_1$.

59. Using Exercise 57 and 58, determine the necessary and sufficient conditions for the existence of period-$(2k+1)$ solutions when $\{A_n\}_{n=0}^{\infty}$ is a period-$(2k+1)$ sequence $(k \in \mathbb{N})$. **Hint:** Break up into two cases when $\{A_n\}_{n=0}^{\infty}$ is a period-$(4k-1)$ sequence and when $\{A_n\}_{n=0}^{\infty}$ is a period-$(4k+1)$ sequence $(k \in \mathbb{N})$.

Consider the **Max-Type Δ.E.:**

$$x_{n+2} = \max\left\{ \frac{1}{x_{n+1}}, \frac{C}{x_n} \right\}, \quad n = 0, 1, \ldots,$$

where $C > 0$. In problems 60–71:

60. Suppose that $C < 1$ and $C^7 < x_0^2 < C^5$. Determine the pattern of the transient terms and the period-2 solutions.

61. Suppose that $C < 1$ and $C^9 < x_0^2 < C^7$. Determine the pattern of the transient terms and the period-2 solutions.

62. Using Exercise 60 and 61, suppose that $C < 1$ and $C^{2k+1} < x_0^2 < C^{2k-1}$ $(k \in \mathbb{N})$. Determine the pattern of the transient terms and the period-2 solutions.

63. Suppose that $C < 1$ and $C < x_0^2 < \frac{1}{C}$. Determine the pattern of the transient terms and the period-2 solutions.

64. Suppose that $C < 1$ and $\frac{1}{C} < x_0^2 < \frac{1}{C^3}$. Determine the pattern of the transient terms and the period-2 solutions.

65. Suppose that $C < 1$ and $\frac{1}{C^3} < x_0^2 < \frac{1}{C^5}$. Determine the pattern of the transient terms and the period-2 solutions.

66. Using Exercises 63–65, suppose that $C < 1$ and $\frac{1}{C^{2k-1}} < x_0^2 < \frac{1}{C^{2k+1}}$ (for $k \geq 1$). Determine the pattern of the transient terms and the period-2 solutions.

67. Suppose that $C > 1$. Determine the necessary and sufficient conditions for the existence of period-4 solutions.

68. Suppose that $C > 1$. Determine the necessary and sufficient conditions for the existence of period-4 solutions with three transient terms.

69. Suppose that $C > 1$. Determine the necessary and sufficient conditions for the existence of period-4 solutions with six transient terms.

70. Suppose that $C > 1$. Determine the necessary and sufficient conditions for the existence of period-4 solutions with nine transient terms.

71. Using Exercises 68–70, suppose that $C > 1$. Determine the pattern of the 3k transient terms ($k \in \mathbb{N}$) and the period-4 solutions.

CHAPTER 6

ADVANCED CHARACTERISTICS AND NEW RESEARCH QUESTIONS

Our aims of this chapter is to widen our knowledge from the previous chapters to third and higher order difference equations and systems of difference equations. This chapter will focus on solving third and higher order linear difference equations, analyzing their monotonic and periodic characters, solving systems of linear difference equations and determining their monotonic and periodic characters. Furthermore, we will extend our studies on applications of third and higher order difference equations and systems of difference equations in signal processing, population dynamics and neural networking.

6.1. Higher Order Linear Difference Equations

In Chapter 4, recall a homogeneous linear A.E. of order $m \geq 3$ in the form:

$$x_{n+m} + \sum_{i=1}^{m} a_i x_{n+i-1} = 0, \quad n = 0, 1, \ldots, \tag{6.176}$$

where $a_1, a_2, a_3, \ldots, a_m \in \Re$. The corresponding characteristic polynomial of Eq. (6.176) is:

$$\lambda^m + \sum_{i=1}^{m} a_i \lambda^{m-i} = 0.$$

The following examples are parallel to examples in Chapter 4 and will determine the general solution of Eq. (6.176).

Example 1. Solve:

$$x_{n+3} - x_{n+2} - 4x_{n+1} + 4x_n = 0, \quad n = 0, 1, \ldots. \tag{6.177}$$

Solution: The **characteristic polynomial** of Eq. (6.177) is:

$$\lambda^3 - \lambda^2 - 4\lambda + 4 = 0,$$

whose three distinct roots are $\lambda_1 = 1$, $\lambda_2 = 2$ and $\lambda_3 = -2$. Hence:

$$x_n = C_1 + C_2 2^n + C_3 (-2)^n, \quad n = 0, 1, \ldots.$$

Example 2. Solve:

$$x_{n+4} - 13x_{n+2} + 36x_n = 0, \quad n = 0, 1, \ldots. \tag{6.178}$$

Solution: The **characteristic polynomial** of Eq. (6.178) is:

$$\lambda^4 - 13\lambda^2 + 36 = 0,$$

whose four distinct roots are $\lambda_1 = 2$, $\lambda_2 = -2$, $\lambda_3 = 3$ and $\lambda_4 = -3$. Thus:

$$x_n = C_1 2^n + C_2 (-2)^n + C_3 3^n + C_4 (-3)^n, \quad n = 0, 1, \ldots.$$

Example 3. Solve:

$$x_{n+4} - 8x_{n+2} + 16x_n = 0, \quad n = 0, 1, \ldots. \tag{6.179}$$

Solution: The **characteristic polynomial** of Eq. (6.179) is:

$$\lambda^4 - 8\lambda^2 + 16 = 0,$$

whose repeated characteristic roots are $\lambda_1 = \lambda_2 = 2$ and $\lambda_3 = \lambda_4 = -2$. Therefore:

$$x_n = C_1 2^n + nC_2 2^n + C_3 (-2)^n + nC_4 (-2)^n, \quad n = 0, 1, \ldots.$$

The following theorem (**Clark's Theorem**) states the necessary conditions for asymptotic stability of $\bar{x} = 0$ of the following $(k+1)$st order Δ.E.:

$$x_{n+k+1} + p x_{n+k} + q x_n = 0, \quad n = 0, 1, \ldots, \tag{6.180}$$

where $q \neq 0$. To prove Clark's Theorem, we will need to apply **Rouche's Theorem**.

Theorem 41. *Let f and g be analytic functions on a simply connected domain D. Also let $\gamma : [a, b] \to D$ be a simple closed curve. Assume that*

$|f(\gamma(t))| > |g(\gamma(t))|$ *for all* $t \in [a, b]$. *Then* f *and* $f + g$ *have the same number of zeros (counting multiplicities) lying in the interior of* γ.

Theorem 42. *Let* $\{x_n\}_{n=0}^{\infty}$ *be a solution of Eq. (6.180) and* $p, q \in \Re$ *and* $k \in \mathbb{N}$. *Suppose that* $|p| + |q| < 1$. *Then*

$$\lim_{n \to \infty} x_n = 0.$$

Proof. We will apply Rouche's Theorem (Theorem 41). The characteristic polynomial of Eq. (6.180) is:

$$\lambda^{k+1} + p\lambda + q = 0. \tag{6.181}$$

Our plan is to show that all the roots of the Eq. (6.181) lie inside the unit disk $|\lambda| < 1$. Now consider the domain $D = \mathbb{C}$ and define the functions

(i) $f : D \to \mathbb{C}$
(ii) $g : D \to \mathbb{C}$

as follows:

$$f(\lambda) = \lambda^{k+1} \quad \text{and} \quad g(\lambda) = p\lambda^k + q.$$

Observe that both functions are analytic on D. Now define $\gamma : [0, 2\pi] \to D$ as:

$$\gamma(t) = e^{it}.$$

Notice that $\gamma(t)$ is a simple connected curve and observe:

$$|g(\gamma(t))| = |g(e^{it})| = |p(e^{it})^k + q|$$
$$\leq |p||(e^{it})^k| + |q|$$
$$\leq |p| + |q| < 1.$$

Also note:

$$|f(\lambda(t))| = |f(e^{it})| = \left|(e^{it})^{k+1}\right| = 1.$$

Hence we see that $|f(\gamma(t))| > |g(\gamma(t))|$ for all $t \in [0, 2\pi]$ and thus Rouche's Theorem (Theorem 41) applies. Now since $f(\gamma(t))$ has $k + 1$ roots (including multiplicities) lying inside the interior of $\gamma(t)$, it follows that all zeros of

$$h(t) = f(\gamma(t)) + g(\gamma(t))$$

lie in the interior of $\gamma(t)$. Therefore all roots of Eq. (6.181) have modulus less than one. $\qquad \square$

The next section will study the periodic traits of Eq. (6.176).

6.2. Periodic Traits of Third and Higher Order Linear Difference Equations

It is of paramount interest to determine the periodic character, patterns of periodic solutions and the necessary and sufficient conditions for the existence of periodic solutions of Eq. (6.176). The periodic character of solutions of Eq. (6.176) has been studied in [29, 30, 31 and 35]. We will start our journey by suggesting the following **Open Problems** that are analogous to what we established in Chapters 2 and 4.

Open Problem 1. Suppose that $m \geq 3$ and $\{a_n\}_{n=0}^{\infty}$ is a period-k sequence ($k \geq 2$). Determine the necessary and sufficient conditions for the existence of periodic solutions of:

$$x_{n+m} = a_n x_n, \quad n = 0, 1, \ldots.$$

Open Problem 2. Suppose that $m \geq 3$ and $\{a_n\}_{n=0}^{\infty}$ is a period-k sequence ($k \geq 2$). Determine the necessary and sufficient conditions for the existence of periodic solutions of:

$$x_{n+m} = x_n + a_n, \quad n = 0, 1, \ldots.$$

Open Problem 3. Suppose that $m \geq 3$ and $\{a_n\}_{n=0}^{\infty}$ is a period-k sequence ($k \geq 2$). Determine the necessary and sufficient conditions for the existence of periodic solutions of:

$$x_{n+m} = -x_n + a_n, \quad n = 0, 1, \ldots.$$

Open Problem 4. Suppose that $m \geq 3$ and $\{a_n\}_{n=0}^{\infty}$ and $\{b_n\}_{n=0}^{\infty}$ are period-k sequences ($k \geq 2$). Determine the necessary and sufficient conditions for the existence of periodic solutions of:

$$x_{n+m} = a_n x_n + b_n, \quad n = 0, 1, \ldots.$$

Hint: To establish theorems from Open Problems 1–4, we perform several examples with different values of m and k. In fact, break up into different cases when k and m are both even, both odd, k is even and m is odd and vice versa. We will commence with examples of theorems that remit Open Problem 1.

Suppose $\{a_n\}_{n=0}^{\infty}$ is a period-k sequence ($k \geq 2$) and consider the non-autonomous third order linear Δ.E.:

$$x_{n+3} = a_n x_n, \quad n = 0, 1, \ldots, \tag{6.182}$$

where $x_0 \neq 0$. The following theorem retorts the questions addressed in Open Problem 1 and outlines the periodic nature of solutions of Eq. (6.182).

Theorem 43. *Suppose that $\{a_n\}_{n=0}^{\infty}$ is a period-k sequence ($k \geq 2$) and $x_0 \neq 0$. Then the following statements are true:*

(i) *If $\{a_n\}_{n=0}^{\infty}$ is a period-3 sequence, then Eq. (6.182) has no period-3 cycles and for all $n \in \mathbb{N}$:*

$$\begin{cases} x_{3n} = a_0^n \, x_0, \\ x_{3n+1} = a_1^n \, x_1, \\ x_{3n+2} = a_2^n \, x_2. \end{cases}$$

Then every solution of Eq. (6.182) is unbounded provided that $a_i < 1$ for all $i = 0, 1, 2$. Every solution of Eq. (6.182) converges to 0 provided that $a_i < 1$ for all $i = 0, 1, 2$.

(ii) *If $\{a_n\}_{n=0}^{\infty}$ is a period-3 sequence, then every solution of Eq. (6.182) is periodic with period-6 if and only if $a_0 = \pm 1$, $a_1 = \pm 1$ and $a_2 = \pm 1$ and are not all equal to each other.*

(iii) *If $\{a_n\}_{n=0}^{\infty}$ is a period-3k sequence ($k \geq 2$), then every solution of Eq. (6.182) is periodic with period-3k if and only if for all $j = 0, 1, 2$:*

$$\prod_{i=0}^{k-1} a_{3i+j} = 1.$$

(iv) *If $\{a_n\}_{n=0}^{\infty}$ is a period-$(3k+1)$ sequence ($k \in \mathbb{N}$), then every solution of Eq. (6.182) is periodic with period-3$(3k+1)$ if and only if:*

$$\prod_{i=0}^{3k} a_i = 1.$$

(v) *If $\{a_n\}_{n=0}^{\infty}$ is a period-$(3k+2)$ sequence ($k \geq 0$), then every solution of Eq. (6.182) is periodic with period-3$(3k+2)$ if and only if:*

$$\prod_{i=0}^{3k+1} a_i = 1.$$

Theorem 43 is proved by induction and will be left as an exercise to prove at the end of the chapter. Now suppose $\{a_n\}_{n=0}^{\infty}$ is a period-k sequence $(k \geq 2)$ and consider the non-autonomous linear $\Delta.E.$ of order m $(m \geq 3)$:

$$x_{n+m} = a_n x_n, \quad n = 0, 1, \ldots. \tag{6.183}$$

Now we will extend Theorem 43 to the following theorem.

Theorem 44. *Suppose that $\{a_n\}_{n=0}^{\infty}$ is a period-k sequence $(k \geq 2)$ and $x_0 \neq 0$. Then the following statements are true:*

(i) *If $\{a_n\}_{n=0}^{\infty}$ is a period-m sequence $(m \geq 3)$, then Eq. (6.183) has no period-m cycles, and for all $n \in \mathbb{N}$ and for all $j = 0, 1, \ldots, m - 1$:*

$$x_{mn+j} = a_j^n x_j.$$

Thus every solution of Eq. (6.182) is unbounded provided that $a_j > 1$ for $j = 0, 1, 2, \ldots, m - 1$. Also, every solution of Eq. (6.182) converges to 0 provided that $a_j < 1$ for all $j = 0, 1, 2, \ldots, m - 1$.

(ii) *If $\{a_n\}_{n=0}^{\infty}$ is a period-m sequence, then every solution of Eq. (6.183) is periodic with period-2m if and only if either $a_i = \pm 1$ for all $i = 0, 1, \ldots, m - 1$ and are not all equal to each other.*

(iii) *If $\{a_n\}_{n=0}^{\infty}$ is a period-mk sequence $(k \geq 2)$, then every solution of Eq. (6.183) is periodic with period-mk if and only if for all $j = 0, 1, \ldots, m - 1$:*

$$\prod_{i=0}^{k-1} a_{mi+j} = 1.$$

(iv) *If $\{a_n\}_{n=0}^{\infty}$ is a period-$(mk + j)$ $(j = 1, \ldots, m - 1)$, then every solution of Eq. (6.183) is periodic with period-$m(mk + j)$ if and only if:*

$$\prod_{i=0}^{mk+j-1} a_i = 1.$$

We will shift our focus on Open Problem 2. Suppose $\{a_n\}_{n=0}^{\infty}$ is a period-k sequence $(k \geq 2)$ and consider the non-autonomous third order linear $\Delta.E.$:

$$x_{n+3} = x_n + a_n, \quad n = 0, 1, \ldots. \tag{6.184}$$

The following theorem addresses the questions in Open Problem 2 and the periodicity character of Eq. (6.184).

Theorem 45. *Suppose that $\{a_n\}_{n=0}^{\infty}$ is a period-k sequence $(k \geq 2)$ and $x_0 \in \Re$. Then the following statements are true:*

(i) *If* $\{a_n\}_{n=0}^{\infty}$ *is a period-3 sequence, then Eq.* (6.184) *has no period-3 cycles and for all* $n \in \mathbb{N}$:

$$\begin{cases} x_{3n} = x_0 + na_0, \\ x_{3n+1} = x_1 + na_1, \\ x_{3n+2} = x_2 + na_2. \end{cases}$$

Hence every solution of Eq. (6.184) *is unbounded.*

(ii) *If* $\{a_n\}_{n=0}^{\infty}$ *is a period-3k sequence* $(k \geq 2)$, *then every solution of Eq.* (6.184) *is periodic with period-3k if and only if for all* $j = 0, 1, 2$:

$$\sum_{i=0}^{k-1} a_{3i+j} = 0.$$

(iii) *If* $\{a_n\}_{n=0}^{\infty}$ *is a period-$(3k + 1)$ sequence* $(k \in \mathbb{N})$, *then every solution of Eq.* (6.184) *is periodic with period-$3(3k + 1)$ if and only if:*

$$\sum_{i=0}^{3k} a_i = 0.$$

(iv) *If* $\{a_n\}_{n=0}^{\infty}$ *is a period-$(3k + 2)$ sequence* $(k \geq 0)$, *then every solution of Eq.* (6.184) *is periodic with period-$3(3k + 2)$ if and only if:*

$$\sum_{i=0}^{3k+1} a_i = 0.$$

6.3. Applications of Higher Order Linear Difference Equations in Signal Processing

Our goal is to pursue the study of the LTI (Linear and Time Invariance) of digital signal processing that we commenced on Eq. (2.24) in Chapter 2 and on Eq. (4.143) in Chapter 4. From these equations we obtain:

(i) x_{n+i} for $i = 0, 1, 2, \ldots, N$ are the input signals.
(ii) y_{n+i} for $i = 0, 1, 2, \ldots, M$ are the output signals.

Then we acquire the following **LTI Δ.E.**:

$$bx_n - \left[y_{n+k} + \sum_{i=1}^{k} a_i y_{n+k-i} \right] = 0, \tag{6.185}$$

where b is the **feed-forward coefficient** and a_i for $i \in \mathbb{N}$ are the **feedback coefficients** that characterize the filter. Eq. (6.185) is applied for computing an output sample at time n based on the current and previous samples in the time domain. We can also rewrite Eq. (6.185) as:

$$y_{n+k} + \sum_{i=1}^{k} a_i y_{n+k-i} = b x_n. \tag{6.186}$$

Example 4. Solve the following **LTI** Δ**.E.**:

$$y_{n+3} = a y_n + b x_n. \tag{6.187}$$

Solution: By iterations and induction we get:

$$y_3 = a y_0 + b x_0,$$
$$y_4 = a y_1 + b x_1,$$
$$y_5 = a y_2 + b x_2,$$
$$y_6 = a y_3 + b x_3 = a^2 y_0 + a b x_0 + b x_3,$$
$$y_7 = a y_4 + b x_4 = a^2 y_1 + a b x_1 + b x_4,$$
$$y_8 = a y_5 + b x_5 = a^2 y_2 + a b x_2 + b x_5.$$
$$\vdots$$

Thus for all $n \in \mathbb{N}$:

$$\begin{cases} y_{3n} = a^n y_0 + \left[\sum_{i=0}^{n-1} a^{n-(i+1)} b x_{3i} \right], \\[2mm] y_{3n+1} = a^n y_1 + \left[\sum_{i=0}^{n-1} a^{n-(i+1)} b x_{3i+1} \right], \\[2mm] y_{3n+2} = a^n y_2 + \left[\sum_{i=0}^{n-1} a^{n-(i+1)} b x_{3i+2} \right]. \end{cases}$$

The solution of Eq. (6.187) consists of two components:

(i) $a^n y_0$, $a^n y_1$ and $a^n y_2$ are the **natural responses** that depend on the initial condition x_0.

(ii) $\sum_{i=0}^{n-1} a^{n-(i+1)} b x_{3i}$, $\sum_{i=0}^{n-1} a^{n-(i+1)} b x_{3i+1}$ and $\sum_{i=0}^{n-1} a^{n-(i+1)} b x_{3i+1}$ are the **forced responses** that depend on the input signal x_n.

We can also extend Eq. (6.185) to the following LTI A.E.:

$$y_n = \sum_{i=0}^{M} b_i x_{n-i} - \sum_{i=1}^{N} a_i y_{n-i},$$

where b_i are the **feed-forward coefficients** and a_i are the **feedback coefficients**. We can rewrite the above equation as:

$$\sum_{i=0}^{N} a_i y_{n-i} + \sum_{i=0}^{M} b_i x_{n-i} = 0.$$

6.4. Systems of Linear Difference Equations

We will first start off with the following homogeneous system of linear difference equations:

$$\begin{cases} x_{n+1} = a x_n + b y_n \\ \\ y_{n+1} = c x_n + d y_n \end{cases} \quad n = 0, 1, 2, \ldots,$$

where $a, b, c, d \in \Re$ and the initial conditions $x_0, y_0 \in \Re$. The above system of linear difference equations can be rewritten in the following matrix form:

$$\begin{bmatrix} x_{n+1} \\ y_{n+1} \end{bmatrix} = \begin{bmatrix} a & b \\ c & d \end{bmatrix} \begin{bmatrix} x_n \\ y_n \end{bmatrix},$$

whose solution is:

$$\begin{bmatrix} x_n \\ y_n \end{bmatrix} = \left(\begin{bmatrix} a & b \\ c & d \end{bmatrix} \right)^n \begin{bmatrix} x_0 \\ y_0 \end{bmatrix}.$$

The characteristic polynomial of the represented matrix is:

$$(\lambda - a)(\lambda - d) - bc = \lambda^2 - \lambda(a + d) + (ad - bc) = 0.$$

Now using Theorem 19, we acquire that $\lim_{n \to \infty} x_n = 0$ and $\lim_{n \to \infty} y_n = 0$ if and only if

$$|a + d| < 1 + ad - bc < 2.$$

Example 5. Solve the following Initial Value Problem:

$$\begin{cases} x_{n+1} = \dfrac{x_n}{2} + y_n \\[2mm] y_{n+1} = \dfrac{y_n}{2} \\[1mm] x_0 = 1, \\ y_0 = 1. \end{cases} \qquad n = 0, 1, 2, \ldots,$$

Solution: First of all for all $n \geq 0$:

$$y_n = \left(\frac{1}{2}\right)^n y_0 = \left(\frac{1}{2}\right)^n.$$

Now by iterations and induction we obtain:

$x_0 = 1,$

$x_1 = \dfrac{x_0}{2} + y_0 = 1 + \dfrac{1}{2},$

$x_2 = \dfrac{x_1}{2} + y_1 = \dfrac{1}{2}\left[1 + \dfrac{1}{2}\right] + \dfrac{1}{2} = 2 \cdot \dfrac{1}{2} + \left(\dfrac{1}{2}\right)^2,$

$x_3 = \dfrac{x_2}{2} + y_2 = \dfrac{1}{2}\left[2 \cdot \dfrac{1}{2} + \left(\dfrac{1}{2}\right)^2\right] + \left(\dfrac{1}{2}\right)^2 = 3 \cdot \left(\dfrac{1}{2}\right)^2 + \left(\dfrac{1}{2}\right)^3,$

$x_4 = \dfrac{x_3}{2} + y_3 = \dfrac{1}{2}\left[3 \cdot \left(\dfrac{1}{2}\right)^2 + \left(\dfrac{1}{2}\right)^3\right] + \left(\dfrac{1}{2}\right)^3 = 4 \cdot \left(\dfrac{1}{2}\right)^3 + \left(\dfrac{1}{2}\right)^4,$

$\vdots$

Hence for all $n \in \mathbb{N}$:

$$\begin{cases} x_n = n\left(\dfrac{1}{2}\right)^{n-1} + \left(\dfrac{1}{2}\right)^n, \\[4mm] y_n = \left(\dfrac{1}{2}\right)^n. \end{cases}$$

6.5. Periodic Traits of Systems of Linear Difference Equations

Our next goal is to establish the patterns of periodic solutions of particular systems of linear difference equations. We will exhibit several examples of various systems of linear difference equations and study their periodic traits.

Example 6. Determine the necessary and sufficient conditions for the existence of periodic solutions of:

$$\begin{cases} x_{n+2} = (-1)^n y_n \\ \\ y_{n+2} = x_n \end{cases} \quad n = 0, 1, 2, \ldots. \tag{6.188}$$

Solution: By iteration we get:

$$\begin{array}{ll} x_0 & y_0 \\ x_1 & y_1 \\ x_2 = y_0 & y_2 = x_0 \\ x_3 = -y_1 & y_3 = x_1 \\ x_4 = y_2 = x_0 & y_4 = y_2 = x_0. \end{array}$$

Hence every solution of System (6.188) is periodic with period-4.

Example 7. Suppose that $\{a_n\}_{n=0}^{\infty}$ and $\{b_n\}_{n=0}^{\infty}$ are period-2 sequences. Determine the necessary and sufficient conditions for the existence of periodic solutions of:

$$\begin{cases} x_{n+1} = a_n y_n \\ \\ y_{n+1} = b_n x_n \end{cases} \quad n = 0, 1, 2, \ldots. \tag{6.189}$$

Solution: Observe:

$$\begin{array}{ll} x_0 & y_0 \\ x_1 = a_0 y_0 & y_1 = b_0 x_0 \\ x_2 = a_1 [y_1] = a_1 b_0 x_0 = x_0 & y_2 = b_1 [x_1] = b_1 a_0 y_0 = y_0 \\ \quad (\text{if } a_1 b_0 = 1). & \quad (\text{if } b_1 a_0 = 1). \end{array}$$

Thus every solution of System (6.189) is periodic with period-2 if and only if $a_1 b_0 = 1$ and $b_1 a_0 = 1$.

Example 8. Suppose that $\{a_n\}_{n=0}^{\infty}$ and $\{b_n\}_{n=0}^{\infty}$ are period-3 sequences. Determine the necessary and sufficient conditions for the existence of periodic solutions of:

$$\begin{cases} x_{n+1} = a_n y_n \\ \\ y_{n+1} = b_n x_n \end{cases} \quad n = 0, 1, 2, \ldots. \tag{6.190}$$

Solution: Notice:

x_0

$x_1 = a_0 y_0$

$x_2 = a_1 [y_1] = a_1 b_0 x_0$

$x_3 = a_2 [y_2] = a_2 b_1 a_0 y_0 = y_0$
    (if $a_2 b_1 a_0 = 1$)

$x_4 = a_0 [y_3] = a_0 y_3$

$x_5 = a_1 [y_4] = a_1 b_0 x_3$

$x_6 = a_2 [y_5] = a_2 b_1 a_0 y_3 = y_3 = x_0$

y_0

$y_1 = b_0 x_0$

$y_2 = b_1 [x_1] = b_1 a_0 y_0$

$y_3 = b_2 [x_2] = b_2 a_1 b_0 x_0 = x_0$
    (if $b_2 a_1 b_0 = 1$)

$y_4 = b_0 [x_3] = b_0 x_3$

$y_5 = b_1 [x_4] = b_1 a_0 y_3$

$y_6 = b_2 [x_5] = b_2 a_1 b_0 x_3 = x_3 = y_0.$

Every solution of System (6.190) is periodic with period-6 if and only if $a_2 b_1 a_0 = 1$ and $b_2 a_1 b_0 = 1$.

In Examples 7 and 8 we notice the contrasts when $\{a_n\}_{n=0}^{\infty}$ and $\{b_n\}_{n=0}^{\infty}$ are both periodic sequences with an even ordered period and with an odd ordered period. The following two theorems generalize these observations.

Theorem 46. *Suppose that $\{a_n\}_{n=0}^{\infty}$ and $\{b_n\}_{n=0}^{\infty}$ are periodic sequences with an even ordered period-$2k$ ($k \in \mathbb{N}$). Then every solution of*

$$\begin{cases} x_{n+1} = a_n y_n \\ \\ y_{n+1} = b_n x_n \end{cases} \quad n = 0, 1, 2, \dots$$

is periodic with period-$2k$ if and only if

$$\prod_{i=1}^{k} a_{2i-1} b_{2i-2} = 1 \quad and \quad \prod_{i=1}^{k} b_{2i-1} a_{2i-2} = 1.$$

To prove Theorem 46, test several examples when $k = 2, 4, \dots$, and then generalize by induction.

Theorem 47. *Suppose that $\{a_n\}_{n=0}^{\infty}$ and $\{b_n\}_{n=0}^{\infty}$ are periodic sequences with an odd ordered period $2k + 1$ ($k \geq 1$). Then every solution of*

$$\begin{cases} x_{n+1} = a_n y_n \\ \\ y_{n+1} = b_n x_n \end{cases} \quad n = 0, 1, 2, \dots$$

is periodic with period-2(2k + 1) if and only if

$$\prod_{i=1}^{k} a_{2i-2}b_{2i-1} = 1 \quad and \quad \prod_{i=1}^{k} b_{2i-2}a_{2i-1} = 1.$$

To prove Theorem 47, try various examples when $k = 3, 5\ldots$, and then generalize by induction. We will proceed with more examples of systems of difference equations and their periodicity nature of solutions.

Example 9. Suppose that $\{a_n\}_{n=0}^{\infty}$ and $\{b_n\}_{n=0}^{\infty}$ are period-2 sequences. Determine the necessary and sufficient conditions for the existence of period-2 solutions of:

$$\begin{cases} x_{n+1} = (-1)^n \, y_n + a_n \\ \\ y_{n+1} = (-1)^n \, x_n + b_n \end{cases} \qquad n = 0, 1, 2, \ldots. \qquad (6.191)$$

Solution: Observe:

$$
\begin{aligned}
&x_0 && y_0 \\
&x_1 = y_0 + a_0 && y_1 = x_0 + b_0 \\
&x_2 = -\,[y_1] + a_1 && y_2 = -\,[x_1] + b_1 \\
&\quad = -x_0 - b_0 + a_1 = x_0 && \quad = -y_0 - a_0 + b_1 = y_0.
\end{aligned}
$$

We obtain $x_0 = \frac{a_1 - b_0}{2}$ and $y_0 = \frac{b_1 - a_0}{2}$ with the following period-2 pattern:

$$x_0 = \frac{a_1 - b_0}{2} \qquad y_0 = \frac{b_1 - a_0}{2}$$

$$x_1 = \frac{b_1 + a_0}{2} \qquad y_1 = \frac{a_1 + b_0}{2}.$$

Example 10. Suppose that $\{a_n\}_{n=0}^{\infty}$ and $\{b_n\}_{n=0}^{\infty}$ are period-4 sequences. Determine the necessary and sufficient conditions for the existence of period-4 solutions of:

$$\begin{cases} x_{n+1} = (-1)^n \, y_n + a_n \\ \\ y_{n+1} = (-1)^n \, x_n + b_n \end{cases} \qquad n = 0, 1, 2, \ldots. \qquad (6.192)$$

Solution: We get:

$$x_0$$
$$x_1 = y_0 + a_0$$
$$x_2 = -[y_1] + a_1$$
$$= -x_0 - b_0 + a_1$$
$$x_3 = [y_2] + a_2$$
$$= -y_0 - a_0 + b_1 + a_2$$
$$x_4 = -[y_3] + a_3$$
$$= x_0 + b_0 - a_1 - b_2 + a_3$$
$$= x_0$$
$$(\text{if } b_0 - b_2 = a_1 - a_3)$$

$$y_0$$
$$y_1 = x_0 + b_0$$
$$y_2 = -[x_1] + b_1$$
$$= -y_0 - a_0 + b_1$$
$$y_3 = [x_2] + b_2$$
$$= -x_0 - b_0 + a_1 + b_2$$
$$y_4 = -[x_3] + b_3$$
$$= y_0 + a_0 - b_1 - a_2 + b_3$$
$$= y_0$$
$$(\text{if } a_0 - a_2 = b_1 - b_3).$$

Every solution of System (6.192) is periodic with period-4 if and only if $b_0 - b_2 = a_1 - a_3$ and $a_0 - a_2 = b_1 - b_3$.

In Examples 9 and 10 there are variations when $\{a_n\}_{n=0}^{\infty}$ and $\{b_n\}_{n=0}^{\infty}$ are both periodic sequences with period-$(4k-2)$ and period-$4k$ $(k \in \mathbb{N})$. The following two theorems extend the results.

Theorem 48. *Suppose that $\{a_n\}_{n=0}^{\infty}$ and $\{b_n\}_{n=0}^{\infty}$ are periodic sequences with period-$(4k-2)$ $(k \geq 1)$. Then the system of difference equations*

$$\begin{cases} x_{n+1} = (-1)^n \, y_n + a_n \\ \\ y_{n+1} = (-1)^n \, x_n + b_n \end{cases} \quad n = 0, 1, 2, \ldots$$

has a unique period-$(4k-2)$ cycle where:

$$x_0 = \frac{\sum_{i=1}^{2k-1} (-1)^{n+1} a_{2i-1} + \sum_{i=1}^{2k-1} (-1)^n \, b_{2i-2}}{2}, \quad and$$

$$y_0 = \frac{\sum_{i=1}^{2k-1} (-1)^{n+1} b_{2i-1} + \sum_{i=1}^{2k-1} (-1)^n \, a_{2i-2}}{2}.$$

To prove Theorem 48, seek more examples when $k = 6, 10, \ldots$.

Theorem 49. *Suppose that* $\{a_n\}_{n=0}^{\infty}$ *and* $\{b_n\}_{n=0}^{\infty}$ *are periodic sequences with period-4k* $(k \geq 1)$*. Then every solution of*

$$\begin{cases} x_{n+1} = (-1)^n \, y_n + a_n \\ \\ y_{n+1} = (-1)^n \, x_n + b_n \end{cases} \qquad n = 0, 1, 2, \ldots$$

is periodic with period-4k if and only if:

$$\sum_{i=1}^{2k} (-1)^{n+1} \, b_{2i-2} = \sum_{i=1}^{2k} (-1)^{n+1} \, a_{2i-1}, \quad and$$

$$\sum_{i=1}^{2k} (-1)^{n+1} \, a_{2i-2} = \sum_{i=1}^{2k} (-1)^{n+1} \, b_{2i-1}.$$

To prove Theorem 49, seek more examples when $k = 8, 12, \ldots$.

6.6. Applications of Systems of Linear Difference Equations in Signal Processing

In Chapters 2 and 4 and in this chapter we study the applications of linear non-autonomous difference equations in signal processing. Our plan is to extend the applications of systems of linear difference equations by emerging with the following homogeneous system of linear difference equations:

$$\begin{cases} x_{k+1}^1 = a_{11}x_k^1 + \cdots + a_{1n}x_k^n + b_1 u_k \\ x_{k+1}^2 = a_{21}x_k^1 + \cdots + a_{2n}x_k^n + b_2 u_k \\ \vdots \qquad \vdots \\ x_{k+1}^n = a_{n1}x_k^1 + \cdots + a_{nn}x_k^n + b_n u_k \end{cases} \tag{6.193}$$

where the initial conditions $x_0^1, \ldots, x_0^n$, b_i are the **feed-forward coefficients** and a_{ij} are the **feedback coefficients** that characterize the filter. Now rewrite System (6.193) in the following matrix form:

$$\begin{cases} x_{k+1} = Ax_k + Bu_k \\ x_0, \end{cases} \tag{6.194}$$

where x_0 is the $1 \times n$ matrix:

$$\begin{bmatrix} x_0^1 \\ \vdots \\ x_0^n \end{bmatrix},$$

A is the following $n \times n$ matrix:

$$\begin{bmatrix} a_{11} & \cdots & a_{1n} \\ \vdots & & \vdots \\ a_{n1} & \cdots & a_{nn} \end{bmatrix},$$

and B is the following $1 \times n$ matrix:

$$\begin{bmatrix} b_1 \\ \vdots \\ b_n \end{bmatrix}.$$

Then we acquire the following solution of System (6.194):

$$x_k = A^k x_0 + \sum_{i=0}^{k-1} A^i B u_{k-1-i}.$$

The solution of System (6.194) consists of two components:

(i) $A^k x_0$ is the **natural response** that depends on the initial condition x_0.
(ii) $\sum_{i=0}^{k-1} A^i B u_{k-1-i}$ is the **forced response** that depends on the input signal x_n.

6.7. Systems of Nonlinear Difference Equations

Our aim is to study the long-term behavior of solutions of systems of nonlinear difference equations in the form:

$$\begin{cases} x_{n+1} = f(x_n, y_n) \\ \\ y_{n+1} = g(x_n, y_n) \end{cases} \qquad n = 0, 1, 2, \ldots, \qquad (6.195)$$

where $f(x, y)$ and $g(x, y)$ are continuously differentiable functions defined on $I \times I \longrightarrow I$ and the initial conditions $x_0, y_0 \in I$. The equilibrium point $(\bar{x}, \bar{y})$ of System (6.195) satisfies:

$$\begin{cases} \bar{x} = f(\bar{x}, \bar{y}) \\ \bar{y} = g(\bar{x}, \bar{y}) \end{cases}.$$

The Linearized Stability Matrix $J(\bar{x}, \bar{y})$ about the equilibrium point $(\bar{x}, \bar{y})$ of System (6.195) is the following matrix:

$$J(\bar{x}, \bar{y}) = \begin{bmatrix} f_x(\bar{x}, \bar{y}) & f_y(\bar{x}, \bar{y}) \\ g_x(\bar{x}, \bar{y}) & g_y(\bar{x}, \bar{y}) \end{bmatrix}.$$

The following example will determine the stability nature of equilibrium points of System (6.195).

Example 11. Determine all the equilibrium point(s) and their local stability character of:

$$\begin{cases} x_{n+1} = \dfrac{A y_n}{1 + x_n} \\[3mm] y_{n+1} = \dfrac{B x_n}{1 + y_n} \end{cases} \qquad n = 0, 1, 2, \ldots, \qquad (6.196)$$

where $x_0, y_0, A, B > 0$.

Solution: System (6.196) has two equilibrium points $(0, 0)$ and $(A-1, B-1)$ (when $A, B > 1$). In addition:

$$\begin{cases} f(x, y) = \dfrac{Ay}{1 + x} \\[3mm] g(x, y) = \dfrac{Bx}{1 + y} \end{cases}.$$

Also:

(i) $f_x(x, y) = \frac{-Ay}{(1+x)^2}$ and $f_y(x, y) = \frac{A}{1+x}$.
(ii) $g_x(0, 0) = \frac{B}{1+y}$ and $g_y(0, 0) = \frac{-Bx}{(1+y)^2}$.

Then:

(i) $f_x(0, 0) = 0$ and $f_y(0, 0) = A$.
(ii) $g_x(0, 0) = B$ and $f_y(0, 0) = 0$.
(iii) $f_x(A - 1, B - 1) = -\frac{B-1}{A}$ and $f_y(A - 1, B - 1) = 1$.
(iv) $g_x(A - 1, B - 1) = 1$ and $g_y(A - 1, B - 1) = -\frac{A-1}{B}$.

The characteristic polynomial about $(0, 0)$ is:

$$\lambda^2 - AB = 0.$$

The characteristic polynomial about $(A - 1, B - 1)$ (when $A, B > 1$) is:

$$\lambda^2 + \left(\frac{A-1}{B} + \frac{B-1}{A} \right) \lambda + \left(\frac{B-1}{A} \right) \left(\frac{A-1}{B} \right) - 1 = 0.$$

Thus from Theorem 29 we procure:

(i) $(0,0)$ is locally asymptotically stable if $AB < 1$.
(ii) $(0,0)$ is unstable if $AB > 1$.
(iii) $(A - 1, B - 1)$ is unstable if $A, B > 1$.

Systems of Nonlinear Difference Equations have been studied in [1, 21, 52, 64–66]. Now we will analyze several applications of Systems of Nonlinear Difference Equations.

6.7.1. *The Host Parasitoid Model*

The **Host Parasitoid Model** is resembled by the following system of difference equations:

$$\begin{cases} H_{t+1} = r \cdot H_t \cdot u\,(H_t) \cdot p\,(P_t), \\ P_{t+1} = s \cdot H_t \cdot [1 - P_t] \end{cases},$$

where:

(i) $u\,(H_t)$ is the Probability of the host to survive in next generation in the absence of the parasitoid, $p(P_t) = 1$.
(ii) r is the Host Multiplicity: Eggs laid by the host that survive.
(iii) $p\,(P_t)$ is the Probability of the host to escape from parasitism.
(iv) s is the Parasitoid Multiplicity: Eggs laid by parasitoid on a single host that survive.

6.7.2. *May's Host Parasitoid Model*

May's Host Parasitoid Model is described by the following system of difference equations:

$$\begin{cases} X_{n+1} = \dfrac{\alpha X_n}{1 + \beta Y_n} \\[2mm] Y_{n+1} = \dfrac{\beta X_n Y_n}{1 + \beta Y_n} \end{cases} \qquad n = 0, 1, 2, \ldots,$$

where $x_0, y_0, \alpha, \beta > 0$. Determining the stability nature of equilibrium points will be left as an exercise at the end of the chapter.

6.7.3. *System of Beverton−Holt Equations*

The **System of Beverton−Holt Equations** is represented as the following system of difference equations in exponential form:

$$\begin{cases} x_{n+1} = \dfrac{\lambda x_n}{1 + x_n + a y_n} \\[4mm] y_{n+1} = \dfrac{\lambda y_n}{1 + y_n + a x_n} \end{cases} \qquad n = 0, 1, 2, \ldots,$$

where $x_0, y_0, \lambda, a > 0$. Determining the stability character of equilibrium points will be left as an exercise at the end of chapter.

6.7.4. *System of Ricker Equations*

The **System of Ricker Equations** is represented as the following system of difference equations in exponential form of:

$$\begin{cases} x_{n+1} = x_n e^{r_1 - x_n - a y_n} \\[2mm] y_{n+1} = y_n e^{r_2 - y_n - b x_n} \end{cases} \qquad n = 0, 1, 2, \ldots,$$

where $x_0, y_0, r_1, r_2, a, b > 0$. Determining the stability nature of equilibrium points will be left as an exercise at the end of chapter.

6.7.5. *Predator-Prey Model*

The **Predator-Prey Model** in [36] is resembled as the following *System of Logistic Difference Equations*:

$$\begin{cases} x_{n+1} = \mu_x y_n x_n (1 - x_n) \\[2mm] y_{n+1} = \mu_y x_n y_n (1 - y_n) \end{cases} \qquad n = 0, 1, 2, \ldots,$$

where:

(i) x_n, y_n are interdependent species with a logistic evolution and interaction.
(ii) x_n is the predator.
(iii) y_n is the prey.
(iv) μ_x is the varying growth rate of species x.
(v) μ_y is the varying growth rate of species y.

Now let λ be the mixed reproduction rate and we acquire the following *System of Logistic Difference Equations*:

$$\begin{cases} x_{n+1} = \lambda(3y_n + 1)x_n(1 - x_n) \\ \\ y_{n+1} = \lambda(4 - 3x_n)y_n(1 - y_n) \end{cases} \quad n = 0, 1, 2, \ldots.$$

Other Predator-Prey Models have been studied such as the Lotka–Volterra Model in [6] and the Moose Predator-Prey Model in [32].

6.7.6. *Applications of systems of difference equations in synchronization*

Systems of difference equations have been used in synchronization. The following system of difference equations describes synchronization:

$$\begin{cases} V_{xj} = -\alpha A(V_{yj} + V_{zj}) \\ V_{yj} = \alpha[BV_{xj} + CV_{yj} + \sigma_{ji}(V_{yi} - V_{yj})], \\ V_{zj} = \alpha[D + EV_{zj}(V_{xj} - F)] \end{cases}$$

where V_{xj}, V_{yj}, V_{zj} are the output voltages, α is the time scale coefficient, σ_{ji} is the coupling strength between the oscillators j and i defined by the parameters of the coupler, A, B, C, D, E, F are the parameters expressed in terms of electronic components as illustrated in the diagram below:

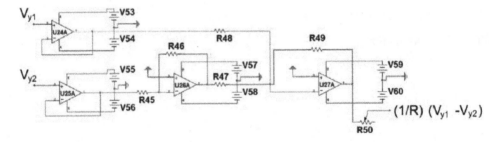

The dynamics of this system were studied in [37] and the existence of chaos was shown.

6.8. Advanced Periodic Characteristics of Higher Order Nonlinear Difference Equations

In the previous chapters we explored varieties of periodic traits of linear difference equations, piecewise difference equations, rational difference equations and Max-Type difference equations. First of all, we noticed how the periodicity nature varied from existence of unique periodic cycles to every solution being periodic. Second of all, we discovered the necessary and sufficient conditions for existence of periodic cycles. Furthermore, we perceived the disparity between patterns of the even ordered periodic cycles and odd ordered periodic cycles with uniqueness of solutions and alternating patterns of periodic cycles. Our next aim is to broaden our developed knowledge to ascertain the periodicity essence of third and higher order difference equations, systems of difference equations when the periodic sequence $\{A_n\}_{n=0}^{\infty}$ is periodic with period-k ($k \geq 2$), and study new systems of piecewise difference equations and neural networking models. How will these criteria for the existence of periodic cycles be similar or different in comparison with our current mastery from the previous chapters? What new periodic traits can we expect that will be quite different? How will the delay $m \geq 3$ affect the patterns of new periodic traits? Will even and odd values of delay $m \geq 3$ influence the new periodic traits? We will pose conjectures that will lead to new theorems and results based on our previous studies and will pose new research questions.

6.9. Third and Higher Order Rational Difference Equations

From Chapter 3 and Chapter 5 we investigated the periodicity nature of solutions of Rational Difference Equations. We will commence with the investigation of periodic character of solutions of third and higher order **Rational Δ.E.** in the form:

$$x_{n+m} = \frac{Ax_n}{1 + \sum_{i=i}^{m} x_{n+m-i}}, \quad n = 0, 1, \ldots, \tag{6.197}$$

where $m \geq 3$ and $x_0, x_1, \ldots, x_{m-1} > 0$. Eq. (6.197) will lead us to the following Conjectures.

Conjecture 6. *Suppose that m is an even positive integer. Then every positive solution of*

$$x_{n+m} = \frac{Ax_n}{1 + \sum_{i=i}^{m} x_{n+m-i}}, \quad n = 0, 1, \ldots$$

(i) *converges to 0 is $A \leq 1$*
(ii) *converges to a period-2 cycle if $A > 1$.*

Conjecture 7. *Suppose that m is an odd positive integer. Then every positive solution of*

$$x_{n+m} = \frac{A x_n}{1 + \sum_{i=i}^{m} x_{n+m-i}}, \quad n = 0, 1, \ldots$$

(i) *converges to 0 if $A \le 1$*
(ii) *converges to the positive equilibrium if $A > 1$.*

6.10. Third and Higher Order Non-autonomous Rational Difference Equations

In Chapters 3 and 5 we investigated the periodic character of solutions of various nonlinear difference equations such as the Riccati Δ.E., Piecewise Difference Equations, Max-Type Difference Equations and Rational Difference Equations. We will commence with the investigation of periodic character of third and higher order **Riccati Δ.E.** in the form:

$$x_{n+m} = \frac{A_n}{x_n}, \quad n = 0, 1, \ldots, \tag{6.198}$$

where $m \ge 3$ and $\{A_n\}_{n=0}^{\infty}$ is a period-k sequence ($k \ge 2$). Eq. (6.198) will then guide us to the following **Open Problems** remitting the periodic traits of solutions.

Open Problem 5. Suppose that $m = 2l$ ($l \in \mathbb{N}$) and $\{A_n\}_{n=0}^{\infty}$ is a period-$2k$ sequence ($k \in \mathbb{N}$). Determine the necessary and sufficient conditions for the existence of periodic solutions of Eq. (6.198).

Open Problem 6. Suppose that $m = 2l$ ($l \in \mathbb{N}$) and $\{A_n\}_{n=0}^{\infty}$ is a period-$(2k+1)$ sequence ($k \in \mathbb{N}$). Determine the necessary and sufficient conditions for the existence of periodic solutions of Eq. (6.198).

Open Problem 7. Suppose that $m = 2l + 1$ ($l \in \mathbb{N}$) and $\{A_n\}_{n=0}^{\infty}$ is a period-$2k$ sequence ($k \in \mathbb{N}$). Determine the necessary and sufficient conditions for the existence of periodic solutions of Eq. (6.198).

Open Problem 8. Suppose that $m = 2l + 1$ ($l \in \mathbb{N}$) and $\{A_n\}_{n=0}^{\infty}$ is a period-$(2k + 1)$ sequence ($k \in \mathbb{N}$). Determine the necessary and sufficient conditions for the existence of periodic solutions of Eq. (6.198).

We will proceed with the analysis of periodicity properties of the non-autonomous rational Δ.E. in the form:

$$x_{n+m} = \frac{A_n x_n}{1 + x_{n+1}}, \quad n = 0, 1, \ldots, \tag{6.199}$$

where $m \geq 3$ and $\{A_n\}_{n=0}^{\infty}$ is a period-k sequence ($k \geq 2$). Eq. (6.199) will then lead to the following **Open Problems** describing the periodic nature of solutions.

Open Problem 9. Suppose that $m = 2l$ ($l \in \mathbb{N}$) and $\{A_n\}_{n=0}^{\infty}$ is a period-2k sequence ($k \in \mathbb{N}$). Determine the necessary and sufficient conditions for the existence of periodic solutions of Eq. (6.199).

Open Problem 10. Suppose that $m = 2l$ ($l \in \mathbb{N}$) and $\{A_n\}_{n=0}^{\infty}$ is a period-$(2k+1)$ sequence ($k \in \mathbb{N}$). Determine the necessary and sufficient conditions for the existence of periodic solutions of Eq. (6.199).

Open Problem 11. Suppose that $m = 2l + 1$ ($l \in \mathbb{N}$) and $\{A_n\}_{n=0}^{\infty}$ is a period-2k sequence ($k \in \mathbb{N}$). Determine the necessary and sufficient conditions for the existence of periodic solutions of Eq. (6.199).

Open Problem 12. Suppose that $m = 2l + 1$ ($l \in \mathbb{N}$) and $\{A_n\}_{n=0}^{\infty}$ is a period-$(2k + 1)$ sequence ($k \in \mathbb{N}$). Determine the necessary and sufficient conditions for the existence of periodic solutions of Eq. (6.199).

We will advance with the study of periodic character of the non-autonomous rational Δ.E. in the form:

$$x_{n+m} = \frac{A_n x_n}{1 + \sum_{i=i}^{m} x_{n+m-i}}, \quad n = 0, 1, \ldots, \tag{6.200}$$

where $m \geq 3$ and $\{A_n\}_{n=0}^{\infty}$ is a period-k sequence ($k \geq 2$). Eq. (6.200) will then direct us to the following **Open Problems** portraying the periodic nature of solutions.

Open Problem 13. Suppose that $m = 2l$ ($l \in \mathbb{N}$) and $\{A_n\}_{n=0}^{\infty}$ is a period-2k sequence ($k \in \mathbb{N}$). Determine the necessary and sufficient conditions for the existence of periodic solutions of Eq. (6.200).

Open Problem 14. Suppose that $m = 2l$ ($l \in \mathbb{N}$) and $\{A_n\}_{n=0}^{\infty}$ is a period-$(2k+1)$ sequence ($k \in \mathbb{N}$). Determine the necessary and sufficient conditions for the existence of periodic solutions of Eq. (6.200).

Open Problem 15. Suppose that $m = 2l + 1$ ($l \in \mathbb{N}$) and $\{A_n\}_{n=0}^{\infty}$ is a period-2k sequence ($k \in \mathbb{N}$). Determine the necessary and sufficient conditions for the existence of periodic solutions of Eq. (6.200).

Open Problem 16. Suppose that $m = 2l + 1$ ($l \in \mathbb{N}$) and $\{A_n\}_{n=0}^{\infty}$ is a period-$(2k + 1)$ sequence ($k \in \mathbb{N}$). Determine the necessary and sufficient conditions of the existence of periodic solutions of Eq. (6.200).

6.11. More on Max-Type Difference Equations

In Chapter 5 we investigated the periodicity properties of Max-Type Δ.E. in the form:

$$x_{n+2} = \max\left\{\frac{1}{x_{n+1}}, \frac{C}{x_n}\right\}, \quad n = 0, 1, \ldots,$$

where $C > 0$. Our next aim is to expand the exploration of periodic and eventually periodic solutions when $\{C_n\}_{n=0}^{\infty}$ is a period-p sequence ($p \geq 2$). This will then guide us to the investigation of periodic character of:

$$x_{n+2} = \max\left\{\frac{1}{x_{n+1}}, \frac{C_n}{x_n}\right\}, \quad n = 0, 1, \ldots,$$

where $\{C_n\}_{n=0}^{\infty}$ is a period-2 sequence. Furthermore, our aim is to study the periodic nature of:

$$x_{n+2} = \max\left\{\frac{B_n}{x_{n+1}}, \frac{C_n}{x_n}\right\}, \quad n = 0, 1, \ldots,$$

where $\{B_n\}_{n=0}^{\infty}$ and $\{C_n\}_{n=0}^{\infty}$ are periodic sequences. Moreover, our intents are to study the periodic nature of:

$$x_{n+m} = \max\left\{\frac{B_n}{x_{n+m-l}}, \frac{C_n}{x_{n+m-k}}\right\}, \quad n = 0, 1, \ldots,$$

where $m \geq 3$, $0 \leq k, l < m$ and $k \neq l$.

6.12. Non-autonomous Piecewise Difference Equations and Systems of Piecewise Difference Equations

In Chapter 3 we studied the Tent-Map and other Piecewise Difference Equations; in particular, the Piecewise Δ.E. in the form:

$$x_{n+1} = \beta_n x_n - g(x_n), \quad n = 0, 1, 2, \ldots,$$

where $x_0 \in \Re$, $\{\beta_n\}_{n=0}^{\infty}$ is a period-2 sequence and

$$g(x) = \begin{cases} 1 & \text{if } x \geq 0, \\ -1 & \text{if } x < 0. \end{cases}$$

Our next goal is to establish the periodic traits of solutions when $\{\beta_n\}_{n=0}^{\infty}$ is a period-k sequence $(k \geq 2)$. The following graph below illustrates an eventually periodic solution with period-4 with 11 transient terms:

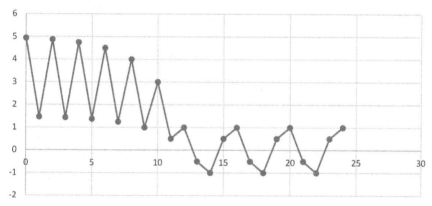

Eventually Periodic with Period-4 with 11 Transient Terms

We will then constitute the following conjecture.

Conjecture 8. *Consider the* $\Delta.E.$:

$$x_{n+1} = \beta_n x_n - g(x_n), \quad n = 0, 1, 2, \ldots, \tag{6.201}$$

where $x_0 \in \Re$, $\{\beta_n\}_{n=0}^{\infty}$ *is a period-k sequence,* $k \geq 2$ *and*

$$g(x) = \begin{cases} 1 & \text{if } x \geq 0, \\ -1 & \text{if } x < 0. \end{cases}$$

Then the following statements hold true:

(1) *Eq. (6.201) has cycles with period-kN, for all* $N \in \mathbb{N}$.
(2) *Eq. (6.201) has eventually periodic solutions with period-kN for all* $N \in \mathbb{N}$.

Now we will advance with investigating the periodic character of solutions of the following system of Piecewise Difference Equations:

$$\begin{cases} x_{n+1} = |x_n| - y_n - 1 \\ \\ y_{n+1} = x_n + |y_n| \end{cases} \quad n = 0, 1, 2, \ldots.$$

This system of piecewise difference equations was investigated in [42] and [58] and showed that there are two period-5 cycles. The above system can be extended to the following system of piecewise difference equations:

$$\begin{cases} x_{n+1} = |x_n| + a y_n + b \\ \\ y_{n+1} = x_n + c|y_n| + d \end{cases} \quad n = 0, 1, 2, \ldots,$$

where the coefficients a, b, c, and d are either $-1, 0$ or 1.

6.12.1. *Applications of systems of piecewise difference equations in neural networking*

Systems of piecewise difference equations have been used in modeling neural networks. The following system of piecewise difference equations (**Rulkov Model**) has been used in neural networking:

$$\left. \begin{array}{l} x_{n+1} = \frac{\alpha}{1-x_n} + y_n \\ \\ y_{n+1} = y_n - \mu(x_n + 1) + \mu\sigma \end{array} \right\}, \quad n = 0, 1, \ldots, \qquad (6.202)$$

when $x_n \leq 0$,

$$\left. \begin{array}{l} x_{n+1} = \alpha + y_n \\ \\ y_{n+1} = y_n - \mu(x_n + 1) + \mu\sigma \end{array} \right\}, \quad n = 0, 1, \ldots, \qquad (6.203)$$

when $x_n \leq \alpha + y_n$ and $x_{n-1} \leq 0$,

$$\left. \begin{array}{l} x_{n+1} = -1 \\ \\ y_{n+1} = y_n - \mu(x_n + 1) + \mu\sigma \end{array} \right\}, \quad n = 0, 1, \ldots, \qquad (6.204)$$

when $x_n > \alpha + y_n$ or $x_{n-1} > 0$. We will discover quite contrasting periodic behaviors ranging from very steady periodic cycles, periodic cycles with different spikes, eventually periodic behavior and irregular periodic cycles or chaotic orbits. Similar to what we have encountered in analogous Piecewise Difference Equations as the Tent-Map and the Neuron Model in Chapter 3, we can detect the strong sensitivity to the initial conditions and the relationship between the parameters. We will present several graphical examples depicting various periodic characters in the **Rulkov Model** [70, 76]:

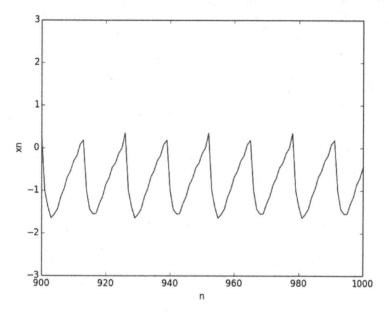

In the diagram above we have a periodic cycle with a steady pattern.

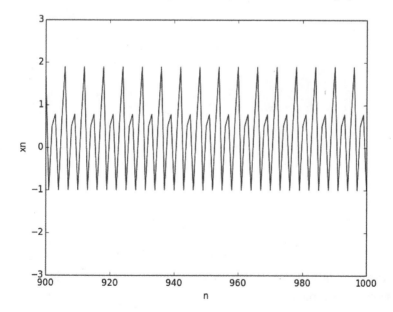

In the diagram above we have a periodic cycle with several patterns as we can see spikes with different heights.

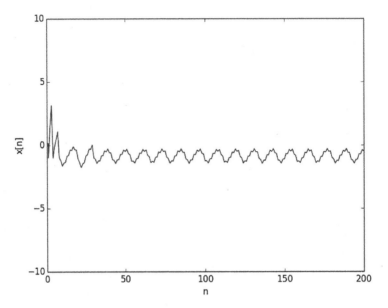

In the diagram above we have an eventually periodic cycle with several spiking patterns.

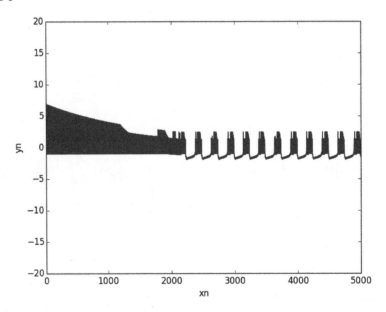

In the diagram above we have an eventually periodic cycle with several clusters of spiking patterns.

6.13. Additional Examples of Periodicity Graphs

Throughout the book we encountered various patterns of periodic and eventually periodic solutions. We can find distinct graphs that render decomposition of isolated clusters of periodic sub-cycles that describe the entire cycle. For example, in the graph below:

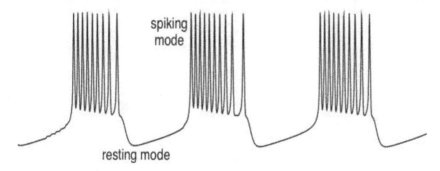

we can see clusters of spikes separated from each other with a steady transition. This particular pattern was discovered in the **Izhikevich Neural Networking Model**. More patterns of these spiking patterns can be found in [43]. We can also find similar periodic behaviors in **Signal Processing in Sigma–Delta Domain** in [25] and [67]. Now we will switch gears by analyzing the graph below:

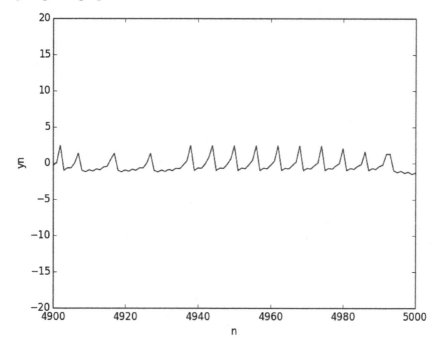

where one pattern transitions to another pattern. However, the second pattern does not hold steady and therefore becomes unstable. We noticed similar chaotic behavior in the Logistic Difference Equation, Tent-Map and the Neuron Model. This is where very careful computer observations are vital in order to come to these conclusions. We will conclude this chapter and the book with a diagram of another unstable periodic orbit.

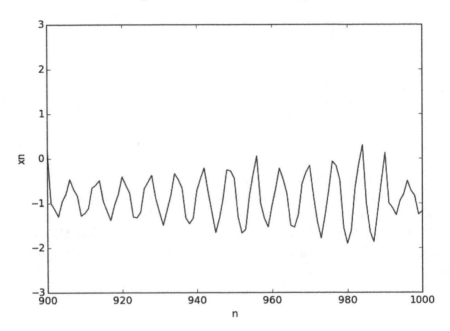

6.14. Chapter 6 Exercises

In problems 1–10, determine the **general solution** to each Δ.E.

1. $x_{n+3} - x_{n+2} - x_{n+1} + x_n = 0, \quad n = 0, 1, \ldots.$
2. $x_{n+3} - 3x_{n+2} + 3x_{n+1} - x_n = 0, \quad n = 0, 1, \ldots.$
3. $x_{n+4} - 10x_{n+2} + 9x_n = 0, \quad n = 0, 1, \ldots.$
4. $x_{n+4} - 3x_{n+2} - 4x_n = 0, \quad n = 0, 1, \ldots.$
5. $x_{n+4} - 4x_{n+3} + 6x_{n+2} - 4x_{n+1} + x_n = 0, \quad n = 0, 1, \ldots.$
6. $x_{n+3} - x_{n+2} - x_{n+1} + x_n = 2, \quad n = 0, 1, \ldots.$
7. $x_{n+4} - 5x_{n+2} + 4x_n = 4, \quad n = 0, 1, \ldots.$
8. $x_{n+3} - x_{n+2} - 9x_{n+1} + 9x_n = 3^n, \quad n = 0, 1, \ldots.$
9. $x_{n+3} + x_{n+2} - x_{n+1} - x_n = (-1)^n, \quad n = 0, 1, \ldots.$
10. $x_{n+3} + 3x_{n+2} + 3x_{n+1} + x_n = (-1)^n, \quad n = 0, 1, \ldots.$

In problems 11–14, solve the given **Initial Value Problem**:

11.
$$\begin{cases} x_{n+1} = -x_n \\ y_{n+1} = x_n + 2y_n \\ x_0 = -1, \\ y_0 = 1. \end{cases} \qquad n = 0, 1, 2, \ldots,$$

12.
$$\begin{cases} x_{n+1} = 2x_n \\ y_{n+1} = x_n + 2y_n \\ x_0 = 2, \\ y_0 = 1. \end{cases} \qquad n = 0, 1, 2, \ldots,$$

13.
$$\begin{cases} x_{n+1} = 3x_n \\ y_{n+1} = x_n + 6y_n \\ x_0 = 3, \\ y_0 = 1. \end{cases} \qquad n = 0, 1, 2, \ldots,$$

14.
$$\begin{cases} x_{n+1} = ax_n \\ y_{n+1} = x_n + by_n \\ x_0 = a, \\ y_0 = 1. \end{cases} \qquad n = 0, 1, 2, \ldots,$$

In problems 15–18, determine the general solution to each **LTI Δ.E.**

15. $y_{n+k} = ay_n + bx_n$.
16. $y_{n+k} = ay_n + x_n + x_{n+1}$.
17. $y_{n+k} = ay_n + x_n + x_{n+1} + x_{n+2}$.
18. $y_{n+k} = ay_n + \left[\sum_{i=0}^{N-1} x_{n+i} \right]$.

In problems 19–26, determine the **local stability character** of all the equilibrium point(s) of each system of difference equations; assume that $A, B, C, D > 0$ and $x_0, y_0 \geq 0$.

19.
$$\begin{cases} x_{n+1} = \dfrac{Ax_n}{1 + y_n} \\[3mm] y_{n+1} = \dfrac{By_n}{1 + x_n} \end{cases} \qquad n = 0, 1, 2, \ldots$$

20.
$$\begin{cases} x_{n+1} = \dfrac{Ay_n}{1 + x_n} \\[3mm] y_{n+1} = \dfrac{Bx_n}{1 + x_n + y_n} \end{cases} \qquad n = 0, 1, 2, \ldots$$

21.
$$\begin{cases} x_{n+1} = \dfrac{Ax_n}{1+y_n} \\[4mm] y_{n+1} = \dfrac{By_n}{1+x_n+y_n} \end{cases} \qquad n = 0,1,2,\ldots$$

22.
$$\begin{cases} x_{n+1} = \dfrac{Ax_n + By_n}{1+x_n} \\[4mm] y_{n+1} = \dfrac{Cx_n + Dy_n}{1+y_n} \end{cases} \qquad n = 0,1,2,\ldots$$

23.
$$\begin{cases} x_{n+1} = \dfrac{Ax_n}{1+x_n+Cy_n} \\[4mm] y_{n+1} = \dfrac{By_n}{1+y_n+Dx_n} \end{cases} \qquad n = 0,1,2,\ldots$$

24.
$$\begin{cases} x_{n+1} = Ax_n + y_n e^{-x_n} \\[3mm] y_{n+1} = By_n + x_n e^{-y_n} \end{cases} \qquad n = 0,1,2,\ldots$$

25.
$$\begin{cases} x_{n+1} = \dfrac{Ax_n}{1+By_n} \\[4mm] y_{n+1} = \dfrac{Bx_n y_n}{1+By_n} \end{cases} \qquad n = 0,1,2,\ldots$$

26.
$$\begin{cases} x_{n+1} = Ax_n e^{1-x_n-Cy_n} \\[3mm] y_{n+1} = By_n e^{1-y_n-Dx_n} \end{cases} \qquad n = 0,1,2,\ldots$$

In problems 27–32, determine the necessary and sufficient conditions for the existence of periodic solutions:

27. Existence of Periodic Solutions of:

$$x_{n+m} = x_n + a_n, \qquad n = 0,1,\ldots,$$

where $m \geq 3$ and $\{a_n\}_{n=0}^{\infty}$ is a period-k sequence $(k \geq 2)$.

28. Existence of Periodic Solutions of:

$$x_{n+3} = -x_n + a_n, \qquad n = 0,1,\ldots,$$

where $\{a_n\}_{n=0}^{\infty}$ is a period-k sequence $(k \geq 2)$.

29. Existence of Periodic Solutions of:

$$x_{n+m} = -x_n + a_n, \quad n = 0, 1, \ldots,$$

where $m \geq 3$ and $\{a_n\}_{n=0}^{\infty}$ is a period-k sequence $(k \geq 2)$.

30. Existence of Periodic Solutions of:

$$x_{n+3} = a_n x_n + b_n, \quad n = 0, 1, \ldots,$$

where $\{a_n\}_{n=0}^{\infty}$ and $\{b_n\}_{n=0}^{\infty}$ are period-2 sequences.

31. Existence of Periodic Solutions of:

$$x_{n+3} = a_n x_n + b_n, \quad n = 0, 1, \ldots,$$

where $\{a_n\}_{n=0}^{\infty}$ and $\{b_n\}_{n=0}^{\infty}$ are period-3 sequences.

32. Existence of Periodic Solutions of:

$$x_{n+3} = a_n x_n + b_n, \quad n = 0, 1, \ldots,$$

where $\{a_n\}_{n=0}^{\infty}$ and $\{b_n\}_{n=0}^{\infty}$ are period-k sequences $(k \geq 2)$.

CHAPTER 7

ANSWERS TO SELECTED
ODD-NUMBERED PROBLEMS

7.1. Answers to Chapter 1 Exercises

1. For all $n \geq 0$:
$$\begin{cases} x_{n+1} = x_n + 5(n+1), \\ x_0 = 1. \end{cases}$$

3. For all $n \geq 0$:
$$\begin{cases} x_{n+1} = x_n + n(n+1), \\ x_0 = 1. \end{cases}$$

5. For all $n \geq 0$:
$$\begin{cases} x_{n+1} = x_n + (n+1)^2, \\ x_0 = 1. \end{cases}$$

7. For all $n \geq 0$:
$$\begin{cases} x_{n+1} = 4x_n, \\ x_0 = 3. \end{cases}$$

9. For all $n \geq 0$:
$$\begin{cases} x_{n+1} = \dfrac{3x_n}{4}, \\ x_0 = 64. \end{cases}$$

11. For all $n \geq 0$:

$$\begin{cases} x_{n+1} = \left[\prod_{k=0}^{n} (2k+1) \right] x_n, \\ x_0 = 1. \end{cases}$$

13. For all $n \geq 0$:

$$\begin{cases} x_{n+1} = \dfrac{(n+3)x_n}{n+1}, \\ x_0 = 2. \end{cases}$$

15. For all $n \geq 0$:

$$\begin{cases} x_{n+1} = \dfrac{2(n+3)x_n}{2(n+1)}, \\ x_0 = 8. \end{cases}$$

17. For all $n \geq 0$:

$$\begin{cases} x_{n+1} = x_n + 2n + 3, \\ x_0 = 1. \end{cases}$$

19. For all $n \geq 0$:

$$\begin{cases} x_{n+1} = x_n + \left(\dfrac{1}{2} \right)^{n+1}, \\ x_0 = 1. \end{cases}$$

21. $x_n = 4^n x_0$, for all $n \geq 0$.

23. $x_n = (-2)^n x_0$, for all $n \geq 0$.

25. $\dfrac{1}{3}$, 3, $\dfrac{1}{3}$, 3, ...

27. 2, 3, 2, 3, ...

29. 2, $\dfrac{1}{2}$, -2, $-\dfrac{1}{2}$, ...

31. 3, 5, $5\sqrt{2} - 3$, $5 - 3\sqrt{2}$, -3, -5, $3 - 5\sqrt{2}$, $3\sqrt{2} - 5$, ...

33. 2, 4, $\dfrac{1}{2}$, $-\dfrac{1}{4}$, 2, -4, $\dfrac{1}{2}$, $\dfrac{1}{4}$, ...

35. Period-8.

37. Period-12.

39. Not Periodic.

41. Period-5.

43. Period-7.

45. Period-4 cycle and terms in the numerator double from neighbor to neighbor.

47. Period-4 cycle and terms in the numerator shift by 1 under modulo 3 arithmetic.

49. Period-4 cycle and terms in the denominator shift by 1 under modulo 4 arithmetic.

51. Sequence is bounded and limit exists as:

$$\lim_{n\to\infty} x_{2n} = \lim_{n\to\infty} x_{2n+1} = 0.$$

53. Sequence is bounded but limit does not exist:

$$\lim_{n\to\infty} x_{2n} = 2 \neq \lim_{n\to\infty} x_{2n+1} = 1.$$

55. Sequence is bounded but limit does not exist:

$$\lim_{n\to\infty} x_{3n} = \lim_{n\to\infty} x_{3n+1} = 0 \neq \lim_{n\to\infty} x_{3n+2} = 1.$$

57. Sequence is unbounded as:

$$\lim_{n\to\infty} x_{4n+1} = +\infty \quad \text{and} \quad \lim_{n\to\infty} x_{4n+3} = +\infty.$$

7.2. Answers to Chapter 2 Exercises

7. $x_n = 9(-1)^{n+1} \left(\dfrac{5}{3}\right)^{n-1}$ for all $n \geq 0$.

9. $x_n = 4\left(-\dfrac{7}{2}\right)^n + 2$ for all $n \geq 0$.

11. $x_n = 3n - 5$ for all $n \geq 0$.

13. $x_n = \begin{cases} -2 & \text{if } n \text{ is even,} \\ 9 & \text{if } n \text{ is odd.} \end{cases}$

15. $x_n = n^2$ for all $n \geq 0$.

17. $x_n = \dfrac{n(n+1)(2n+1)}{6}$ for all $n \geq 0$.

19. $x_n = 2n(n+1) + \dfrac{3}{2}\left[3^{n+1} - 1\right]$ for all $n \geq 0$.

21. $\lim_{n\to\infty} x_n = \bar{x} = 3$.

23. $\lim_{n\to\infty} x_n$ does not exist.

25. $\lim_{n\to\infty} x_n = +\infty$.

27. $\lim_{n\to\infty} x_n = x_0 + e$.

29. $\lim_{n\to\infty} x_n = x_0 + 9$.

31. $y_n = a^n y_0 + a^{n-1} x_0 + \sum_{i=1}^{n-1} [a^{n-i} + a^{n-i-1}] x_i + x_n$ for all $n \in \mathbb{N}$.

33. $y_n = a^n y_0 + a^{n-1} b_1 x_0 + \sum_{i=1}^{n-1} [a^{n-i} b_2 + a^{n-i-1} b_1] x_i + b_2 x_n$ for all $n \in \mathbb{N}$.

35. $y_n = a^n y_0 + a^{n-1} x_0 + \sum_{i=1}^{2} [a^{n-1} + a^{n-2}] x_i + \sum_{i=0}^{n-1-k} [a^i] x_{3+k} + x_{n+2}$ for all $k = 0, 1, \ldots (n-2)$ and for all $n \geq 2$.

7.3. Answers to Chapter 3 Exercises

1. Intersection between $y = x$ and $y = \dfrac{2+x}{3+x}$:

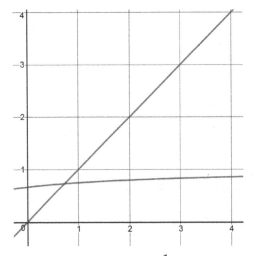

3. Intersection between $y = x$ and $y = \dfrac{1}{x^2+1}$:

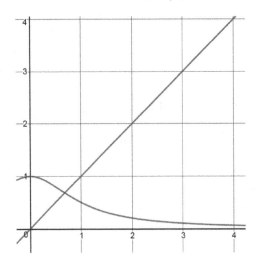

5. Intersection between $y = x$ and $y = \dfrac{1}{e^x}$:

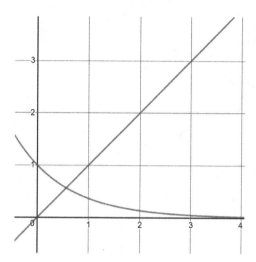

7. Intersection between $y = x$ and $y = x^4 - x^2$:

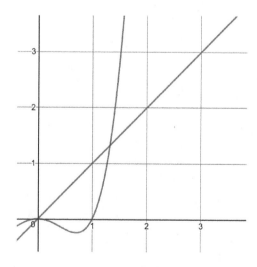

9. $\bar{x} = 1$ is Locally Asymptotically Stable.

11. $\bar{x} = 1$ is Locally Asymptotically Stable.

13. $\bar{x} = \sqrt{a-1}$ is Locally Asymptotically Stable for $a > 1$.

15. $\bar{x}$ is Locally Asymptotically Stable if $\bar{x} < \sqrt{a}$.

17. $\bar{x} = ab$ is Locally Asymptotically Stable if $a < 2$.

19. Globally Asymptotically Stable for all $x_0 \geq 0$:

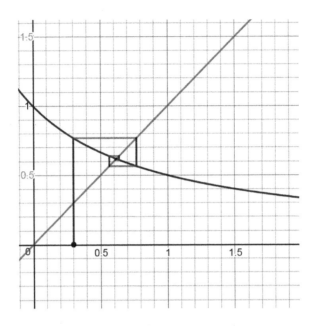

21. Globally Asymptotically Stable for all $x_0 \geq 0$:

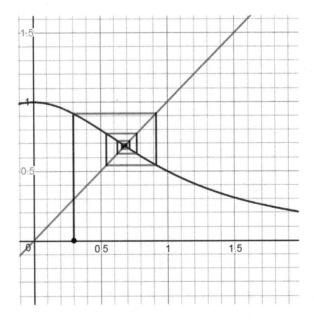

23. Globally Asymptotically Stable for all $x_0 \geq 0$:

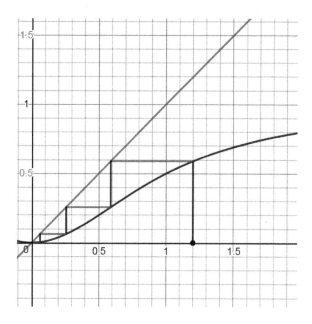

25. Globally Asymptotically Stable for all $x_0 \geq 0$:

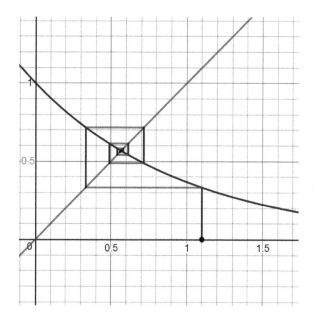

27. Convergence to Period-2 for all $x_0 \in (0, 1)$:

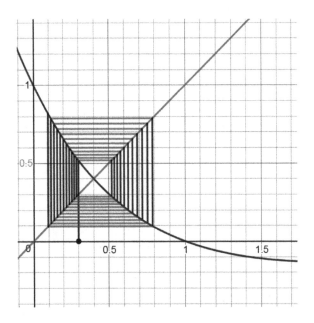

29. $x_0 > x_1 > x_2 > \ldots > x_n > x_{n+1} > \ldots$ for all $n \geq 0$.

31. $x_0 > x_1 > x_2 > \ldots > x_n > x_{n+1} > \ldots$ for all $n \geq 0$.

33. Result follows from Theorem 9.

35. One of the following period-2 cycles:

$$\frac{a_0a_1 + \sqrt{(a_0a_1)^2 + 4a_0a_1}}{2a_0}, \quad \frac{a_0a_1 + \sqrt{(a_0a_1)^2 + 4a_0a_1}}{2a_1}$$

$$\frac{a_0a_1 - \sqrt{(a_0a_1)^2 + 4a_0a_1}}{2a_0}, \quad \frac{a_0a_1 - \sqrt{(a_0a_1)^2 + 4a_0a_1}}{2a_1}$$

51. $x_n = \dfrac{3}{4}$ for all $n \geq 0$.

53. Period-10 cycle.

55. Eventually Constant with 2 transient terms.

57. Eventually Periodic with Period-4 with 5 transient terms.

59. $\dfrac{2}{2^5 + 1}, \dfrac{2^2}{2^5 + 1}, \dfrac{2^3}{2^5 + 1}, \dfrac{2^4}{2^5 + 1}, \dfrac{2^5}{2^5 + 1}$.

61. $\dfrac{2^{i+1}}{2^k + 1}$ for all $i = 0, 1, \ldots, k - 1$.

63. $\left[\dfrac{1}{2080}, \dfrac{1}{1040}, \dfrac{1}{520}, \dfrac{1}{260}, \dfrac{1}{130}, \dfrac{1}{65}\right], \dfrac{2}{65}, \dfrac{4}{65}, \dfrac{8}{65}, \dfrac{16}{65}, \dfrac{32}{65}, \dfrac{64}{65}.$

67. $\dfrac{A}{A^2+1}, \dfrac{A^2}{A^2+1}.$

69. $\dfrac{A}{A^4+1}, \dfrac{A^2}{A^4+1}, \dfrac{A^3}{A^4+1}, \dfrac{A^4}{A^4+1}.$

71. $\left[\dfrac{1}{A^3(A^2+1)}, \dfrac{1}{A^2(A^2+1)}, \dfrac{1}{A(A^2+1)}, \dfrac{1}{A^2+1}\right], \dfrac{A}{A^2+1}, \dfrac{A^2}{A^2+1}.$

73. $\left[\dfrac{1}{A^j(A^k+1)}\right], \dfrac{A^{i+1}}{A^k+1}$ for all $j = 0, 1, \ldots, N-1$ and for all $i = 0, 1, \ldots, k-1.$

7.4. Answers to Chapter 4 Exercises

11. $x_n = C_1(-5)^n + C_2 4^n$ for all $n \geq 0.$

13. $x_n = C_1 3^n + C_2 7^n$ for all $n \geq 0.$

15. $x_n = C_1 6^n + nC_2 6^n$ for all $n \geq 0.$

17. $x_n = \left(\dfrac{1}{2}\right)^n \left[C_1 \cos\left(\dfrac{n\pi}{2}\right) + C_2 \sin\left(\dfrac{n\pi}{2}\right)\right]$ for all $n \geq 0.$

19. $x_n = C_1 \cos\left(\dfrac{n\pi}{4}\right) + C_2 \sin\left(\dfrac{n\pi}{4}\right)$ for all $n \geq 0.$

21. $x_n = 2^n \left[C_1 \cos\left(\dfrac{n\pi}{3}\right) + C_2 \sin\left(\dfrac{n\pi}{3}\right)\right]$ for all $n \geq 0.$

23. $x_n = [C_1 2^n + C_2 5^n] + 4$ for all $n \geq 0.$

25. $x_n = [C_1 3^n + C_2 6^n] + \dfrac{3}{2}$ for all $n \geq 0.$

27. $x_n = [C_1 + C_2 5^n] - \dfrac{n}{2}$ for all $n \geq 0.$

29. $x_n = [C_1 2^n + C_2 3^n] + \dfrac{4^n}{2}$ for all $n \geq 0.$

31. $x_n = [C_1 + C_2 2^n] + n2^{n-1}$ for all $n \geq 0.$

33. $x_n = [C_1 4^n + nC_2 4^n] + \dfrac{n^2}{2} 4^{n-2}$ for all $n \geq 0.$

35. $x_n = 2 + 2^n$ for all $n \geq 0.$

37. $x_n = -4^n + 2(-3)^n$ for all $n \geq 0.$

39. $x_n = -2 + 2(5)^n - n$ for all $n \geq 0.$

41. Period-6 pattern:

$$x_0, \ x_1, \ x_1 - x_0, \ -x_0, \ -x_1, \ x_0 - x_1.$$

43. Period-12 pattern:

$$x_0, \ x_1, \ \sqrt{3}x_1 - x_0, \ 2x_1 - \sqrt{3}x_0, \ \sqrt{3}x_1 - 2x_0, \ x_1 - \sqrt{3}x_0,$$
$$-x_0, \ -x_1, \ x_0 - \sqrt{3}x_1, \ \sqrt{3}x_0 - 2x_1, \ 2x_0 - \sqrt{3}x_1, \ \sqrt{3}x_0 - x_1.$$

45. Linearly Independent.

47. Linearly Independent.

49. Linearly Independent.

51. Transforms to $y_{n+2} - y_{n+1} - y_n = 0$ and $\lim_{n\to\infty} x_n = \dfrac{1+\sqrt{5}}{2}$.

53. Transforms to $y_{n+2} - 5y_{n+1} + 3y_n = 0$ and $\lim_{n\to\infty} x_n = \dfrac{-3+\sqrt{13}}{2}$.

55. Transforms to $y_{n+2} - 5y_{n+1} + 4y_n = 0$ and $\lim_{n\to\infty} x_n = 3$.

57. $|p| < 1 + q < 2$ satisfies and $\lim_{n\to\infty} x_n = 0$.

59. $|p| = 1 + q < 2$ does not satisfy and $\lim_{n\to\infty} x_n \neq 0$.

61.
$$\begin{cases} y_{2n} = a^n y_0 + \left[\displaystyle\sum_{i=0}^{n-1} a^{n-i-1} \left[x_{2i} + x_{2i+1} \right] \right], \\[4mm] y_{2n+1} = a^n y_1 + \left[\displaystyle\sum_{i=0}^{n-1} a^{n-i-1} \left[x_{2i+1} + x_{2i+2} \right] \right]. \end{cases}$$

63.
$$\begin{cases} y_{2n} = a^n y_0 + \left[\displaystyle\sum_{i=0}^{n-1} a^{n-i-1} \left[x_{2i} + x_{2i+1} + x_{2i+2} \right] \right], \\[4mm] y_{2n+1} = a^n y_1 + \left[\displaystyle\sum_{i=0}^{n-1} a^{n\ i-1} \left[x_{2i+1} + x_{2i+2} + x_{2i+3} \right] \right]. \end{cases}$$

7.5. Answers to Chapter 5 Exercises

1. $- \ \bar{x} = 0$ is Locally Asymptotically Stable if $A + B < \alpha$.

   $- \ \bar{x} = \dfrac{A + B - \alpha}{\beta}$ is Locally Asymptotically Stable if $A + B > \alpha$.

3. $- \ \bar{x} = \dfrac{B}{\alpha + \beta}$ is Locally Asymptotically Stable if $\alpha < \dfrac{1}{2}$.

5. $- \ \bar{x} = \dfrac{A}{\alpha + \beta}$ is Locally Asymptotically Stable for all $A, \alpha, \beta > 0$.

7. $- \ \bar{x} = 0$ is Locally Asymptotically Stable if $A < \gamma$.

   $- \ \bar{x} = \dfrac{A - \gamma}{\beta}$ is Locally Asymptotically Stable if $A > \gamma$.

9. $-\bar{x} = \sqrt{\dfrac{A}{2}}$ is Locally Asymptotically Stable for all $A > 0$.

11. $-\bar{x} = \sqrt{A + B}$ is Locally Asymptotically Stable for all $A, B > 0$.

13. $-\bar{x} = 0$ is Locally Asymptotically Stable.

15. $-\bar{x} = 0$ is Locally Asymptotically Stable if $B < 1$.
   - $\bar{x} = Ln(B)$ is Locally Asymptotically Stable if $1 < B < e$.

17. $-\bar{x} = 0$ is Locally Asymptotically Stable if $B < 1$.
   - $\bar{x} = Ln(B)$ is Locally Asymptotically Stable if $B < e^{\frac{2}{B}}$.

19. $-\bar{x} = 0$ is Locally Asymptotically Stable if $A < 1$.
   - $\bar{x} = Ln(B)$ is Locally Asymptotically Stable if $A < e^{\frac{2}{A}}$.

21. Period-2 cycles exist if and only if $D = C$ and $x_0 + x_1 = B$ with one of the following patterns:

   - $x_0, B - x_0, x_0, B - x_0, \ldots$
   - $B - x_1, x_1, B - x_1, x_1, \ldots$

23. Period-2 cycles exist if and only if $B = A + 1$ and $A[x_0 + x_1] = Cx_0x_1$ with one of the following patterns:

   $$- \frac{Ax_1}{Cx_1 - A}, x_1, \frac{Ax_1}{Cx_1 - A}, x_1, \ldots$$

   $$- x_0, \frac{Ax_0}{Cx_0 - A}, x_0, \frac{Ax_0}{Cx_0 - A}, \ldots$$

25. Period-2 cycles exist if and only if $B > A + 1$ and $x_0 + x_1 = \dfrac{B - 1 - A}{D}$ with one of the following patterns:

   $$- x_0, \frac{B - 1 - A}{D} - x_0, x_0, \frac{B - 1 - A}{D} - x_0, \ldots$$

   $$- \frac{B - 1 - A}{D} - x_1, x_1, \frac{B - 1 - A}{D} - x_1, x_1, \ldots$$

27. Two unique period-2 cycles exist if and only if $x_0 = -x_1$ with one of the following patterns:

   - $\sqrt{2}, -\sqrt{2}, \sqrt{2}, -\sqrt{2}, \ldots$
   - $-\sqrt{2}, \sqrt{2}, -\sqrt{2}, \sqrt{2}, \ldots$

29. Every non-trivial solution is periodic with the following period-3 pattern:

   $$x_0, x_1, \frac{1}{x_0x_1}, x_0, x_1, \frac{1}{x_0x_1}, \ldots$$

31. Every non-trivial solution is periodic with the following period-6 pattern:

$$x_0, x_1, \frac{1}{x_0 x_1}, -x_0, -x_1, \frac{-1}{x_0 x_1}, \ldots.$$

33. Every non-trivial solution is periodic with the following period-6 pattern:

$$x_0, x_1, \frac{x_1}{x_0}, \frac{-1}{x_0}, \frac{-1}{x_1}, \frac{-x_0}{x_1}, \ldots.$$

7.6. Answers to Chapter 6 Exercises

1. $x_n = C_1 + nC_2 + C_3(-1)^n$ for all $n \geq 0$.

3. $x_n = C_1 3^n + C_2(-3)^n + C_3 + C_4(-1)^n$ for all $n \geq 0$.

5. $x_n = C_1 + nC_2 + n^2 C_3 + n^3 C_4$ for all $n \geq 0$.

7. $x_n = C_1 2^n + C_2(-2)^n + C_3 + C_4(-1)^n - \frac{2n}{3}$ for all $n \geq 0$.

9. $x_n = C_1 + C_2(-1)^n + nC_3(-1)^n - \frac{n^2(-1)^n}{4}$ for all $n \geq 0$.

11. For all $j = 0, 1, \ldots, kn - 1$ and for all $n \in \mathbb{N}$:

$$y_{kn+j} = a^n y_j + \left[\sum_{i=0}^{n-1} a^{(n-1-i)} \, bx_{ki+j} \right].$$

13. For all $j = 0, 1, \ldots, kn - 1$ and for all $n \in \mathbb{N}$:

$$y_{kn+j} = a^n y_j + \left[\sum_{i=0}^{n-1} a^{(n-1-i)} \, [x_{ki+j} + x_{ki+j+1} + x_{ki+j+2}] \right].$$

15. For all $n \in \mathbb{N}$:

$$\begin{cases} x_n = (-1)^{n+1} \\ \\ y_n = \begin{cases} \sum_{k=0}^{n} (-2)^k & \text{if } n \text{ is even,} \\ \sum_{k=0}^{n} -(-2)^k & \text{if } n \text{ is odd.} \end{cases} \end{cases}$$

17. For all $n \in \mathbb{N}$:

$$\begin{cases} x_n = 3^{n+1} \\ y_n = (3)^n \left[\sum_{k=0}^{n} 2^k \right] \end{cases}$$

19. – $(0,0)$ is Locally Asymptotically Stable if $AB < 1$.
    – $(B-1, A-1)$ is Unstable.

21. – $(0,0)$ is Locally Asymptotically Stable if $AB < 1$.
    – $(B-A, A-1)$ is Unstable.

23. – $(0,0)$ is Locally Asymptotically Stable if $AB < 1$.
    – $\left(\dfrac{A}{B}, \dfrac{A-1}{B} \right)$ is Unstable.

25. – $(0,0)$ is Locally Asymptotically Stable if $AB < 1$.

APPENDICES

A.1. Patterns of Sequences

1. Linear Patterns:

$1, 2, 3, 4, 5, 6, 7, \ldots = \{n\}_{n=1}^{\infty}$

$2, 4, 6, 8, 10, 12, 14, \ldots = \{2n\}_{n=1}^{\infty}$

$1, 3, 5, 7, 9, 11, 13, \ldots = \{2n+1\}_{n=0}^{\infty}$

$3, 6, 9, 12, 15, 18, 21, \ldots = \{3n\}_{n=1}^{\infty}$

2. Quadratic Patterns:

$1, 4, 9, 16, 25, 36, 49, \ldots = \{n^2\}_{n=1}^{\infty}$

$4, 16, 36, 64, 100, 144, 196, \ldots = \{(2n)^2\}_{n=1}^{\infty}$

$1, 9, 25, 49, 81, 121, 169, \ldots = \{(2n-1)^2\}_{n=1}^{\infty}$

3. Geometric Patterns:

$1, r, r^2, r^3, r^4, r^5, r^6, \ldots = \{r^n\}_{n=0}^{\infty}$

$2, 4, 8, 16, 32, 64, 128, \ldots = \{2^n\}_{n=1}^{\infty}$

$3, 9, 27, 81, 243, 729, \ldots = \{3^n\}_{n=1}^{\infty}$

A.2. Alternating Patterns of Sequences

1. Alternating Linear Patterns:

$1, -2, 3, -4, 5, -6, 7, \ldots = \{(-1)^{n+1}\, n\}_{n=1}^{\infty}$

$-1, 2, -3, 4, -5, 6, -7, \ldots = \{(-1)^{n}\, n\}_{n=1}^{\infty}$

$1, -3, 5, -7, 9, -11, 13, \ldots = \{(-1)^{n}\, [2n+1]\}_{n=0}^{\infty}$

$-1, 3, -5, 7, -9, 11, -13, \ldots = \{(-1)^{n+1}\, [2n+1]\}_{n=0}^{\infty}$

2. **Alternating Quadratic Patterns:**

$$1,\ -4,\ 9,\ -16,\ 25,\ -36,\ 49,\ldots = \{(-1)^{n+1}\ n^2\}_{n=1}^{\infty}$$
$$-1,\ 4,\ -9,\ 16,\ -25,\ 36,\ -49,\ldots = \{(-1)^{n}\ n^2\}_{n=1}^{\infty}$$

3. **Alternating Geometric Patterns:**

$$1,\ -r,\ r^2,\ -r^3,\ r^4,\ -r^5,\ r^6,\ldots = \{(-1)^{n}\ r^n\}_{n=0}^{\infty}$$
$$-1,\ r,\ -r^2,\ r^3,\ -r^4,\ r^5,\ -r^6,\ldots = \{(-1)^{n+1}\ r^n\}_{n=0}^{\infty}$$

A.3. Finite Series

$$1+2+3+4+5+6+\cdots+n = \sum_{i=1}^{n} i = \frac{n[n+1]}{2}.$$

$$1+3+5+7+9+11+\cdots+[2n-1] = \sum_{i=1}^{n} (2i-1) = n^2.$$

$$1+4+9+16+25+36+\cdots+n^2 = \sum_{i=1}^{n} i^2 = \frac{n[n+1][2n+1]}{6}.$$

$$1\cdot 2+2\cdot 3+3\cdot 4+4\cdot 5+\cdots+n\cdot[n+1] = \sum_{i=1}^{n} i\cdot[i+1] = \frac{n[n+1][n+2]}{3}.$$

$$\frac{1}{1\cdot 2}+\frac{1}{2\cdot 3}+\frac{1}{3\cdot 4}+\frac{1}{4\cdot 5}+\cdots+\frac{1}{n\cdot[n+1]} = \sum_{i=1}^{n} \frac{1}{i\cdot[i+1]} = \frac{n}{n+1}.$$

$$1+r+r^2+r^3+r^4+r^5+\cdots+r^n = \sum_{i=0}^{n} r^i = \frac{1-r^{n+1}}{1-r}.$$

$$1\cdot 2^0+2\cdot 2^1+3\cdot 2^2+\cdots+n\cdot 2^{n-1} = \sum_{i=1}^{n} i\cdot 2^{i-1} = [n-1]2^n+1.$$

$$\binom{n}{0}+\binom{n}{1}+\binom{n}{2}+\cdots+\binom{n}{n-1}+\binom{n}{n} = \sum_{i=0}^{n} \binom{n}{i} = 2^n.$$

A.4. Convergent Infinite Series

$$1+r+r^2+r^3+r^4+r^5+\cdots = \sum_{n=0}^{\infty} r^n = \frac{1}{1-r},\quad |r|<1.$$

$$\frac{1}{1\cdot 2}+\frac{1}{2\cdot 3}+\frac{1}{3\cdot 4}+\frac{1}{4\cdot 5}+\cdots = \sum_{n=1}^{\infty} \frac{1}{n[n+1]} = 1.$$

$$1 + \frac{1}{2} + \frac{1}{6} + \frac{1}{24} + \frac{1}{120} + \frac{1}{720} + \cdots = \sum_{n=0}^{\infty} \frac{1}{n!} = e.$$

$$1 - \frac{1}{2} + \frac{1}{3} - \frac{1}{4} + \frac{1}{5} - \frac{1}{6} + \cdots = \sum_{n=1}^{\infty} \frac{(-1)^{n+1}}{n} = Ln[2].$$

$$1 + \frac{1}{4} + \frac{1}{9} + \frac{1}{16} + \frac{1}{25} + \frac{1}{36} + \cdots = \sum_{n=1}^{\infty} \frac{1}{n^2} = \frac{\pi^2}{6}.$$

A.5. Periodic Sequences and Modulo Arithmetic

Period-2 sequence $\{A_n\}_{n=0}^{\infty}$ and corresponding period-2 pattern:

$$A_0, \ A_1, \ A_0, \ A_1, \ \ldots.$$

Period-2 sequence $\{A_n\}_{n=0}^{\infty}$ and corresponding period-2 pattern:

$$\frac{A_0 A_1 - 1}{1 + A_0}, \ \frac{A_0 A_1 - 1}{1 + A_1}, \ \frac{A_0 A_1 - 1}{1 + A_0}, \ \frac{A_0 A_1 - 1}{1 + A_1}, \ \ldots.$$

Period-3 sequence $\{A_n\}_{n=0}^{\infty}$ and corresponding period-3 pattern:

$$A_0, \ A_1, \ A_2, \ A_0, \ A_1, \ A_2, \ \ldots.$$

Period-3 sequence $\{A_n\}_{n=0}^{\infty}$ and corresponding period-3 pattern:

$$\frac{A_0 A_1}{A_0 A_1 A_2 + 1}, \ \frac{A_1 A_2}{A_0 A_1 A_2 + 1}, \ \frac{A_2 A_0}{A_0 A_1 A_2 + 1}, \ \ldots.$$

Period-4 sequence $\{A_n\}_{n=0}^{\infty}$ and corresponding period-4 pattern:

$$A_0, \ A_1, \ A_2, \ A_3, \ A_0, \ A_1, \ A_2, \ A_3, \ \ldots.$$

Period-4 sequence $\{A_n\}_{n=0}^{\infty}$ and corresponding period-4 pattern:

$$\frac{A_0 + A_1 + A_2}{2}, \ \frac{A_1 + A_2 + A_3}{2}, \ \frac{A_2 + A_3 + A_0}{2}, \ \frac{A_3 + A_0 + A_1}{2}, \ \ldots.$$

A.6. Alternating Periodic Sequences and Modulo Arithmetic

Period-2 sequence $\{A_n\}_{n=0}^{\infty}$ and corresponding period-4 pattern:

$$A_0, \ A_1, \ -A_0, \ -A_1, \ \ldots.$$

Period-3 sequence $\{A_n\}_{n=0}^{\infty}$ and corresponding period-6 pattern:

$$A_0, \ A_1, \ A_2, \ -A_0, \ -A_1, \ -A_2, \ldots.$$

Period-2 sequence $\{A_n\}_{n=0}^{\infty}$ and corresponding period-2 pattern:

$$\frac{A_0 A_1}{A_0 + A_1 + 1}, \quad \frac{-A_0 A_1}{A_0 + A_1 + 1}, \quad \ldots$$

Period-2 sequence $\{A_n\}_{n=0}^{\infty}$ and corresponding period-2 pattern:

$$\frac{A_0 - A_1}{A_0 A_1 + 1}, \quad \frac{A_1 - A_0}{A_0 A_1 + 1}, \quad \ldots$$

Period-2 sequence $\{A_n\}_{n=0}^{\infty}$ and corresponding period-4 pattern:

$$\frac{A_0}{A_0 A_1 + 1}, \quad \frac{A_1}{A_0 A_1 + 1}, \quad \frac{-A_0}{A_0 A_1 + 1}, \quad \frac{-A_1}{A_0 A_1 + 1}, \quad \ldots$$

Period-2 sequence $\{A_n\}_{n=0}^{\infty}$ and corresponding period-4 pattern:

$$\frac{A_0 + A_1}{A_0 A_1 + 1}, \quad \frac{A_0 - A_1}{A_0 A_1 + 1}, \quad \frac{-[A_0 + A_1]}{A_0 A_1 + 1}, \quad \frac{A_1 - A_0}{A_0 A_1 + 1}, \quad \ldots$$

BIBLIOGRAPHY

[1] A. M. Amleh, E. Camouzis, G. Ladas and M. Radin (2010), Patterns of boundedness of a rational system in the plane, *Journal of Difference Equations and Applications*, 16 (10), 1197–1236.

[2] A. M. Amleh, D. A. Georgiou, E. A. Grove and G. Ladas (1999), On the recursive sequence $x_{n+1} = \alpha + \frac{x_{n-1}}{x_n}$, *J. Math. Anal. Appl.*, 233, 790–798.

[3] A. M. Amleh, J. Hoag and G. Ladas (1998), A difference equation with eventually periodic solutions, *Computer Math. Applic.*, 36, 401–404.

[4] A. Anisimova, M. Avotina and I. Bula (2013), Periodic orbits of single neuron models with internal decay rate $0 < \beta \leq 1$, *Mathematical Modelling and Analysis*, 18, 325–345.

[5] A. Anisimova, M. Avotina and I. Bula (2015), Periodic and chaotic orbits of a neuron model, *Mathematical Modelling and Analysis*, 20, 30–52.

[6] M. C. Anisiu (2014), Lotka, Volterra and their model, *Didactica Mathematica*, 32, 917.

[7] V. Avrutin and M. Schanz (2004), Border collision period-doubling scenario, *Phys. Review E*, 70, 026222.

[8] V. Avrutin and M. Schanz (2005), Period-doubling scenario without flip bifurcations in a one-dimensional map, *International Journal of Bifurcations and Chaos*, 15, 1267–1284.

[9] W. F. Basener, B. P. Brooks, M. A. Radin and T. Wiandt (2008), Rat instigated human population collapse on easter island, *Journal of Non-Linear Dynamics, Psychology and Life Sciences*, 12 (3), 227–240.

[10] W. F. Basener, B. P. Brooks, M. A. Radin and T. Wiandt (2008), Dynamics of a population model for extinction and sustainability in ancient civilizations, *Journal of Non-Linear Dynamics, Psychology and Life Sciences*, 12 (1), 29–54.

[11] W. J. Briden, E. A. Grove, C. M. Kent and G. Ladas (1999), Eventually periodic solutions of $x_{n+1} = max\{\frac{1}{x_n}, \frac{A_n}{x_{n-1}}\}$, *Commun. Appl. Nonlinear Anal.*, 6, no. 4.

[12] W. J. Briden, E. A. Grove, G. Ladas and L. C. McGrath (1999), On the non-autonomous equation $x_{n+1} = max\{\frac{A_n}{x_n}, \frac{B_n}{x_{n-1}}\}$, *Proceedings of the Third International Conference on Difference Equations and Applications*, September 1–5, 1997, Taipei, Taiwan, Gordon and Breach Science Publishers, 49–73.

[13] R. J. H. Beverton and S. J. Holt (1957), On the dynamics of exploited fish populations, *Fishery Investigations Series II Volume XIX, Ministry of Agriculture, Fisheries and Food*.

309

[14] R. J. H. Beverton and S. J. Holt (1956), The theory of fishing, In Sea Fisheries: Their Investigation in the United Kingdom, M. Graham ed., pp. 372–441, Edward Arnold, London.

[15] W. J. Briden, G. Ladas and T. Nesemann (1999), On the recursive sequence $x_{n+1} = max\left\{\frac{1}{x_n}, \frac{A_n}{x_{n-1}}\right\}$, *J. Differ. Equations. Appl.*, 5, 491–494.

[16] I. Bula, M. A. Radin and N. Wilkins (2017), Neuron model with a period three internal decay rate, *Electronic Journal of Qualitative Theory of Differential Equations* (EJQTDE), 46, 119.

[17] I. Bula and M. A. Radin (2015), Periodic orbits of a neuron model with periodic internal decay rate, *Applied Mathematics and Computation*, 266, 293–303.

[18] E. Camouzis, G. Ladas, I. W. Rodriques and S. Northsfield (1994), On the rational recursive sequences $x_{n+1} = \frac{\beta x_n^2}{1+x_n^2}$, *Computers Math. Appl.*, 28, 37–43.

[19] V. C. Carmona, E. Freire, E. Ponce and F. Torres (2002), On simplifying and classifying piecewise linear systems, *IEEE Transactions on Circuits and Systems I*, 49, 609–620.

[20] E. Chatterjee, E. A. Grove, Y. Kostrov and G. Ladas (2003), On the trichotomy character of $x_{n+1} = \frac{\alpha+\gamma x_{n-1}}{A+B x_n+x_{n-2}}$, *J. Difference Equa. Appl.*, 9, 1113–1128.

[21] D. Clark and M. R. S. Kulenovic (2002), A coupled system of rational difference equations, *Comput. Math. Appl.*, 43, 849–867.

[22] R. E. Crandall (1978), "On the '$3x+1$' Problem.", *Math. Comp.*, 32, 1281–1292.

[23] J. M. Cushing (1994), Oscillations in age structured population models with an Allee effect, Oscillations in nonlinear systems: applications and numerical aspects, *J. Comput. Appl. Math.*, 52, no. 1–3, 71–80.

[24] J. M. Cushing and J. Li (1995), Oscillations caused by cannibalism in a size structured population model, Proceedings of the G. J. Butler Workshop in Mathematical Biology (Waterloo, ON, 1993), *Canad. Appl. Math. Quart.*, 3, no. 2, 155–172.

[25] V. Da Fonte Dias (1995), Signal processing in the sigma–delta domain, *Microelectronics Journal*, 26, 543–562.

[26] F. Dannan (2004), The asymptotic stability of $x_{n+k} + a x_n + b x_{n-l} = 0$, *Journal of Difference Equations and Applications*, 10 (6), 1–11.

[27] R. L. Devaney (1984), A piecewise linear model for the zones of instability of an area-preserving map, *Physica*, 10D, 387–393.

[28] R. Devault, E. A. Grove, G. Ladas, R. Levins and C. Puccia (1995), Oscillations and stability in a delay model of a perennial grass, *Journal of Difference Equations and Applications*, 1 (2), 173–185.

[29] J. Diblik, M. Ruzickova and E. L. Schmeidel (2009), Existence of asymptotically periodic solutions of system of Volterra difference equations, *Journal of Difference Equations and Applications*, 15 (11–12), 1165–1177.

[30] J. Diblik, M. Ruzickova and E. L. Schmeidel (2010), Asymptotically periodic solutions of system of Volterra difference equations, *Computers and Mathematics with Applications*, 59, 2854–2867.

[31] J. Diblik, M. Ruzickova, E. L. Schmeidel and M. Zbaszyniak (2011), Weighted Asymptotically Periodic Solutions of Linear Volterra Difference Equations, *Hindawi Publishing Corporation Abstract and Applied Analysis*.

[32] L. L. Eberhardt (2000), Reply: Predator-prey ratio dependence and regulation of moose populations, *Canadian Journal of Zoology*, 78 (3), 511–513.

[33] S. Elaydi (2005), *An Introduction to Difference Equations*, Springer.

[34] H. Eli-Metwally, E. A. Grove, G. Ladas, R. Levins and M. Radin (2001), On the difference equation $x_{n+1} = a + bx_{n-1}e-x_n$, *Journal of Nonlinear Dynamics*, 47, 4623–4634.

[35] K. R. Janglajew and E. L. Schmeidel (2012), Periodicity of solutions of nonhomogeneous linear difference equations, *Advances in Difference Equations*, 195.

[36] D. Fournier-Prunaret and R. Lopez-Ruiz (2005), Indirect Allee effect, bistability, and chaotic oscillations in a predator-prey discrete model of logistic type, *Chaos, Solutions and Fractals*, 24, 85–101.

[37] M. A. Garca-Vellisca, R. Jaimes-Retegui and A. N. Pisarchik (2016), Experimental evidence of deterministic coherence resonance in coupled chaotic systems with frequency mismatch, *Phys. Rev.*, E94, 012218.

[38] C. Gibbons, M. R. S. Kulenovic and G. Ladas (2000), On the recursive sequence $x_{n+1} = \frac{\alpha+\beta x_{n-1}}{\gamma+x_n}$, *Math. Sci. Res. Hot-Line*, 4 (2), 1–11.

[39] E. A. Grove and G. Ladas (2005), *Periodicities in Nonlinear Difference Equations*, Chapman and Hall/CRC, New York.

[40] E. A. Grove, G. Ladas, M. Predescu and M. Radin, (2001), On the global character of $x_{n+1} = \frac{px_n+n_{n-1}}{q+x_n}$, *Mathematical Science Research Hot-Line*, 5 (7), 25–39.

[41] E. A. Grove, G. Ladas, M. Predescu and M. Radin (2003), On the global character of the difference equation $x_{n+1} = \frac{\alpha+\gamma x_{n-(2k+1)}+\delta x_{n-2l}}{A+x_{n-2l}}$, *J. Difference Equa. Appl.*, 9, 171–200.

[42] E. A. Grove, E. Lapierre and W. Tikjha (2012), On the global behavior of $x_{n+1} = |x_n| - y_n - 1$ and $y_{n+1} = x_n + |y_n|$, *Cubo A Mathematica Journal*, 14 (2), 111–152.

[43] E. M. Izhikevich (2003), Simple model of spiking neurons, *IEEE Transactions on Neural Networks*, 14 (6), 1569–1572.

[44] G. L. Karakostas and S. Stevic (2004), On the recursive sequence $x_{n+1} = B + \frac{x_{n-k}}{a_0 x_n+\cdots+a_{k-1}x_{n-k+1}+\gamma}$, *J. Difference Equa. Appl.*, 10, 809–815.

[45] C. M. Kent, E. A. Grove, G. Ladas and M. A. Radin (2001), On $x_{n+1} = max\left\{\frac{1}{x_n}, \frac{A_n}{x_{n-1}}\right\}$ with a period 3 parameter, *Fields Institute Communications*, 29.

[46] C. M. Kent, M. Kustesky, A. Q. Nguyen and B. V. Nguyen, Eventually Periodic Solutions of $x_{n+1} = max\left\{\frac{A_n}{x_n}, \frac{B_n}{x_{n-1}}\right\}$, With Period Two Cycle Parameters, Dynamics of Continuous, Discrete and Impulsive Systems, Series A, Mathematical Analysis 10 (2003), 33–49.

[47] C. M. Kent and M. A. Radin (2013), On the boundedness of positive solutions of a reciprocal MaxType difference equation with periodic parameters, *International Journal of Difference Equations*, 8 (2), 195–213.

[48] V. V. Khuong and M. N. Phong (2013), On a system of two difference equations of exponential form, *International Journal of Difference Equations*, 8 (2), 215–223.

[49] V. L. Kocic and T. Darensburg, (2004), On the discrete model of west Nile-like epidemic, *Proceedings of Dynamic Systems and Applications*, 4, 358–366.

[50] M. R. S. Kulenovic, G. Ladas and N. R. Prokup (2000), On the recursive sequence $x_{n+1} = \frac{ax_n+bx_{n-1}}{A+x_n}$, *J. Differ. Equations Appl.*, 6 (5), 563–576.

[51] M. R. S. Kulenovic, G. Ladas and W. S. Sizer (1998), On the recursive sequence $x_{n+1} = \frac{\alpha x_n+\beta x_{n-1}}{\gamma x_n+\delta x_{n-1}}$, *Math. Sci. Res. Hot-Line*, 2 (5), 1–16.

[52] M. R. S. Kulenović and M. Nurkanović (2006), Asymptotic behavior of a competitive system of linear fractional difference equations, *Advances in Difference Equations*, 3, 1–13.

[53] S. Kuruklis (1994), The asymptotic stability of $x_{n+1} - ax_n + bx_{n-k} = 0$, *J. Math. Anal. Appl.*, 188, 719–731.

[54] S. A. Kuruklis and G. Ladas (1992), Oscillation and global attractivity in a discrete delay logistic model, *App. Math.*, 50, 227–233.

[55] G. Ladas, (1996), On the recursive sequence $x_{n+1} = max\left\{\frac{A_0}{x_n}, \ldots, \frac{A_k}{x_{n-k}}\right\}$, *J. Diff. Equa. Appl.*, 2 (2), 339–341.

[56] J. C. Lagarias (1985), "The $3x + l$ problem and its generalizations." *Amer. Math. Monthly*, 92, 3–21.

[57] J. C. Lagarias and A. Weiss (1992), "The $3x + l$ problem: Two stochastic models." *Ann. Appl. Prob.*, 2, 229–61.

[58] E. Lapierre, Y. Lenbury and W. Tikjha (2012), On the global character of the system of piecewise linear difference equations $x_{n+1} = |x_n| - y_n - 1$ and $y_{n+1} = x_n + |y_n|$, *Advances in Difference Equations*, CUBO A Mathematical Journal Vol. 14, no 2, 111–152.

[59] E. Lapierre, Y. Lenbury and W. Tikjha (2015), Periodic solutions of a generalized system of piecewise linear difference equations, *Advances in Difference Equations*, 248–263.

[60] G. Ladas, A. Tovbis and G. Tzanetopoulos (1996), On may's host parasitoid model, *Journal of Difference Equations and Applications*, 2 (2), 195–204.

[61] T. Y. Li and J. A. Yorke (1975), Period three implied chaos, *The American Mathematical Monthly*, 82 (10), 985–992.

[62] E. N. Lorenz (1963), Deterministic non-periodic flow, *Journal of the Atmospheric Sciences*, 20, 130141.

[63] E. N. Lorenz (2005), Designing chaotic models, *Journal of the Atmospheric Sciences*, 62 (5), 15741587.

[64] E. Magnucka-Blandzi and J. Popenda (1999), On the asymptotic behavior of a rational system of difference equations, *J. Difference Equ. Appl.*, 5, no. 3, 271–286.

[65] G. Papaschinopolous, M. Radin and S. Schinas (2011), On the system of two difference equations in exponential form, *Journal of Mathematical and Computer Modeling*, 54, 2969–2977.

[66] G. Papaschinopoulos, C. J. Schinas and G. Stefanidou (2010), On a system of two exponential type difference equations, *Comm. Appl. Nonlinear Anal.*, 17, no. 2, 113.

[67] M. A. Pervez, H. V. Sorensen and J. Van der Spiegel (1996), An overview of sigma–delta converters, *IECE Signal Processing Magazine*, 61–84.

[68] E. C. Pielou (1969), *An Introduction to Mathematical Ecology*, Wiley Interscience, New York.

[69] E. C. Pielou (1974), *Population and Community Ecology*, Gordon and Breach, New York.

[70] A. N. Pisarchik, M. A. Radin and R. Vogt (2015), Non-autonomous discrete neuron model with multiple periodic and eventually periodic solutions. *Discrete Dynamics in Nature and Society*, Article ID 147282, 6 pages.

[71] M. Radin (2018), *Periodic Character and Patterns of Recursive Sequences*, Springer.

[72] O. Orlova and M. Radin (2018), University level teaching styles with high school students and international teaching and learning, *International Scientific Conference "Society, Integration, Education"*.

[73] M. Radin and V. Riashchenko (2017), Effective Pedagogical management as a road to successful international teaching and learning, *Forum Scientiae Oeconomia*, 5 (4), 71–84.

[74] W. E. Ricker (1954), Stock and recruitment, *Journal of the Fisheries Research Board of Canada*, 11 (5), 559623. doi:10.1139/f54-039.

[75] W. E. Ricker (1975), Computation and interpretation of biological statistics of fish populations, *Bulletin of the Fisheries Research Board of Canada*, no. 119, Ottawa.

[76] N. F. Rulkov (2002), Modeling of spiking-bursting neural behavior using two-dimensional map, *Physical Review E*, 65, 041922.

[77] R. J. Sacker (2007), A note on periodic Ricker Maps, *Journal of Difference Equations and Applications*, 13 (1), 89–92.

[78] P. A. Samuelson (1939), Interaction between the multiplier analysis and the principle of acceleration, *Rev. Econm. Statist.*, 21, 75–78.

[79] J. Steele (2009), Human dispersals: mathematical models and the archeological record, *Human Biology*, 81 (2/3), 121–140.

[80] S. Stević (2007), On the recursive sequence $x_{n+1} = \frac{\alpha + \sum_{i=1}^{k} \alpha_i x_{n-p_i}}{1 + \sum_{j=1}^{m} \beta_j x_{n-q_j}}$, *J. Difference Equa. Appl.*, 13, 41–46.

[81] P. F. Verhulst (1838), "Notice sur la loi que la population suit dans son accroissement", *Correspondance mathmatique et physique*, 10, 113121. Retrieved 2013-02-18.

[82] Q. Wang, F. Zeng, G. Zang and X. Liu (2006), Dynamics of the difference equation $x_{n+1} = \frac{\alpha + B_1 x_{n-1} + B_3 x_{n-3} + \cdots + B_{2k+1} x_{n-2k-1}}{A + B_0 x_n + B_2 x_{n-2} + \cdots + B_{2k} x_{n-2k}}$, *J. Difference Equa. Appl.*, 12, 399–417.

[83] M. Williamson (1974), The analysis of discrete time cycles, In M. B. Usher and M. H. Williamson, eds., *Ecological Stability*, Chapman and Hall, 17–33.

[84] Z. Zhou and J. Wu (2003), Stable periodic orbits in nonlinear discrete-time neural networks with delayed feedback, *Computers and Mathematics with Applications*, 45, 935–942.

[85] Z. Zhou (2003), Periodic orbits on discrete dynamical systems, *Computers and Mathematics with Applications*, 45, 1155–1161.

[86] H. Zhu and L. Huang (2004), Dynamics of a class of nonlinear discrete-time neural networks, *Computers and Mathematics with Applications*, 48, 85–94.

[87] Z. Yuan, L. Huang and Y. Chen (2002), Convergence and periodicity of solutions for a discrete-time network model of two neurons, *Mathematical and Computer Modelling*, 35, 941–950.

[88] Z. Yuan and L. Huang (2004), All solutions of a class of discrete-time systems are eventually periodic, *Applied Mathematics and Computation*, 158, 537–546.

INDEX

CPSIA information can be obtained
at www.ICGtesting.com
Printed in the USA
FFHW021411270919
55209985-60940FF